THE NATURAL DEATH HANDBOOK

THE NATURAL DEATH HANDBOOK

FOR IMPROVING THE QUALITY OF LIVING AND DYING

Edited by Nicholas Albery, Gil Elliot and Joseph Elliot

Chapter heading illustrations by Yvonne Malik

This edition first published in Great Britain in 1993 by
Virgin Books
an imprint of Virgin Publishing Ltd
332 Ladbroke Grove
London W10 5AH

Material collected, laserset and laid out by
The Natural Death Centre
20 Heber Road,
London NW2 6AA
tel 081 208 2853
fax 081 452 6434

Copyright © The Natural Death Centre 1993

All royalties from this book are going to the Natural Death Centre, an educational charity, towards its work in supporting those dying at home. The Centre is grateful to all the many people and publishers who freely contributed items and is apologetic to any whom it failed to trace or acknowledge. Sources are given either in the text or in the booklist starting on p. 205. Please send all corrections, updates and suggested additions to the Centre at the above address. The Centre is especially grateful to Joseph Elliot and Gil Elliot for the first draft editions which they prepared of chapters two, four, five and eight; to The Network for Social Change for a grant during the preparation of this book; to Nicholas Saunders and his Neal's Yard DeskTop Publishing Centre for his financial help since the beginning; to Yvonne Malik for the drawings at the start of each chapter; to Richard Doust for his free design consultancy for the book's lay-out; to Christine Mills for researching the funerals chapter and for constant help throughout with all the other chapters too; to Yasmin Zaman for helping compile the funeral questionnaire results; to Juliet Solomon for compiling an early draft of chapter three; to Yvonne Ackroyd, J. B. Bradfield, Mary Bradbury, Roger Knights and Marion Schmidt for their research help; to Marcelle Papworth for her translations; to Josefine Speyer for her help; to Geoffrey Cannon for getting the book accepted for publication; to all those who suggested improvements to the early drafts including Heather Albery, Des Banks, Sheila Barratt, Denise Brady, Joanna Gilpin, Christianne Heal, John Horbury, Avril Jackson, Margaret Hayworth, Elizabeth Lawlor, Julian Litten, David Lorimer, Yvonne Malik, Dr Mary Neal, Renée O'Sullivan, Derek Roberts-Morgan, Caroline Sherwood, Jane Spottiswoode, Solveig Taylor, Sheila Thompson and Pam Williams; and to Rosalind Oliver for her proof-reading.

A catalogue record for this book is available from the British Library
ISBN 0 86369 687 2
Printed and bound in Great Britain by Mackays of Chatham PLC, Chatham, Kent

CONTENTS

Chapter 1

The Natural Death Movement

The idea that launched the Natural Death Centre

The Natural Death Centre is an educational charity, founded in 1991 by three psychotherapists – Christianne Heal, myself and my wife Josefine Speyer. The idea for the Centre grew from our experience of the birth of our son. Back in 1975, Josefine was pregnant and I'd taken a long spell off work to help her to fulfil a cherished fantasy of travelling by horse and cart. With our horse Patience (on £2 a week rent from the Heavy Horse Preservation Society) and our converted manure tip cart, we meandered our way through the wilder parts of Wales, looking for a cottage for the winter and the birth. Josefine was adamant that she wanted to be at home for the birth. As she put it: 'I'm not ill, why should I go into hospital?' At last we found a place by the river Teifi and a doctor who was willing to come to the farm cottage – 'I don't mind if you give birth on a haystack, I'll come wherever you want,' he told Josefine.

In the event we were very lucky. It was a quick, almost painfree and ecstatic labour for Josefine, and all the preparation helped – the Raspberry Leaf tea, the natural birth books and classes, the visualisations and breathing exercises – and the doctor and midwife were like guests in our home for this Leboyer-style birth of low lights and quiet.

In 1988, my father died at home and his death triggered in me a realisation of the need for a natural death movement to parallel the natural childbirth movement, and to spread the tenets of good hospice care to home care for those dying of all causes, not just cancer. It wouldn't suit everybody, but why shouldn't those families who wanted it be fully supported by the NHS in looking after the dying person at home, with generous financial and other help for carers? Wouldn't more people, if it were possible, prefer to die at home amongst friends rather than in the anonymity of a big and noisy hospital? As with birth, could preparation, exercises and rituals help reduce the anxieties that people feel about dying? Could dying at least for a lucky few become as easy and as ecstatic a process as our experience of birth? Granted that no one can be certain what happens after death, could it be that preparation matters, as the Tibetans argue, to enable the soul at the point of death to merge fearlessly with that bright light reported by many who have recovered from Near-Death Experiences? I remembered how a friend's mother insisted on being given her travelling rug to die with; could the process of dying be the labour pains of the soul, with sometimes the same feeling of expectation and transition as at birth?

Just as many people want to experience birth as consciously as possible, so some people want to face death with minds as unclouded as their circumstances permit. It is here that the analogy between birth and death breaks down somewhat, for drugs are more likely to be necessary to relieve pain for the dying, if only because dying can be a much more long drawn-out labour than giving birth – but nevertheless further research is needed into drugs that are strong enough to relieve terminal pain whilst enhancing alertness.

As related later in this book, Aldous Huxley sat by his wife Maria at her death, urging her with hypnotic repetition to 'go towards the light'. Perhaps many people would like an Aldous Huxley-type figure sitting by them as they go. Perhaps there could be a new profession of 'Midwives for the Dying', people skilled in holistic care of the dying patient's practical, emotional and spiritual needs (and the needs of the family), and more intent on creating a calm and supportive atmosphere than on high tech medical interventions to prolong life to the utmost. There is a need for such skills in modern life, for as Aldous Huxley wrote: 'The living can do a great deal to make the passage easier for the dying, to raise the most purely physiological act of human existence to the level of awareness and perhaps even of spirituality.'

Introduction by Nicholas Albery, co-editor of The Natural Death Handbook.

As the sixties-generation Green movement people age, so the natural death movement will inevitably become a force in health politics, bringing about a redirection of NHS and other resources towards home care and proper provision for carers. The Natural Death Centre aims to be in the vanguard of such changes. It will act as a kind of Society for Home Deaths, and will work to implement its long-term plans for Midwives for the Dying, with lay helpers or 'Personal Assistants for the dying' to back up the midwife. In the meantime, it will do what it can to help improve the quality of living and dying. Christianne Heal offers Living With Dying workshops for the general public on preparing for dying. Josefine Speyer gives talks to nurses, doctors and others concerned with looking after the dying and offers individual counselling to the anxious or the bereaved.

At present, dying mostly happens 'off stage', as it were, in old people's homes and hospitals, and many people are superstitious enough to believe that the less they think about the subject the longer they will live. Two thirds of the UK population have not even taken the first step of writing a will, thus potentially leaving additional problems for their survivors. The Centre wants to make death and dying an unexceptional topic for daily meditation and conversation, and to that end is hosting a series of large dinner discussions with candlelit tables and gourmet food and wine on subjects ranging from care of the dying to Near-Death Experiences. It is also organising an English Day of the Dead celebration for the third Sunday in April each year, inspired by the Mexican Day of the Dead festivities.

Once a family has looked after a dying person at home, they are more likely to want to take care of the dead body themselves too. But whatever the reason, the Centre has found itself submerged in mail from families wanting Green, inexpensive funerals, without using undertakers. A great deal of research later, the material for the two chapters in this book, 'D-i-y Funerals' and the 'Good Funeral Guide', was assembled, not only on how to run a funeral without using an undertaker, at a fifth of the normal average cost, but also on who are the best professionals to approach, should you want help.

The Centre now acts as a sort of 'Which?' type body, available by phone or letter, giving for the first time an in depth consumer's perspective on the whole funeral trade. It also perforce has had to campaign on behalf of the public with the National Association of Funeral Directors, the Office of Fair Trading and the Department of Trade and Industry, to try to ensure, for instance, that itemised price breakdowns on funerals are available to the public and that coffins are sold to those people who want to organise a funeral themselves. The kind of changes in policy that seem necessary are outlined in the chapter 'Manifesto for the Dying' which also includes a Declaration of Rights for the person dying at home.

The Centre is financed on a shoestring and has survived to date mainly thanks to financial help from Nicholas Saunders and his Neal's Yard DeskTop Publishing Studio, and thanks to two small grants, one from the Gulbenkian Foundation and another during the writing of this book from the Network for Social Change. The Centre has no full-time staff and has only shared office space. It will rely in part for its continuation on members of the public becoming Friends of the Natural Death Centre by filling in a banker's order, normally for £20 a year. If you can afford this or any other sum on a regular basis please make contact. This Handbook too requires your assistance if it is to become ever more useful in future editions – if you have a recommendation, update, correction, tip or experience you are willing to share with others, please send it in.

The purpose of this book is not only to collect together all the information that the Centre has gathered to date, but also to introduce readers to the great pioneers of the natural death movement and to the ideas in their writings. Some of the very best books on the subject (marked ❸❸❸ in the Resources chapter) have been published in the United States but deserve a wider readership in the UK. Information for ordering them is at the back of this book and, if not available through your local bookshop, most can be obtained either from the publishers or via the Centre itself (if urgent, by phone call quoting an Access or Visa credit card number).

What have these other writers had to say about the need for a natural death movement? Douglas Harding has emphasised our resistance to thinking about our own mortality:

The cult of youth-at-all-costs

Our current resistance to such an investigation, to any candour or realism concerning our own mortality, can scarcely be exaggerated. Witness the popular cult of youth-at-all-costs in the worlds of advertising and fashion. Witness those communities of old folk dedicated to being 'as young as you feel' and to avoiding all reminders of old age, sickness, and death. Witness the newspeak and double-talk of 'seventy years young' in place of 'seventy years old' and 'elderly person' or 'senior citizen' in place of 'old man', 'old woman'. Witness the funerary nonsense so tellingly described in Evelyn Waugh's 'The Loved One'. Witness Cryonics – the freezing of the newly dead for revival when technology is further developed, thus giving effect to the view that 'death is an imposition on the human race, and no longer acceptable'. Witness the cultists who seriously maintain that death is unnecessary and unnatural, and we can choose to live as long as we wish. How unlike the veneration of old age and the preoccupation with death and the hereafter which are such marked features of some great cultures! And again, what a contrast with the *memento mori* (remember you must die) of earlier centuries of our own civilisation – its human skulls carved on tombstones and displayed on mantelpieces, its countless engravings and paintings confronting the living with the grim spectacle of Death the Reaper and the imagined sequel!

Reproduced by permission of Penguin Books Ltd from 'The Little Book of Life and Death' by D. E. Harding.

For fuller details of all main book references see the Resources chapter.

Ivan Illich in 1975 wrote about the torments inflicted on the dying in some hospitals:

The medicalisation of society

Today, the man best protected against setting the stage for his own dying is the sick person in critical condition. Society, acting through the medical system, decides when and after what indignities and mutilations he shall die. The medicalisation of society has brought the epoch of natural death to an end.

From 'Medical Nemesis: The Expropriation of Health' by Ivan Illich, Calder and Boyars Ltd, '75.

The isolation of the dying and the bereaved in a centralised society that has lost almost all sense of neighbourhood has been highlighted by Tony Walter:

Neighbours no longer share the loss

Because the elderly person who has died may well not have been widely known by the friends of those left behind, the grief of the bereaved is not shared. When someone dies in Ambridge, or in an African village, or in a police unit, an entire community feels the loss: everyone knew the person and everyone to some degree mourns the loss. But when most old people in Britain die today, only a few close relatives are still in touch to feel the loss.

Nor is this true only when the deceased is elderly. In a relatively isolated nuclear family in which outsiders have played little if any role in child care, the death of a child may be a uniquely isolating experience. Contrast this account by Miller after the destruction of the primary school in Aberfan: 'One bereaved mother told me that when she lost her child the company she sought was not that of other bereaved mothers but of her neighbours. They might not have lost a child themselves, but she realised they had lost her child. It was the neighbours who had helped to bring him up, who had minded him when she went out, had watched him grow and had taken pride in his achievements. In a very real sense they shared her grief.' Usually though, friends and neighbours may be sympathetic, but they do not know the child well enough truly to share the loss. Friends in their thirties or younger may never have experienced any close bereavement.

So the bereaved today often are isolated, and may well report being treated as lepers.

From 'Modern Death: Taboo or Not Taboo?' by Tony Walter, Sociology, Vol. 25, No. 2.

Tony Walters shares the Natural Death Centre's perception that the Green movement and the natural childbirth movement will tend to lead to the acceptance of death and dying as natural processes to be shared with our family and friends:

Natural childbirth leads to natural death

The Green movement surely must lead to a more realistic acceptance of the fact that human beings are natural creatures who must die. This movement has prompted all of us to question our technological hubris; we all know now that we are part of a delicate natural system; we are less able to split a heroic, rational soul from an inconvenient body.

This new attitude surely underlies the natural childbirth movement. Giving birth may be painful, but it is part of the natural human experience, and many women would not wish it anaesthetised away. Nor do they want to be socially isolated; they want to share this miracle of nature with their partners and their other children.

Death is also a natural part of being human, and therefore I do not wish to be drugged into oblivion: I want the pain to be controlled, but I would like to be conscious and in control as far as is possible. And I would like to share this unrepeatable and important event with my partner and my children.

From 'Funerals and How to Improve Them' by Tony Walter.

There are, however, many kinds of natural death. It is just as much a part of nature to die abruptly or in agony, through accidents or violence or illness, as it is to die with ease and dignity. But even in such circumstances, to feel prepared for any eventuality may help. Gandhi was assassinated, but his almost automatic reaction to the bullets was to chant the name of God. He was prepared, in his own way.

As Jung appreciated:

Death as a goal in old age

Willy-nilly, the ageing person prepares himself for death. Thoughts of death pile up to an astonishing degree as the years increase. That is why I think that nature herself is always preparing for the end. Objectively it is a matter of indifference what the individual consciousness may think about it. But subjectively it makes an enormous difference whether consciousness keeps in step with the psyche or whether it clings to opinions of which the heart knows nothing. It is just as neurotic in old age not to focus upon the goal of death as it is in youth to repress fantasies which have to do with the future.

From 'The Soul and Death' by C. G. Jung in 'The Collected Works, series XX, vol. viii, translated by R. F. C. Hull, Princeton University Press, 1969.

Many people ask: Is it not morbid to think about death and dying earlier in life? No, it is necessary, for preparing for dying is half a lifetime's work. The main preparation is that which the Dalai Lama advises: 'For most of us ordinary people who lead busy lives, what is important is to develop a kind, generous heart to others. If we can do that and live accordingly, we will be able to die peacefully.' And for those who have the opportunity and the necessary circumstances, he adds, there are higher spiritual preparations available through religious and yogic practices. But above all, an awareness of death can sweeten every remaining living moment. Yeats is not the only poet to warn:

'Begin the preparation for your death'

Get all the gold and silver that you can,
Satisfy ambition, animate
The trivial days and ram them with the sun ...

But then:

No longer in Lethean foliage caught
Begin the preparation for your death
And from the fortieth winter by that thought
Test every work of intellect or faith,
And everything that your own hands have wrought,
And call those works extravagance of breath
That are not suited for such men as come
Proud, open eyed and laughing to the tomb.
From 'Vacillation' by W. B. Yeats

Ageing to Yeats was a growing of the soul:

An aged man is but a paltry thing,
A tattered coat upon a stick, unless
Soul clap its hands and sing, and louder sing
For every tatter in its mortal dress.
From 'Sailing to Byzantium'.

Stephen Levine sees death as the graduation ceremony for this cocoon-abandoning soul:

Death as graduation

Death is another transformation through which we move, an adventure to surpass
all adventures, an opening, an incredible moment of growth, a graduation.
From 'Who Dies?' by Stephen Levine.

To adopt this new outlook, we have first to rid ourselves of a great deal of cultural
conditioning. Paula Hendrick has surveyed the natural death movement from an American
perspective and concludes that our technological mastery of nature and our focus on
personal autonomy and self-development have made it very hard for us to accept the
inevitability of death:

Natural dying – an American perspective

In the world of nature, death provides a service because it makes room in an
ecological niche for a young one. People are part of nature, too, and when people
die, they make room for more people. In a time of population explosion, it would
be useful to be able to die without making too much of a fuss about it. But we
humans, particularly in the affluent cultures of the first world, face the final
journey of life with a load of weighty baggage. We avoid talk of death, and we
dread the realities of the aging process.

We as individuals don't necessarily create and lug around this excess baggage
on our own. Something pervasive in our society moulds our collective choices.
Michael Ignatieff, writing in 'The New Republic', offers this explanation:
'Cultures that live by the values of self-realisation and self-mastery are not
especially good at dying, at submitting to those experiences where freedom ends
and biological fate begins. Why should they be? Their strong side is Promethean
ambition: the defiance and transcendence of fate, the material and social limit.
Their weak side is submitting to the inevitable.'

We have become victims of the health care system that our cultural values have
created. The dying process has been transformed into a series of wrenching

choices. A woman, getting along pretty well after a stroke at age eighty – some confusion, but lots of independence and zest for life – develops increasing heart problems. She has no family support, just a few friends who do the best they can. The doctor recommends a pacemaker. She says no but he persuades her. There are complications during surgery. Now she's totally disorientated and can barely walk even with assistance. Her pacemaker keeps her going.

Out of the apparently needless suffering of countless people has grown a strong movement towards patients' rights and natural death – that is, death with a minimum of medical intervention. Advances are continually – albeit slowly – being made in legislation and public education. The Patient Self-Determination Act, which went into effect in the States in December 1991, requires health care facilities to inform patients of their rights to refuse treatment and to formulate advance directives such as a living will or health care proxy. Difficult moral dilemmas are also being debated on the topic of 'aid-in-dying', or physician-assisted suicide. The goals of the broader 'natural death movement' are to guarantee choice for individuals and to bring about a large-scale cultural shift. An article in The Economist of London describes such a large scale shift this way: 'To civilise death, to bring it home and make it no longer a source of dread, is one of the great challenges of the age ... Gradually, dying may come to hold again the place it used to occupy in the midst of life: not a terror but a mystery so deep that man would no more wish to cheat himself of it than to cheat himself of life.'

Excerpted from In Context magazine No. 31 (subs. $31, airmail $42, from PO Box 11470, Bainbridge Island, WA98110, USA, tel 0101 206 842 0216).

May this present Handbook prove a useful contribution to the contemplation of all aspects of this magnificent and awe-inspiring subject. Above all, may it help allow people to 'die in character' as Elisabeth Kübler-Ross puts it. Dr Buckman in his book on how to support a dying person is rightly adamant on this point:

It should be your objective as friend and supporter – as it is my objective when I'm looking after dying patients – to help your friend let go of life *in his own way*. It may not be your way, and it may not be the way you read about in a book or magazine, but it's his way and consistent with the way he's lived his life. You can and should help your friend achieve that.

From 'I Don't Know What To Say – How to Help and Support Someone who is Dying' by Dr Robert Buckman.

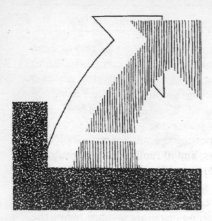

Chapter 2

BRAVE AND 'CONSCIOUS' DEATHS

Ancient Models

Natural death is as old as the hills. As ancient as the burial mounds that fit neatly into the landscapes of Europe. But that image would not satisfy all cultures, for only a proportion of the world's peoples plant their dead in the ground. In India, with one of the largest populations, they are consigned to the flames, in Tibet to the air in the ceremony of sky burial. Earth, fire and air. The elements of natural death are varied, and the ways of dying follow the natural forms of life itself. To speculate about the deaths of individuals in other cultures and historical periods has a natural and secret fascination. Could my death be like that? Should it be? Will I get the chance to practise that virtue, that wisdom? We can have a model inside us of how we wish to die, we may even plan for it. But the actual moment of death remains unpredictable. A modern master of the ancient Zen tradition built this unpredictability into his dying words:

Death of Zen master Taji

As Zen master Taji (1889-1953) approached death, his senior disciples assembled at his bedside. One of them, remembering the master was fond of a certain kind of cake, had spent half a day searching the pastry shops of Tokyo for this confection, which he now presented to him. With a wan smile the dying master accepted a piece of the cake and slowly began munching it. As he grew weaker, his disciples inquired whether he had any final words for them.

'Yes,' the master replied.

The disciples leaned forward eagerly so as not to miss a word. 'Please tell us!'

'My, but this cake is delicious!' And with that he slipped away.

From 'The Wheel of Life and Death' by Philip Kapleau.

In the Buddhist tradition there is something natural and healthy about making use of your death. The death of the *Buddha* himself is neither a monument nor an icon, but a practical demonstration. Thus he used his death to deliver a sermon of practical advice to his disciples. According to tradition he predicted his own passing: 'Reckoned from today, I will sustain my life for only three more months.' When the time came he gave a practical model of how to meet death, couched in a few sentences that are worth savouring.

Death of the Buddha

'It is not appropriate,' the Buddha tells his disciples, ' to grieve in an hour of joy. You all weep, but is there any real cause for grief? We should look upon a sage as a person escaped from a burning mansion.' Instead of binding them to him, he releases his disciples in his last moment, just as he is about to be released from life. 'It does not matter whether I am here or not; salvation does not depend upon me but upon practising the Dharma, just as a cure depends not upon seeing the doctor but upon taking his medicine.

'My time has come, my work is done. Everything eventually comes to an end, even if it should last for an aeon. The time of parting is bound to come one day. I have done what I could for myself and others, and to remain longer would be without purpose. I have trained all whom I could train.' The final send-off begins: 'My teachings shall last for many generations, so do not be disturbed. Recognise that all that lives is subject to the laws of impermanence, and strive for eternal wisdom.' And ends: 'When the light of knowledge dispels ignorance, when the world is seen as without substance, the end of life is seen as peace and as a cure to disease. Everything that exists is bound to perish. Be therefore mindful of your salvation. The time of my passing has come.' Having said these words the master 'entered into a profound meditation and passed away'.

From 'Death and Dying, The Tibetan Tradition' by Glenn H. Mullin.

The Tibetan yogi Milarepa (eleventh century), by knowingly accepting poisoned food, consciously used his death in such a way as to make his murderer repent, and convert to righteous ways!

Ancient models of the 'brave and conscious death' – death faced with full consciousness, not denied – provide a lively contrast to the modern custom of avoiding or passing over the moment of death or, worse still, draping it in artificial gloom. In the following examples death is approached with vigorous human emotions of curiosity, technical interest and celebration. The Arab *Amr Ibn Al-As* responded on his deathbed with a precise image of what dying felt like: 'breathing through the eye of a needle'. The methods of *Himalayan yogis* present themselves as an exact science of dying, clearly attainable only after long and conscious study of techniques. As a model of natural death none could be richer and more rewarding of study than the Native American way, as told by *Sun Bear,* who himself died in 1992. Within this spacious tradition there is room for each person to make his death according to his natural bent, whether in solitary praise and ritual, in celebration with friends or even in the heat of action.

Death of the Arab Amr Ibn Al-As

As Amr lay on his death-bed a friend said to him: 'You have often remarked that you would like to find an intelligent man at the point of death, and to ask him what his feelings were. Now I ask you that question.' Amr replied, 'I feel as if heaven lay close upon the earth and I between the two, breathing through the eye of a needle.'

Amr Ibn Al-As, the Arab conqueror of Egypt, died in 664; quoted in 'The Oxford Book of Death' edited by D. J. Enright.

Himalayan yogis

The techniques of dying which are used by yogis are very methodical, painless and conscious. This is unusual in the Western world, but not in the Himalayas. It is not like committing suicide, but is an exact process or way of leaving that body which is no longer an instrument for enlightenment. Such a body is considered to be a burden – an obstacle which might obstruct the journey of the dying man when he goes through his vast unconscious reservoir of memories. Only those who are not competent in higher techniques and not self-reliant on their yogic will-power and control accept the normal methods of dying, which are definitely inferior to the yogic methods.

One which is traditional to certain Himalayan yogis is to seat yourself in meditation, enter the state of consciousness called samadhi, and then allow the body to freeze in the cold mountain air. Another technique – very rare – involves meditating on the solar plexus in a certain way that generates great internal heat, inducing spontaneous combustion of the body.

From 'A Practical Guide to Death and Dying' by John White.

Sun Bear on the Native American way of dying

In the old way, when it was time to die, old ones would go off by themselves, feeling that the moment of death was as intimate between them and the Earth Mother as the moment of birth is between human mother and child. They would find a quiet place and there make prayers to the Great Spirit, thanking him for the life they had enjoyed. They would sing their song, and they would die.

There is a story of one old-timer who felt his time had come. He invited all of his friends to a gathering where they sang songs and made a feast. He had a big give-away, giving gifts to all his friends, telling them how happy he had been with their friendship. They, in turn, all spoke their good thoughts of him. Then, while they were singing songs, he closed his eyes and died. Many Indian people have been known to predict the exact date and time they would die.

Warrior societies used to let the old men go into battle one last time. When they went the young men would stand aside and say, 'Let the old man count one last coup.'

Another Indian custom was to give away or make arrangements to give away everything a person had before he died. That way there was nothing for anyone to fight over after the person was gone.

Like all other things in life, death is not permanent. It is but a change from one world, from one state of being into another. For those of us who learn to love life, with all of its changes, death should not be a fearful event. It should be a time of celebrating the continual evolution of the soul. When it is your time to pass, it should be with your mind wide open and your prayer in your heart. When one dear to you dies, besides sadness at your loss you should feel happiness that now the soul is free to soar to Kitche Manitou, the Great Spirit, our common Creator. Where there is love, there is no room for fear.

From Many Smokes magazine (now entitled Wild Fire), Bear Tribe Medicine Society, PO Box 9167, Spokane, WA 99209-9167, USA.

The deaths of Jesus and Socrates provide the models for the blend of Christian and classical attitudes to facing death that has moulded Western tradition. Given that modern Western culture seems to have lost the feel for natural death we should look closely at our own tradition to see what happened to the brave and conscious death along the way. Is there some inherent feature in the Western way of dying that has led to modern attitudes of denial? Judging by the two examples that follow, the answer would be a resounding No.

St Francis met his end by singing a welcome to death. According to another version of the story his Christian cheerfulness set up such a racket in the Bishop's palace that the singing saint was not allowed to die in the main building. Plato's account of the death of *Socrates* shows the philosopher dying as he lived, choosing to die rather than compromise his principles at the command of the state, and surrounded by his tearful but admiring friends.

Death of St Francis

St Francis of Assisi, as his life neared its end, was taken to the palace of the Bishop of Assisi. A doctor was fetched to treat him. St Francis, wanting to know how long he had to live, asked the doctor, who avoided a direct answer for some time but finally said that the disease was incurable and that he might die soon. St. Francis, overjoyed, raised his hands and cried, 'Welcome, Sister Death!' He bade farewell to his friends and friars, and dictated some letters. A few days later, near to death, he asked the doctor to announce the arrival of Sister Death. 'She will open for me the door of life,' he explained. Then, following his instructions, the Franciscan brothers spread a coarse cloth on the ground, placed their mentor on it, and sprinkled him with dust and ashes. St Francis was heard to mutter faintly the 142nd psalm. After that he struggled to sing his own 'Canticle of the Creatures', which contains these lines:

> And Death is our sister, we praise Thee for Death,
> Who releases the soul to the light of Thy gaze;
> And dying we cry with the last of our breath
> Our thanks and our praise.

But St. Francis' voice failed at that moment. He died singing the praise of death.

Quoted in 'Philosophy of Death and Dying' by M. V. Kamath.

Death of Socrates

'We'll try to follow your wishes,' said Crito. 'But how should we bury you?'

'However you please,' replied Socrates, 'that is, if you can catch me and I don't slip away from you.'

The slave went out and stayed away a long time and then returned with the man who was to administer the poison; he brought it in a cup ready for use. When Socrates saw him he said 'Well, my good man, you know about these things; what must I do?'

'Nothing,' he replied, 'except drink it and then walk about until your legs feel heavy, and then lie down. Then the poison will act of its own accord.'

'What do you say about pouring a libation from this drink to a god? Is it permitted, or not?'

'We prepare only as much as we think is enough, Socrates,' he replied.

'I understand,' said Socrates. 'But I may and must pray to the gods that my departure from this world may be fortunate. So I offer this as my prayer and may it be granted.' With these words, with no sign of disgust and quite calmly, he drank the cup to the last drop in one breath.

Socrates walked about, and when his legs were heavy, he lay down on his back – that was what the man advised. The man who had administered the poison laid his hand upon Socrates, and after a little while examined his legs and feet; then pinched his foot hard and asked if he felt it. Socrates said No. Then he pinched his legs; and moving upwards in this way he showed us that he was getting cold and rigid. The man felt him again and said that when it reached the heart, Socrates would be gone.

The chill had now reached his belly when Socrates uncovered his face – which he had covered up – and said (these were his last words): 'Crito, we owe a cock to Aesculapius. Don't neglect this.'

From Plato's 'Phaedo', translated by Marcelle Papworth.

The seamless death

The seamless death is when the fabric of life and death is so closely knit you cannot see the joins. Sometimes this seems to be an enviable quality, at other times more dubious. When the New York wit Dorothy Parker was told of the death of President Warren G. Harding, not the most charismatic of men, she is said to have retorted, 'How can they tell?' A more admirable case of the seamless death is that of America's first President, *George Washington*. On his deathbed he gave matter-of-fact instructions to his aide, as if dying were a daily occurrence:

Death of George Washington

I find I am going, my breath cannot continue long; I believed from the first attack it would be fatal; do you arrange and record all my late military letters and papers; arrange my accounts and settle my books, as you know more about them than anyone else.

Quoted in 'Philosophy of Death and Dying' by M. V. Kamath.

This is natural death, Western-style. Washington died as he lived, polite and civil to the end. Another of the founding fathers of the United States, President *Thomas Jefferson*, author of the Declaration of Independence, was determined to die on the fourth of July.

Death of Thomas Jefferson

On the third of July Jefferson slept throughout the day only to wake up in the evening, about seven o'clock. By his side were his faithful grandson Jefferson Randolph and Nicholas Trist, husband of his granddaughter Virginia. He stirred. 'This is the fourth of July,' he noted, but had to be reminded that it wasn't. It was the third. At 9pm his doctor came to administer some medicine, but Jefferson wanted none of it. 'No, doctor, nothing more,' he said, his voice still clear and distinct.

He was getting restless. He sat up in bed, leaned forward as if in a gesture of writing. He was delirious. 'The Committee of Safety must be warned,' he mumbled. In the corner, a grandfather clock ticked the minutes away. At 11pm Jefferson looked at Trist, asked, his voice a bare whisper: 'This is the 4th?' Trist pretended he had not heard. Afraid Jefferson was dying and even more afraid to tell a dying man an untruth, Trist was miserable. Jefferson repeated the question. Mutely, Trist nodded assent. 'Ah!' he heard Jefferson sigh, as if satisfied with the knowledge that he had seen the fiftieth anniversary of his beloved republic arrive. Now others joined Trist and Randolph at the great leader's bedside. Jefferson fell into a disturbed sleep. The midnight hour struck. Conscious or not, Jefferson had realised his desire. At 4 am on the morning of July 4th, Jefferson stirred and called for Burwell, one of the slaves he had freed in his last will and testament. He did not speak again. On the noon of July 4th, fifty minutes past meridian, Jefferson ceased to breathe.

Quoted in 'Philosophy of Death and Dying' by M. V. Kamath.

In the eighteenth century early Christian and classical influences are still discernible in the way of dying. The poet William Blake sang halleluiahs, in the style of St. Francis, as he went to meet his Maker. This was typical of Blake who was once found by a friend reading 'Paradise Lost' to his wife in the conservatory of their home. Both were nude, befitting the setting of Milton's poem in the Garden of Eden.

The philosopher *David Hume* took leave of life in a calm, stoical manner reminiscent of Socrates:

Death of Scottish philosopher David Hume

The Scottish philosopher died in 1776, aged sixty-five. Though he had had a long life by eighteenth-century standards, it was also a remarkably fulfilled life and enabled Hume to approach his death with dignity and wry good humour. Just before his death he talked to fellow Scot, Adam Smith. Since reading Lucien's 'Dialogues of the Dead' Hume had mused about what excuses he might offer Charon, boatman to the other world, for not wishing to come on board. He could find none: he had no house to finish, he had no daughter to provide for, he had no enemies upon whom he wished to revenge himself: 'I have done everything of consequence which I ever meant to do, and I could at no time expect to leave my relations and friends in a better situation than that in which I am now likely to leave them: I therefore have all reason to die content.'

From 'The Fireside Book of Death' by Robert Wilkins.

Yet death was not always as seamless as it appeared in the outwardly confident, mannered society of that time. Christian faith was alive, but assailed by doubts and terrors. James Boswell, the great biographer was driven to his wits' end, and, by his own account, to drink and whoring, by his father's Christian cheerfulness. The father, an Edinburgh judge and classical scholar, was everything that a pillar of his time ought to be but Jamie was a bit ahead of his time with twentieth-century existential hang-ups. Had he been around in the nineteen-sixties he would certainly have worn beads and experimented with pot. Nevertheless Boswell faithfully recorded the death of his hero and the subject of his biography, *Dr Samuel Johnson*, in the spirit of the times:

Death of Dr Samuel Johnson

When Dr Warren, in the usual style, hoped that he was better, his answer was, 'No, Sir; you cannot conceive with what acceleration I advance towards death.'

As he opened a note which his servant brought to him, he said, 'An odd thought strikes me: we shall receive no letters in the grave.'

He requested three things of Sir Joshua Reynolds: to forgive him thirty pounds which he had borrowed of him; to read the Bible; and never to use his pencil on a Sunday. Sir Joshua readily acquiesced.

Johnson, with that native fortitude, which, amidst all his bodily distress and mental sufferings, never forsook him, asked Dr Brocklesby, as a man in whom he had confidence, to tell him plainly whether he could recover. 'Give me' (said he) 'a direct answer.' The Doctor having first asked him if he could bear the whole truth, which way so ever it might lead, and being answered that he could, declared that, in his opinion, he could not recover without a miracle. 'Then' (said Johnson) 'I will take no more physick, not even my opiates: for I have prayed that I may render up my soul to God unclouded.'

From 'Life of Johnson' by James Boswell.

John Keats, the romantic poet, when he discovered blood on his sheet at the young age of twenty-five, looked at it steadfastly:

Death of John Keats

'I know the colour of that blood; it is arterial blood. I cannot be deceived by that colour; that drop of blood is my death warrant. I must die.'

He was persuaded to travel to Italy:

In Rome, the friends took rooms at the bottom of the famous Spanish Steps in the Piazza di Spagna. Keats rested but he had now no illusion of what was coming. To Brown he wrote: 'I have an habitual feeling of my real life having past and that I am leading a posthumous existence.'

All of December and the January and February following, Severn watched Keats with fraternal care and affection. Then the end came. On Friday, February 23rd, 1821, around four o'clock in the afternoon, Severn heard himself called. Keats was calling for him. 'Severn, Severn, lift me up, for I am dying. I shall die easy; don't be frightened. Thank God it has come!'

Severn rushed to his friend's bedside, took the young poet in his strong arms and waited. Severn was still holding Keats tightly when the poet died. In his 'Ode to a Nightingale' he had written:

Darkling I listen; and, for many a time
I have been half in love with easeful death,
Called him soft names in many a mused rhyme,
To take into the air my quiet breath;
Now more than ever seems it rich to die,
To cease upon the midnight with no pain.

Quoted in 'Philosophy of Death and Dying' by M. V. Kamath.

A little nearer to our day *Henry David Thoreau*, the philosopher of the woods and natural living, died as he lived, at peace with the world:

Death of Thoreau

Ill as he was, he never once complained. On the contrary, he seemed to be full of cheer. To a friend who tried to console him somewhat undiplomatically by saying: 'Well, Mr. Thoreau, we must all go,' Thoreau replied, 'When I was a very little boy I learned that I must die, and I set that down, so, of course, I am not disappointed now. Death is as near to you as it is to me.' He retained his sense of humour. When his aunt Louisa asked him if he had made his peace with God, Thoreau replied: 'I did not know we had ever quarrelled, Aunt.' A friend, Parker Pillsbury, visited Thoreau just a few days before the end came and casually asked: 'You seem so near the brink of the dark river, that I almost wonder how the opposite shore may appear to you.' Thoreau answered: 'One world at a time.'

As his mother, sister and aunt watched him, his breathing grew fainter and fainter and without the slightest struggle, as if he was going gently into the good night, he died at nine o'clock. A man who was ever at peace with himself, died peacefully.

Quoted in 'Philosophy of Death and Dying' by M. V. Kamath.

And yet around this time there was a growing sense that the Western tradition had begun to forget the purpose of ritual in meeting death, and to fail to recognise it in other cultures. Walt Whitman introduced the spirit of modernity to American poetry and art but was at the same time one of the first to recognise the importance of Eastern philosophies. Whitman used the ancient wisdom of the Upanishads in his verse in a way that later inspired the Beat movement of the nineteen-fifties which led to the hippy flowering of the Sixties. Whitman's poem describes the death of *Osceola*, an American Indian, at the time of the civil war. Osceola, imprisoned in an alien culture, reached into his own tradition in order to die bravely and consciously. The real-life background to the poem is equally important. It is prophetic of a modern phenomenon, namely the ancient cultures that have died 'of a broken heart' whilst Western technological society looks on, unaware of its own impoverishment and, in particular, of the importance of ceremony in natural death.

Death of Osceola, an American Indian, by Whitman

When I was nearly grown to manhood in Brooklyn, New York (middle of 1838), I met one of the return'd U.S. Marines from Fort Moultrie, S.C., and had long talks with him – learn'd the occurrence below described – death of Osceola. The latter was a young, brave, leading Seminole, in the Florida war of that time – was surrender'd to our troops, imprison'd, and literally died of 'a broken heart', at Fort Moultrie. He sicken'd of his confinement – the doctor and officers made every allowance and kindness possible for him; then the close:

> When his hour for death had come,
> He slowly rais'd himself from the bed on the floor,
> Drew on his war-dress, shirt, leggings, and girdled the belt around his waist,
> Call'd for vermillion paint (his looking-glass was held before him),
> Painted half his face and neck, his wrists, and back-hands,
> Put the scalp-knife carefully in his belt – then lying down, resting a moment,
> Rose again, half sitting, smiled, gave in silence his extended hand to each
>   and all,
> Sank faintly low to the floor (tightly grasping the tomahawk handle),
> Fix'd his look on wife and children – the last.

From 'Leaves of Grass' by Walt Whitman.

There comes a point where the Western tradition of seamless death does not work any more. The lack of distinction between life and death becomes a negative, a denial of death. Coming right up to our own time, the following description of a hospital death shows a peculiar alienation. The seamless death has come to mean a pretence that death does not exist. Death has been stripped bare of all its ceremony, its connection with home and loved ones, its ritual and celebration – in a word, its relationship to life. It has lost its natural form. 'Bravery' in this example means not consciousness but pretending you're not dying at all! This is Jill, a nurse by profession, describing *Tony*, her husband, dying in a surgical ward. She sums it up in one devastating image: 'like dying on a building site'. A building site!

Luckily in this case the form of natural death was restored when Tony was transferred first to a hospice and then, with their help, back home. The couple ended up fighting bravely for the dignity of the conscious death.

Tony Armstrong – a struggle for death with dignity

'Tony was on a surgical ward and there was no provision whatsoever for dealing with a dying patient. Apart from the doctors initially telling him "the news" it became a taboo subject.' One senior nurse actually said to Jill that if Tony wanted to turn his face to the wall and just die that was fine, but some patients she'd known were brave until the last minute. 'That was the worst moment,' said Jill. 'He was very brave and it was all so sudden. The week before he was swimming in the Mediterranean and the day before he was at work and now he was told he had between 48 hours and six weeks to live. He just couldn't adapt into the happy, smiling patient they wanted him to be.'

Jill felt that hospital staff must try and understand this and modify their 'jollying up' attitude to dying patients. She felt that what would have helped, was for someone to sit down with him and listen to and care about what he was feeling. 'The obvious policy there was that the terminally ill patient is to be avoided at all costs.'

Jill said, 'The pits was his dying on this busy surgical ward, it was like dying on a building site and I used all my back-door contacts to get him out. God help the poor buggers who didn't have those contacts.'

Jill eventually had Tony transferred to a hospice where the tension visibly seeped out of him. 'When he wanted to be alone he was alone, when he wanted to chat, about dying, or anything else, he could.' In fact it gave them the breathing space to decide where he wanted to die and for the last two weeks he went home, with the back-up of the domiciliary hospice service.

Had Jill's concept of herself as a nurse changed since this tragic experience? 'I'll never pass by a bed again without chatting to a dying patient,' she said.

From the Guardian (Oct. 1st 1986).

Modern and natural

The issue of natural death arises in the modern world partly because the artificial morbidities of the Victorian attitude to death have been succeeded by a plain way of dying, often in circumstances that seem drained of humanity. So powerful an effect did Victorian customs have on the imagination that we can be fooled into believing that what we have left behind, with our plain ways, is a series of empty rituals decorated in black crêpe. But we need to recognise that it is not so. What our modern plainness leaves behind, as our examples from the past show, is a rich diversity in ways of dying. Thankfully, modern people are increasingly coming to choose ways of dying that reflect not just the past but the individuality of their own lives. The key to natural death lies in the freedom to choose.

No two people could be more diverse in their lifestyles than the natural-living homesteader Scott Nearing and the sophisticated intellectual Aldous Huxley. Their chosen paths of dying reflect these differences. Yet it is encouraging to note the similarities of choice. Both chose to recognise, in a highly conscious way, the transition between life and death. Both filled this time with a courage and a dignity that were very much alive. And, at the end, both men were in close harmony with themselves and their partners.

A published account of Aldous Huxley's first wife's death describes how *Maria Huxley* came home from hospital with a rapidly deteriorating cancer of the liver. Huxley helped to make her comfortable through hypnosis:

Hypnotic suggestions and the death of Maria Huxley

These suggestions for physical comfort were in every case followed by a much longer series of suggestions addressed to the deeper levels of the mind. I went and sat by Maria's bed and from time to time leaned over and spoke into her ear. I told her that I was with her and would always be with her in that light which was the central reality of our beings. I told her that she was surrounded by human love and that this love was a manifestation of a greater love, by which she was enveloped and sustained. I told her to let go, to forget the body, to leave it lying here like a bundle of old clothes and to allow herself to be carried, as a child is carried, into the heart of the rosy light of love.

For the last hour I sat or stood with my left hand on her head and the right on the solar plexus. Between two right-handed persons this contact seemed to create a kind of vital circuit. For a restless child, for a sick or tired adult, there seems to be something soothing and refreshing about being in such a circuit. And so it proved even in this extremity. The breathing became quieter and I had the impression that there was some kind of release. I went on with my suggestions and reminders, reducing them to their simplest form and repeating them close to the ear. 'Let go, let go. Forget the body, leave it lying here; it is of no importance now. Go forward into the light.' When the breathing ceased, at about six, it was without any struggle.

From 'This Timeless Moment' by Laura Archera Huxley.

Aldous Huxley himself 'died as he lived, doing his best to develop fully in himself one of the essentials he recommended to others – awareness,' writes his second wife Laura Archera Huxley:

Aldous Huxley: death and awareness

Modern psychology has discovered how powerful the birth trauma is for the individual's life. What about the 'death trauma'? If one believes in the continuity of life, should one not give it equal consideration?

The Tibetan Book of the Dead gives the greatest importance to the state of consciousness at the time of death. The guide always addresses the dying person with the salute 'O Nobly Born!' and urges: 'Let not thy mind be distracted.' The guide keeps reminding the dying person not to become entangled in visions, heavenly or hellish, which are not real, but which are only the illusionary projections of his thoughts and emotions, fears and desires. The dying are exhorted 'to go on practising the art of living even while they are dying. Knowing who in fact one is, being conscious of the universal and impersonal life that lives itself through each of us. That's the art of living, and that's what one can help the dying to go on practising. To the very end.'

Laura Huxley gave Aldous on his deathbed, at his request, two injections of 100mg of LSD:

A decision had been made. Suddenly he had accepted the fact of death; now, he had taken this *moksha*-medicine in which he believed. Once again he was doing what he had written in 'Island', and I had the feeling that he was interested and relieved and quiet.

I began to talk to him, saying, 'Light and free you let go, darling; forward and up. You are going forward and up; you are going toward the light. Willingly and consciously you are going, willingly and consciously, and you are doing this beautifully; you are doing this so beautifully – you are going toward the light – you are going toward the light – you are going toward a greater love – you are going forward and up. It is so easy – it is so beautiful.' Once I asked him, 'Do you hear me?' He squeezed my hand; he was hearing me.

The breathing became slower and slower, and there was absolutely not the slightest indication of contraction, of struggle. The ceasing of life was not a drama at all, but like a piece of music just finishing so gently in a *sempre più piano, dolcemente* ... and at five-twenty the breathing stoppped

If the way Aldous died were known, it might awaken people to the awareness that not only this, but many other facts described in 'Island' are possible here and now. Aldous asking for the *moksha*-medicine while dying is not only a confirmation of his open-mindness and courage, but as such a last gesture of continuing importance. Is his way of dying to remain for his friends, and only for us, a relief and consulation, or should others also benefit from it? Aren't we all nobly born and entitled to noble dying?

Adapted from 'This Timeless Moment' by Laura Archera Huxley.

'We rarely if ever,' writes *Scott Nearing*'s wife, 'used doctors, pills or hospitals. Yet Scott lived to a hale and hearty 100 and died when he decided to – by fasting for a month and a half at the very end.'

The Nearings are dissimilar to the Huxleys, but in their togetherness they could be the same couple. Scott's dying, as Helen describes it, was like nature itself:

Scott Nearing – 'death like a leaf falling from a tree'

He did more than his share of mental and physical work up to his last years. At ninety-eight he said 'Well at least I can still split and carry in the wood.' And when he was close to the end, lying in our living room, his one regret at leaving this Earth plane was on watching me lug in the wood for our kitchen stove, 'I wish I could help with that,' he said. He was a help unto the end.

A month or two before he died he was sitting at table with us at a meal. Watching us eat he said, 'I think I won't eat anymore.' 'Alright,' said I. 'I understand. I think I would do that too. Animals know when to stop. They go off in a corner and leave off food.'

So I put Scott on juices: carrot juice, apple juice, banana juice, pineapple, grape – any kind. I kept him full of liquids as often as he was thirsty. He got weaker, of course, and he was as gaunt and thin as Gandhi. Came a day he said, 'I think I'll go on water. Nothing more.' From then on, for about ten days, he only had water. He was bed-ridden and had little strength but spoke with me daily. In the morning of August 24th, 1983, two weeks before his hundredth birthday, when it seems he was slipping away, I sat beside him on his bed.

We were quiet together; no interruptions, no doctors or hospitals. I said, 'It's alright, Scott. Go right along. You've lived a good life and are finished with things here. Go on and up – up into the light. We love you and let you go. It's alright.'

In a soft voice, with no quiver or pain or disturbance he said 'All...right,' and breathed slower and slower and slower till there was no movement anymore and he was gone out of his body as easily as a leaf drops from the tree in autumn, slowly twisting and falling to the ground.

Excerpted from In Context magazine No. 26 (subs. $31, airmail $42, from PO Box 11470, Bainbridge Island, WA98110, USA, tel 0101 206 842 0216).

The familiar modern phrase 'terminal illness' is enough to strike terror into the heart. It suggests an illness for which there is no cure, a failure of modern science. There is no hint of death as a natural event and perhaps that is what is so terrifying, as if death somehow does not fit into the modern world. A group of terminally ill people and their relatives gather together for a popular television programme and are regarded as brave for coming forward and exposing their connection with death. And so they are. Extraordinarily brave. Under the glare of the studio lights they are forced to be bright, cheerful, to perform for the cameras in the same way as a dying patient has to perform for the clinical ambience of the modern hospital with all its sophisticated monitoring and life-saving equipment; to apologise to all that medical technology for being a failure, for dying. Nevertheless they do not lose their dignity. They are facing death with their eyes open. They talk calmly of practical matters, of freeing themselves from the burdens of daily life like credit cards and uncongenial jobs, of preparing their families for the inevitable event. They discuss the false friends who desert them, as if dying were contagious, and the true friends who remain, the families who give support, the husbands, daughters and mothers.

Nobody mentions science or technology, and it is curious how irrelevant these become when a person is finally in charge of his or her own death. *Albert Einstein*, the father of modern physics, was impatient of medical technology at the point of death.

Albert Einstein refusing surgery

The patient was given an electrocardiogram, fixed up in a bed and given morphia injections to kill the pain. The diagnosis was a small leakage of blood from a hardened aorta, but the doctor found Einstein 'very stoical'. More specialists were brought from New York who suggested operating. An operation, it was put to Einstein, gave him a fifty per cent chance of survival. Without the operation, his chances of survival were minimal. Einstein declined the operation. He was 'violently opposed' to the surgery. To Helen Dukas, his housekeeper, he said philosophically: 'The end comes some time; does it matter when?'

From 'Philosophy of Death and Dying' by M.V. Kamath.

In recognising death instead of brushing it aside the people in the television studio as well as the great discoverer of relativity are bravely and consciously taking a stand against the trend of our culture. By contrast the great cultures of the East have continued their recognition of death into modern times. When Ramakrishna Paramahansa became 'terminally ill' with cancer, his body wasted away as his spirit prepared for death. At the end he fell into samadhi as did, sixteen years later, his disciple *Swami Vivekananda* who founded the Ramakrishna Mission and brought the meaning of Hinduism to the West. The death meditation of the Tibetan Buddhists is illustrated in the accounts of an *old man* dying as the Dalai Lama gave a talk, and in the death of the *former abbot* of the Dalai Lama's monastery in Dharamsala.

Death of Swami Vivekananda

Around 1884, when he was forty-eight, his throat began to bleed. At first it was diagnosed as 'clergyman's sore throat' and treated as such. But as the bleeding continued, the malady was recognized for what it was: cancer. Swami Vivekananda had once prophesied that he would not live to be fifty. He died on July 4, 1902, six months before the target he had set for himself.

Soon the chapel bell rang the seven o'clock call for evening worship. Quietly, with a word that none should disturb him, he went to his own room for an hour's meditation. Then he called one of his disciples in and asked him to open all the windows and fan his head. Without a word, he lay down and a silence enveloped the room. The disciple continued to fan the Swami. Minutes passed and not a word was uttered. It was presumed that Vivekananda was either sleeping or gone into deep meditation and in any event it was not for the disciple to disturb him either by word or deed.

At the end of an hour, says Swami Nikhilananda in the Swami's official biography, Vivekananda's hands trembled a little and he seemed to take a deep breath. There followed a shattering silence. The Swami again took a similar deep breath. 'His eyes became fixed in the center of his eyebrows, his face assumed a divine expression and eternal silence fell.'

From 'Philosophy of Death and Dying' by M.V. Kamath.

Old man dying at a Dalai Lama talk

One year in Bodh Gaya the Dalai Lama gave a week of teachings and initiations, and over 100,000 people came from the various Himalayan kingdoms. Babies were born in this time, and several old people died. One night I saw an old man sitting under a tree. He sat in peace and serenity, quietly saying his prayers and rejoicing in his good fortune at having made it to the holy place of Bodh Gaya at such an auspicious time. He looked over at the group I was with and beamed us an enormous smile. A few minutes later he leaned back against the tree and, still sitting in the meditation posture, passed away. His face expressed perfect contentment.

From 'Death and Dying' by Glenn H. Mullin.

Death of former abbot of Dalai Lama monastery

This great guru had served as the abbot of the Gyu-me Tantric College for six years and then as abbot of the Dalai Lama's Nam-gyal Dratsang for fourteen. He then retired from monastic activity due to a heart condition, and lived quietly devoting his time to meditation and to receiving private students.

One day out of the blue he told me, 'For several years I have been promising to give a formal instruction to you. I think the time has now come. If you wish, you can invite some of your friends to attend as well.' Because the teaching was to be given in a group I arranged for a translator, and the day of the event drew near.

The teaching then began; but after about fifteen minutes I noticed that although he looked perfect when he himself would speak, even laughing and telling jokes, when he would stop and let the translator talk his face would change colour and he would curl up slightly and close his eyes to concentrate on his mantras, turning his rosary rather more quickly than usual. After several minutes had passed I leaned over and asked him if anything was wrong. 'Well,' he replied calmly, 'I'm having a heart attack.' At the moment the translator finished speaking and Rinpoche straightened himself again and went on with the discourse as though nothing were wrong. When he had paused again to let the translator speak I leaned over and asked him, 'Goodness, shouldn't we stop the teaching immediately?' He gave me a long, penetrating look.

'As you wish,' he replied, 'we can either go on now or finish another time.' I quickly called a halt to things and got everyone out of the room. Rinpoche moved over to his bed and sat in meditation, and several of his monks rushed in and began chanting to him in low, deep tones. He sat in meditation that evening without moving. The next day I visited his house. He was not well enough to receive me, but sent me a message. 'Rinpoche asks that you remember his teaching,' his attendant informed me. That night the lama sat in meditation and ceased breathing. His heart stopped and bodily functions failed, although he did not manifest the full signs of death. This is the practice of tuk-dam, when a yogi retreats to the heart in death meditation. He sat like this for three days without manifesting the signs of death. Then his head fell to one side and the process was complete. Such is the death of an accomplished yogi.

From 'Death and Dying' by Glenn H. Mullin.

In her book 'Deathing' Anya Foos-Graber makes the link between Eastern and Western ways of dying. 'The introduction of a support person, therefore, is the modern replacement of the supportive lama in Tibetan spiritual intervention in the dying process, who becomes a therapeutic presence, a monitor, and a coach to keep the dying "on course" during the deathing experience.' She goes on to describe the teaching she receives from a Westerner, *Paul Twitchell,* in the Eastern art of consciousness withdrawal, during the process of his dying.

Paul Twitchell and the art of consciousness withdrawal

I have witnessed the deaths of various friends and strangers, including the controlled and final moments of Paul Twitchell, who showed me that 'deathing' was possible. This renowned and skilful adept gave me my first example of conscious and voluntary withdrawal from an impaired and physical body in his final out-of-body experience. I have never forgotten the courage and control he displayed while in acute pain from a massive coronary. I tried to comfort him and act as what I would now call a support person, but at the time I was clumsy in ignorance and inexperience. Although obviously in pain, he showed courtesy and good humour at my awkwardness. Even while dying, he was able to teach me as we shared consciousness. I chanted and breathed with him to keep his attention focused and to ease his transition. This practice, which quieted me as well, is now a fundamental part of the method for conscious deathing.

As Paul died, he laboured with his breath in long-held exhalations, as I recall having done during childbirth's labour. While I had concentrated on my breathing to help the birth, Paul breathed carefully to ease himself out of life. Slowly he performed what I now call consciousness withdrawal; as he did so, the personal connection I had always felt with him winked out. Gone – it was like the ceasing of a song – and its absence made clear what his presence had meant. But in its place was a radiant harmony that permeated the room in a much vaster presence which has never left me.

From 'Deathing' by Anya Foos-Graber.

The connection between dying and birth is close to the hopes of the Natural Death Centre for a holistic midwifery service for the dying.

'People have choice over giving birth, why not mode of death?' asks a letter writer. The Natural Death Centre welcomes accounts of dying experiences under modern conditions. This particular letter contrasts 'two deaths, one where Graham virtually organised his own and the other where Joyce was a victim of the system and not in control'. *Graham* died at home, surrounded by support. *Joyce* died in hospital. In contrast, a *good hospital death* is described by a letter writer who had discussed in advance with her husband how to approach the experience, and who was allowed by the hospital to remain fully involved.

Death of Graham, 'who organised his death at home'

The first death I wish to share with you was our hospital chaplain, a Baptist Minister. His death sparked off some thoughts when I read about The Natural Death Centre, as I feel Graham had as natural a death as possible.

I felt very strained as I had the feeling his wife knew his prognosis but he hadn't a clue. The following week he was to get results of a liver biopsy. The day before these results his GP, a practising Christian, came to warn him that it would be grim news. A week later I steeled myself to visit. His wife said he had taken to his bed too weak to get up. His sister, an SRN, had come home from her missionary job in China. His other sister, another SRN, had also come to stay to nurse him. Graham was aware he hadn't long to live and arrangements had been made years ago that they would care for each other when the time came for any one of them to die. He told his wife he would like to see me two days later. I visited and was concerned to find the spiritual side of him in great distress. He talked to me about his funeral. I mentioned this to his wife who looked shocked, and I asked her to 'grab a space' to talk with him.

That weekend Graham's son, who is a GP, stayed, also his daughter, a nurse. His own GP prescribed painkillers, and half the dose prescribed was given at Graham's request, so as not to be 'knocked out'. The most loyal church members came to his house and had a service on the Sunday evening, and a visiting minister gave communion. I understand this, plus a vicar colleague who counselled him, gave him spiritual peace and strength. His grandchildren visited and cuddled him, bringing him garden flowers. His house meanwhile was filled with flowers and cards. I mentioned to Iris about keeping visitors to family now so he could have dignity. The nurse began to call daily the last four days of his life. Apparently Graham was debating water rates about two hours before he died.

As far as Graham was concerned he probably couldn't have had all his visitors and 'cuddles' in hospital. I'm sure he couldn't have had a service in his room in hospital (perhaps he could in some). I doubt he could have had the privacy to arrange his affairs with his sons.

His family must feel fulfilled in that they gave him the best, with people he loved.

From a letter to The Natural Death Centre.

Death of Joyce, a nurse, in hospital

This death was that of a nursing colleague who had retired. Her husband had cancer of the throat at Christmas. Joyce nursed him and had support from Macmillan nurses and the priest of the Catholic Church. Two weeks ago, after investigations for her sudden weight loss, cancer of the pancreas and liver were diagnosed. Joyce was sent home. She had a massive stroke and was readmitted to hospital that day. Her husband had clear results from his post radiotherapy/ chemotherapy tests. I visited Joyce in hospital: she had been given two weeks to live. She was in a side ward which was clean and pleasant, with flowers. She was very well cared for and four members of the family were there all day. There was no restriction on visiting. Her meal arrived, whilst my friend and I were there; being both nurses we fed her. Joyce knew we were there but she slept quite a lot as she was on MST. I asked her if she felt peaceful; she said, No, she wasn't. Her husband told us she wanted to be at home; Joyce has two daughters and a son. I really felt for her. Between all her loving friends at our hospital we could have maintained a rota without any difficulty. Her husband stayed the night and she died just over a week after admission. Prior to her death a move to a hospice was mentioned, as she was occupying an acute medical bed. Her husband opposed this and she died a day later.

From the same letter as above.

A good hospital death

I am sure you are right in saying that we need to make death and dying a topic of ordinary conversation if we are to prepare for our own deaths, love our partners through their dying and support bereaved friends. Thirteen years ago my husband died after a sub-arachnoid bleed. I was fortunate because I was invited to stay in the hospital for the sixteen days he lived and was treated as part of the caring team. It was one of the greatest experiences of my life. But I think that was so only because we had talked beforehand about what we would do if one of us was so ill that death became preferable to a life of very poor quality. I had no decisions to make and could explain our views to a sympathetic consultant and ward sister, so there was no officious striving. I have never felt more useful and shall always be grateful that, although my husband was in a coma, our relationship continued to grow. Few people understand how sharing dying can be a positive experience and give the courage and strength to grieve and go on to construct a new life alone.

From a letter to The Natural Death Centre.

Natural death, where it is allowed to happen, takes many forms depending on the individual and the specific circumstances. The published account of *Sophie's* death, given below, seems to radiate with the indomitable spirit of life emerging from a grotesquely wasted body. *Mrs Thayler's* death in hospital is described by a 'support person', a true midwife of death who came to realise that the pain of dying was like the pain of labour, giving birth to the soul. Another support person, a Christian priest, describes the ritual of dying among the Alaskan Indians where the active role of the dying person is emphasised. *Old Sarah* organised her own death, assigning a supportive role to the priest who realised about these people that 'few of them required the services of a doctor to tell them they were terminal'.

Death of Sophie in a hospice

When I saw her I thanked goodness for the existence of hospices. The nurses got her care and treatment just right and she was given whatever her heart desired (real filter coffee and rice pudding) to make her last days dignified and comfortable. Her unusual personality was recognised and acknowledged.

Her cancer was now very advanced and she was close to death, a skeleton weighing only four stone. Her hair was matted, her eyes were gummed up, whiskers had sprouted all around her face and a gigantic tumour was growing on her neck, but she was still alert, witty and articulate. Her skin was too tender to be touched anywhere so massage was not appropriate, but I sat with her for hours on end, talking or being silent – whatever she wanted – and I found her a great inspiration. I learned a lot from her remarkable acceptance of death, an attitude I'd always felt and hoped was possible.

'This is the natural outcome of my life and I'm genuinely interested in the process of dying. I only hope it won't be boring after all this. I'm excited by what lies ahead. My bags are packed and I'm ready to go.' She loved to sleep now, she said – everything else required too much energy – and described a special dreaming state she kept slipping into, unlike any she'd ever known, wherein she was already half out of her body. It was a state of great lightness and peace, and she looked forward to it. 'It's like a rehearsal and not at all frightening. I can smell hay and roses and I just hope the real thing will feel like this.'

I toasted her with a glass of champagne in the beautiful French summer countryside and she was there in the warm smell of hay and roses. I thought about her all day, wondering if she could feel the connection as strongly as I did. The next morning I rang the hospice to speak to her and was told she had died the evening before, so I'll never know, but in my heart I shared that day with her.

From 'Acquainted with the Night' by Allegra Taylor.

Mrs Thayler and the 'labour pains' of dying

I only had a little time with her. Enough to share love but not yet to share a space called God. She returned from the operating room and it was clear that she was dying. She lay in agony for hours, every breath a groan. Her pain drove everyone away. Doctors and nurses couldn't stand to come into the room, so I had an opportunity to sit for long periods of time with her undisturbed. I sat open, waiting for anything that needed to come through. Nothing came. Only groans. I sat, willing to do anything to help her soul fly free. And Mrs Thayler struggled on into death. I thought, 'What am I doing here? What kind of presumption is it of me to sit with this one in her agony of death? I know nothing.' Well, knowing nothing is my usual state, so I sat on. She struggled and I felt her struggle. I came away troubled, my body full of her groaning agony.

It wasn't until the next day that understanding came. I came to my friend to talk about this struggle I still felt in my body and lay down with my head in his lap. I couldn't tell the difference between Mrs Thayler and me. Her body, my body, the same. My body began to grow like hers and as I let her, my, our, groaning come, finally it came clear. Exactly the same as when I see a bird singing in the trees. Perfect praise of God. The bird's life, the bird's song, a statement of the perfection of God. And Mrs Thayler's life, her death agony, a song in praise of God. A perfect song, a perfect statement of God. The groans were labour pains, only she was giving birth to her soul out of her mouth, letting it fly free from her body; and the death agony – labour pains. I couldn't see how it was because I wanted her to be out of what appeared to be struggle.

From 'Who Dies?' by Stephen Levine.

Old Sarah in the Arctic – and her sense of timing

By far the most dramatic instance of timing and planning was the dying of old Sarah. About two weeks before her death I received a radio message from Old Sarah summoning me to Arctic Village on a specific day. Nothing like this had happened to me before but I can remember thinking 'she intends to die on that day.' Dutifully I gathered three of her family in Fort Yukon and flew them to Arctic Village on the day designated. I was right about her intentions but wrong about the date. She had a son in another village and wished me to go and bring him to Arctic Village. She allowed enough time for me to bring in the last person. It was quite a company of people, as was fitting for the undisputed matriarch of both the family and the community.

During the morning of the next day she prayed for all the members of her family. At noon we had a great celebration of the Eucharist in her cabin complete with all the hymns and prayers. Old Sarah loved every minute of it, joined in the prayers and the singing and was quite bright throughout the service. Then we all left and at six in the evening she died.

Old Sarah didn't need much bolstering of her will.

She was on familiar ground with familiar people and was carrying out a long tradition. But in our communities today many people die in some kind of isolation; a strange hospital room, the regimen of hospital life, controlled visits, medication (often mind-dulling) and possibly a battery of life-support systems. How can an individual exert much will, continue growing, reaching out, and giving in that kind of setting? That defines the task of those who love him: to break through the isolation and offer human warmth, the liveliness of one personality in contact with another and the opportunity for the dying to be heard and understood and to give his gifts of love.

From 'Dying Among Alaskan Indians' by Murray Trelease in 'Death, the Final Stage of Growth', edited by Elisabeth Kübler-Ross.

A gift for the dying is the theme of what is perhaps the most moving of all the stories collected in this Natural Death Handbook. It concerns the death of a fifteen-year-old girl, *Lee*.

Lee – 'dolphin therapy' for a dying 15-year-old

'It's not easy to die when you are fifteen, but Lee had already accepted her fate,' said Robert. As he spoke, his eyes were full of tears and he could barely keep his voice steady. 'She knew she had an illness that would not spare her. She knew that in spite of their finest efforts the doctors couldn't save her. She suffered a lot but never complained. This particular evening she seemed tranquil and composed but suddenly she said, "Mama, daddy – I think I'm going to die soon and I'm afraid. I know I'm going to a better world than this one and I'm longing for some peace at last but it's hard to accept the idea that I'm going to die at only fifteen."

'We could have lied, telling her of course she wasn't going to die, but we didn't have the heart. Somehow her courage was worth more than our pretence. We just cuddled her and cried together. Then she said, "I always dreamed of falling in love, getting married, having kids ... but above all I would have liked to work in a big marine park with dolphins. I've loved them and wanted to know more about them since I was little. I still dream of swimming with them free and happy in the open sea." She'd never asked for anything, but now she said with all the strength she could muster, "Daddy, I want to swim in the open sea among the dolphins just once. Maybe then I wouldn't be so scared of dying."

'My wife and I talked it over and decided to do everything we could. We had heard of a research centre in the Florida Keys and we phoned them. "Come at once," they said. But that was easier said than done. Lee's illness had used up all our savings and we had no idea how we would be able to afford air tickets to Florida. Then our six year old, Emily, mentioned that she'd seen something on television about a foundation that grants the wishes of very sick children. So I phoned the number and three days later we were all on our way.

'When we arrived at Grass Key, Lee was pale and terribly thin. The chemo-therapy she'd been having had made all her hair fall out and she looked ghastly, but she didn't want to rest for a minute and begged us to take her straight away to the dolphins. It was an unforgettable scene. When she got into the water, Lee was already so weak she hardly had the strength to move. We had all put her in a wet suit so she wouldn't get cold, with a life preserver to keep her afloat.

'I towed her out toward the two dolphins, Nat and Tursi, who were frolicking around about thirty feet away from us. At first they seemed distracted and uninterested but when Lee called them softly by name they responded without hesitation. Nat came over first, raised his head and gave her a kiss on the end of her nose. Then Tursi came over and greeted her with a flurry of little high-pitched squeaks of joy. A second later they picked her up with their mighty fins and carried her out to sea with them.

"It feels like flying!" cried Lee, laughing with delight. I hadn't heard her laugh like that since before she became ill. I could hardly believe it was true, but there she was gripping Nat's fin and challenging the wind and the immensity of the ocean. The dolphins stayed with Lee for more than an hour, always tender, always attentive, never using any unnecessary force, always responsive to her wishes.

'There are no words to describe the effect that swim had on her. When she got out of the water it was as if she had been reborn.

'The next day she was too weak to get out of bed. She didn't even want to talk, but when I took her hand she squeezed it and whispered, "Daddy, don't be sad for me. I'll never be afraid again. The dolphins have made me understand that I have nothing to fear." Then she said, "I know I'm going to die tonight. Promise me that you'll cremate my body and scatter my ashes in the sea where the dolphins swim. They have left me with a great feeling of peace in my heart and I know they will be with me on the long journey that lies ahead." Just before dawn she woke and said, "Hold me, daddy, I'm so cold." And she died like that in my arms a few minutes later – passing from sleep to death without a ripple. I only realised her suffering was over because her body became colder and heavier.

'We cremated her as she wanted and went out the next day to scatter her ashes in the ocean amongst the dolphins. We were all crying, I'm not ashamed to say; not just my wife and I and our three other children, but even the sailors on the boat that had taken us out into the bay. Suddenly, through our tears, we saw the great arching silver shapes of Nat and Tursi leaping out of the water ahead of us. They had come to take our daughter home.'

From 'Acquainted with the Night' by Allegra Taylor.
Note: In the UK, the Starlight Foundation (see under Organisations in the Resources chapter) attempts to grant the wishes of critically ill children.

Remarkable models

Like the ancients, then, we have our own modern models of the brave and conscious death. Finally in this chapter we present three extended accounts of modern deaths which seem to sum up everything the Natural Death Centre was founded to promote. Each one is remarkable. Each one is distinctive. Each one can hardly fail to inspire the rest of us. *Caroline Walker*, campaigner extraordinaire, died as she lived, campaigning. In this account (as told by her husband Geoffrey Cannon, and then by Judy Sadgrove) Caroline was campaigning to be thoroughly in charge of her own death.

Like Scott Nearing, described earlier in this chapter, Caroline, a nutritionist, decided to stop eating for the weeks before she died. Death by fasting, an alternative to euthanasia (as discussed in the Manifesto for the Dying chapter), is a subject which the Natural Death Centre is particularly interested in researching.

'Joan' – very different. She decided to explore her own dying process through an LSD programme. Starting off as a housewife and mother, Joan became a spiritual adventurer, using her death to explore the meaning of her life and to re-experience her childhood.

Andy, Claudia Melnyk's husband, died in her arms at home after Claudia had experienced and rejected the impersonal, regulated hospital environment.

Caroline Walker – a gentle death by fasting

Caroline was exasperated rather than fascinated by her illness. We did learn a lot, though; enough to make another book. For example, when a doctor says you have cancer he (it's usually a he) will no doubt go on to say what will become of you. Our advice is take note, say thank you, shop around, and take your own decisions. After all, if a builder says you have dry rot, you do not immediately take his word for it, sign his estimate without looking at the small print, shut your eyes and resign yourself to the pickaxes. (No disrespect intended, to doctors or builders.)

There again, just as there are societies to encourage home births, there should be societies for home deaths. Being looked after at home is more trouble, of course, just as home cooking takes more time. But dying in hospital as most people do now, stuck full of tubes in white rooms, surrounded by sufferers and strangers, with those you love kept at the end of a telephone, is a sad and bad ending. Caroline thought being sent to hospital to die is like being put in a skip. (Again, no disrespect to builders or doctors.)

At home in August, Caroline finished planting our garden, with seeds and bulbs identified with little flags, so I would know what to expect the next spring and summer. She gave two interviews: one at the beginning of the month, for the

Guardian, on her sense of death, as we ate lunch; the other from her bed, at the end of the month, for 'The Food Programme', on the meaning of her work.

Our home filled with family and friends and flowers. Pain was the only uncertainty. The surgeons had warned me that obstruction caused by the cancer would eventually be horribly painful. Not so; Dr Anne Naysmith, consultant at our local community hospital, a woman about Caroline's age, disagreed; and with a careful cocktail of drugs, Caroline rested at home, and took responsibility for her death, simply by stopping eating, two weeks before she died. Around midnight as her last day began, she foresaw her death. How was it – what did the thought feel like? 'Oh, lovely,' she said; and we laughed. And it was lovely to be with her when she died.

From 'The Good Fight' by Geoffrey Cannon.

That was how Caroline's husband Geofrey Cannon saw her death. Her friend Judy Sadgrove was the Guardian interviewer:

She was resting after a long conversation in which she described what it was like to die. As she spoke, I could forget her gaunt and fleshless body. I'd known her as the campaigning nutritionist, attacking the food industry and the Government.

The ultimate irony was that Caroline was dying from cancer of the colon. Despite her emaciation, her spirit was still strong. Her campaign now was to urge us to come to terms with death in general. We are all so afraid of death, she said.

There was a phase when every time she shut her eyes, she'd see her own face, pallid, yellowish, grey, empty – already dead. She had visions a religious person might construe as significant. Towering crucifixes reared above her. But to Caroline the crosses were simply the archetypal symbol of death. 'After all, when I was young I went to church every week and gazed at crucifixes. Death in Christian society is mentioned only in association with Jesus. Were I a Muslim I would probably dream up quite another symbol.'

She derived most comfort from the regular presence of a healer, Julian Leech. 'I love seeing him. Not because I think he's going to come up with a miracle cure but because he's so relaxing to talk to. He's used to being with people who are dying and he has tremendous respect for the process, with no rejection or fear.'

'I have to live with it. Why can't other people? I know they find it difficult and disgusting, but whoever said that life was easy? Or that dying was a piece of cake? What do they want? Tinsel and gift-wrapping?' These are the people who said 'Poor you' and bought their way out with flowers. Caroline didn't feel poor. She was consumed by pain, which made her sometimes tense and fractious, but she was not poor. She did not want an Enid Blyton attitude to death. Indeed, she felt she had to be viciously blunt in imposing her death on the world. 'Dying is an alien state. You have to make the effort to communicate otherwise you are totally cut off. And you have to help others come to terms. Although I wasted much precious energy trying to prop up other people, I slowly learned who was important and who wasn't.'

Caroline has shone some light on the mystifying business of dying. She has been brave enough to expose her fear and other people's. We cling to life, avoiding thoughts of death until the very end. Surely that's too late?

From The Guardian (Sept. 7th 1988).

'Joan' and LSD therapy for the terminally ill

At her first LSD session Joan began an inward journey packed with illuminating visions and insights.

> Joan felt she 'became electric with fantastic energy' going through her. It was so much energy that no individual could contain it and handle it effectively; it was commensurate with the entire universe. It became clear to her that she contained so much energy that in everyday life she had to deny it, misuse it and project it on other people in a disowning fashion. She had a flash of herself in various stages of her life, trying on different roles – daughter, lover, young wife, mother, artist – and realised that they could not work since they were inadequate containers for her energy. The most important aspect of these experiences was their relevance for the understanding of death. Joan saw the magnificent unfolding of the cosmic design in all its infinite nuances and ramifications. Each individual represented a thread in the beautiful warp of life and was playing a specific role. All these roles were equally necessary for the central energy core of the universe; none of them was more important than others. After death the life energy underwent a transformation and the roles were recast. Joan saw her role in this life to be a cancer patient and was able to accept it.

At her second session:

> 'For what seemed like a fairly long time, I experienced my present family in terms of preparing them for my death. There was a scene in which I finally told them, after preparing myself for some time. In a sequence of scenes I was able to say goodbye to my children, my husband, my father and other relatives, as well as friends and acquaintances. I did it in a very individualised way, with regard to the personality and special sensitivity of each of them. Tears followed, but after a time there was warmth and cheer; at the end they all gathered around me to take care of me. I recall their fixing warm and sweet things to eat. After this I spent some good bit of time saying goodbye to them and to my husband – in turn – and realizing that there were caring people who were going to look after them. I said goodbye to them too, and felt that something of me would live on in them.'

> The second session proved to be very beneficial for Joan. She became reconciled to her situation and decided to spend her remaining days in a spiritual quest. After a vacation that the family spent on the west coast, she decided to say goodbye to her husband and her children. She thought that it would save them from the painful process of watching her progressive deterioration and make it possible for them to remember her full of life and energy. In California Joan remained in close contact with her father, who was himself interested in the spiritual path; he introduced her to a Vedanta group.

At her third and final LSD session:

> 'Toward the end of the day I became suddenly aware that I had found a way to legitimise my lifelong sadness: to become terminally ill. The irony of this situation was that I then found happiness and felt relief in this discovery. I wanted to get into the sources of my sadness. I saw that from very early my mother had not much to give me; that, in fact, she looked to me to give *her*. I did indeed have more to give her than she me. I experienced this as a heavy burden.

'I had much discussion with my father about sadness, what is wrong with it and why it is so discouraged by others. I described to him how much energy I expended pretending to be glad or happy or to smile. I talked about the beauty in sadness – sad sweetness, sweet sadness. I am not sad any longer that I am to die. I have many more loving feelings than ever before.'

After Joan's death her relatives and friends on the east coast received the invitation for a memorial get-together that she wrote personally when she was still alive. After they had all assembled at the appointed time, they were surprised to be addressed by Joan's voice from a cassette tape. It was much more than an unusual and moving farewell. According to the participants, the content and tone of her speech had a powerful comforting effect on those who had come to this meeting with a sense of deepest tragedy.

> From 'The Human Encounter with Death' by Stanislav Grof
> and Joan Halifax.

Death of Andy Melnyk at home

You're dying. Forget sudden death or peaceful coma – you're fully conscious and terminally ill. Given a choice, where would you want to die? Hospital, hospice perhaps – or at home?

Eighteen months ago, my husband Andy was dying. The brain tumour gave him no choices – but I knew which he would prefer. In hospitals he was always confused and disorientated. He lost his identity, becoming the nil-by-mouth or bed two. And visiting him, I was ever, myself, conscious always of other visitors, the routine, the regulations. If our children were allowed in, they fidgeted, wishing themselves elsewhere; if they were not, I worried about them. And I dreaded the return journey, fretted about shopping, household chores, the shortness of days spent travelling, waiting, visiting, travelling.

Medical institutions necessarily dictate conditions – where patients sleep, wash or eat; where, when, and even if they can see visitors. One cannot control the environment – cleaners bang around the beds, telephones ring unanswered, night nurses chatter and patients call out in pain or delirium. My visits often coincided with Andy's periods of irritability or drowsiness, with his meals or with the doctors' rounds, when I would be banished to the corridor. The impersonal atmosphere accentuated the awful distance that can develop between a dying person and those caring for him. Terminal illness involves enormous emotional struggles with guilt, fear, anger and grief. I spent hours staring through train windows blurred by tears. How much easier to cope with all this in the privacy of home.

To allow the choice of dying at home, several factors must coincide. The local health authority must provide nursing back-up, illness and patient must be manageable, and all parties concerned must agree. It is a challenge. But why not think of it as a luxurious alternative package to the NHS? Imagine the brochure:

Choose Home Ward, the truly private scheme; a single room, unrestricted visiting, choice of meals, total privacy. What more could one want?

Home nursing held few fears for me: I was used to helping Andy dress, wash, walk and eat. His progression towards death was a gradual decline, a series of 'lasts'. The last time he could walk, stand or sit without support, raise his head, speak or smile. In hospital, Andy was always 'as well as can be expected'. Now I knew exactly how well he was expected to be – and the nurses knew that I knew. It was such a relief to speak openly – no more clichéd 'comfortable' nights. I knew what he was eating, drinking, even excreting – and I knew exactly when he stopped. I watched his muscles losing power, his eyes losing sight, heard his last words, saw his last smile. When his circulation failed I warmed his chilled flesh with my own body. In hospital I could only hold his hand; at home I slept in his bed.

Family and friends came daily to say goodbye with a kiss, a touch or just a look. As the tumour mounted its final attack, it took with it the bizarre and aggressive behaviour that had blighted our lives and returned the original Andy, gentle, laughing, loving.

Normal family life carried on; his mother sat beside him, the children went to school, the sun shone. June, the district nurse, was briskly down to earth. 'If he dies in the night,' she warned me, 'don't call the doctor until morning, because he won't come!' And although we had accepted for months that Andy was dying, she told me firmly, 'You must let him go.' She was right. I stopped trying to involve Andy in the life that was leaving him behind and concentrated instead on letting him move towards death. Late one night, Andy's breathing became laboured. The locum GP said, 'You do know he is very, very ill?' meaning, 'You do realise this man is dying?' I assured him I knew. Somehow I also knew this night would be our last together. I held Andy in my arms and talked to him for hours. I told him that he was dying, that he need not worry about me, our children or his elderly mother. He had fought long enough: it was time for us both to let go.

He took three last breaths and at 4.43am time stopped for him. Although he lay still and sightless, I knew the essence of him was there with me and I kept right on talking while I closed his eyes, washed his face and called the children in.

The hours after his death were totally private. We could each say goodbye in our own time, our own way. There was no one to pull curtains around his bed, send his body to the mortuary or hand me a bundle of his clothes. We all look back on Andy's final illness as a positive time of immense tenderness which we were privileged to share. Perhaps it was Andy's last gift. With his passing went all our fear of death.

From an article by Claudia Melnyk in The Guardian (March 3rd 1990).

Chapter 3

NEAR-DEATH EXPERIENCES

Accounts from past centuries

Throughout life, preparations are made for the various rites of passage, from weaning a baby, to preparing for retirement, by listening to the voices of those who have already passed through those various stages. Yet the voices of those who may have undergone at least a temporary death are only now beginning to be taken seriously by mainstream society and mainstream science. This is despite the fact that the written descriptions of changes in consciousness during Near-Death Experiences (NDEs) have been available for centuries. The earliest English account comes from the Venerable Bede in the eighth century, who tells the story of a man who was thought to be dead:

An eighth century account

He came back to life and suddenly sat up – those weeping around the body were very upset and ran away. 'I was guided by a handsome man in a shining robe,' he said. 'When we reached the top of a wall, there was there a wide and pleasant meadow, with light flooding in that seemed brighter than daylight or the midday sun. I was very reluctant to leave, for I was enraptured by the place's pleasantness and beauty and by the company I saw there. From now on I must live in a completely different way.' He later left all his wordly responsibilities and entered the Melrose monastery.

Adapted extract from 'A History of the English Church and People' by the Venerable Bede.

Likewise, Montaigne, in the sixteenth century, described the pleasure of nearly dying, having been thrown from his horse. As he lay inanimate:

Pleasure in letting go

My attendants tried to revive me but in vain and, thinking I was dead, they began to carry me with great difficulty to my house.

On the way, after having been taken for dead for over two hours, I began to move and breathe. It seemed to me that life held only from the tip of my lips and I was closing my eyes to keep life out: I was taking pleasure in letting myself go. My life was merely a perception passing fleetingly though my soul, which was as weak as the rest of me, although the whole experience was not only truly free of pain but was reminiscent of the gentle sensation felt by those who abandon themselves to sleep. I believe that this is the same state that people find themselves in whom we see fainting in death agony, and I maintain that we pity them without cause.

From Montaigne's 'Essays', Bk II ch. II, On Training, translated by Marcelle Papworth.

Not only pleasure but an elongation of time were reported by a Victorian parson caught outside in a blizzard:

Review of life during fall

The story of the Reverend Edmund Donald Carr, who miraculously survived on the Lond Mynd on a January night in 1865 can still be found in the libraries of Shropshire country houses. In the weeks preceding Carr's adventure the snow had fallen to a greater depth than in the previous 51 years; however he set off to walk four miles from Woolstaston to Ratlinghope after lunch, to preach to three people, after which he set off home in a blizzard. He was not found for 18 hours, having lost most of his outer clothing before he finally passed out. In the course of one of the many falls he had before this, he experienced what is described as the agonal phenomenon.

'The pace I was going in this headlong descent must have been very great, yet it seemed to me to occupy a marvellous space of time, long enough for the events of the whole of my previous life to pass in review before me.'

From an article by Julian Critchley in the Independent Magazine (May 23rd 1992)

Albert Heim, writing in 1892, made a special study of NDEs resulting from falls, and gave as one instance his own such experience:

A fall in the mountains

As soon as I began to fall I realized that now I was going to be hurled from the crag and I anticipated the impact that would come. With clawing fingers I dug into the snow in an effort to brake myself. My fingertips were bloody but I felt no pain. I heard clearly the blows on my head and back as they hit each corner of the crag and I heard a dull thud as I struck below. But I first felt pain some hours afterward. The earlier-mentioned flood of thoughts began during the fall. What I felt in five to ten seconds could not be described in ten times that length of time. All my thoughts and ideas were coherent and very clear, and in no way susceptible, as are dreams, to obliteration. First of all I took in the possibilities of my fate and said to myself: 'The crag point over which I will soon be thrown evidently falls off below me as a steep wall since I have not been able to see the ground at the base of it. It matters a great deal whether or not snow is still lying at the base of the cliff wall. If this is the case, the snow will have melted from the wall and formed a border around the base. If I fall on the border of snow I may come out of this with my life, but if there is now more snow down there, I am certain to fall on rubble and at this velocity death will be quite inevitable. If, when I strike, I am not dead or unconscious I must instantly seize my small flask of spirits of vinegar and put some drops from it on my tongue. I do not want to let go of my alpenstock; perhaps it can still be of use to me.' Hence I kept it tightly in my hand. I thought of taking off my glasses and throwing them away so that splinters from them might not injure my eyes, but I was so thrown and swung about that I could not muster the power to move my hands for this purpose. A set of thoughts and ideas then ensued concerning those left behind. I said to myself that upon landing below I ought, indifferent to whether or not I were seriously injured, to call immediately to my companions out of affection for them to say, 'I'm all right!' Then my brother and three friends could sufficiently recover from their shock so as to accomplish the fairly difficult descent to me. My next thought was that I would not be able to give my beginning university lecture that had been announced for five days later. I considered how the news of my death would arrive for my loved ones and I consoled them in my thoughts. Then I saw my whole past life take place in many images, as though on a stage at some distance from me. I saw myself as the chief character in the performance. Everything was transfigured as though by a heavenly light and everything was beautiful without grief, without anxiety and without pain. The memory of very tragic experiences I had had was clear but not saddening. I felt no conflict or strife; conflict had been transmuted into love. Elevated and harmonious thoughts dominated and united the individual images, and like magnificent music a divine calm swept through my soul. I became ever more surrounded by a splendid blue heaven with delicate roseate and violet cloudlets. I swept into it painlessly and softly and I saw that now I was falling freely through the air and that under me a snowfield lay waiting. Objective observations, thoughts, and subjective feelings were simultaneous. Then I heard a dull thud and my fall was over.

> *From an article by Albert Heim in Jahrbuch des Schweitzer Alpenklub 27 (1892):327, quoted in 'The Human Encounter with Death' by Stanislav Grof and Joan Halifax.*

Until recently, the main reporters of near-death changes of state were philosophers, mystics and poets, from Plato and Pythagoras to Walt Whitman and Tolstoy. However, today, interest in the phenomenon of Near-Death Experiences (NDEs) is more likely to be promoted by developments in psychiatry and psychology and the resultant interest on the fringes of science in different states of human consciousness. Furthermore, modern resuscitation techniques have increased the number of people now alive who have 'temporarily died' and have generated a considerable amount of new research data.

NDE investigators

The challenge to explore this phenomenon was taken up by the Swiss-born American psychiatrist Elisabeth Kübler-Ross, renowned for her pioneering work with dying patients. She drew public attention to the fact that something quite out of the ordinary happens to a person on the verge of death. And a psychiatry professor, George Ritchie, who during his nine-minute 'death' had found himself in the presence of Christ in a heavenly realm, wrote a book entitled 'Return from Tomorrow'. This inspired Raymond Moody, an American, whose book 'Life after Life' (published in 1975) quickly became a best seller, advertising itself as 'actual case histories that reveal there is life after death' (although Moody himself said 'I am not trying to prove there is life after death. Nor do I think that a "proof" of this is presently possible').

'Life after Life' is based on 150 accounts, and from these accounts Moody extracted the fifteen most frequent elements. He labelled these in the sequence in which they tended to occur as follows: ineffability, hearing the news, feelings of peace and quiet, the noise, the dark tunnel, out of the body, meeting others, the being of light, the review, the border or limit, coming back, telling others, effects on lives, new views of death, and, finally, corroboration. This next account, a descriptive summary by Kenneth Ring, puts flesh on the bones of these elements.

The 'typical' NDE

The experience begins with a feeling of easeful peace and a sense of well-being, which soon culminates in a sense of overwhelming joy and happiness. This ecstatic tone, although fluctuating in intensity from case to case, tends to persist as a constant emotional ground as other features of the experience begin to unfold. At this point, the person is aware that he feels no pain nor does he have any other bodily sensations. Everything is quiet. These cues may suggest to him that he is either in the process of dying or has already 'died'.

He may then be aware of a transitory buzzing or wind-like sound, but, in any event, he finds himself looking down on his physical body, as though viewing it from some external vantage point. At this time, he finds that he can see and hear perfectly; indeed, his vision and hearing tend to be more acute than usual. He is aware of the actions and conversations taking place in the physical environment, in relation to which he finds himself in the role of a passive, detached spectator. All this seems very real – even quite natural – to him; it does not seem at all like a dream or an hallucination. His mental state is one of clarity and alertness.

At some point, he may find himself in a state of dual awareness. While he continues to be able to perceive the physical scene around him, he may also become aware of 'another reality' and feel himself being drawn into it. He drifts or is ushered into a dark void or tunnel and feels as though he is floating through it. Although he may feel lonely for a time, the experience here is predominantly peaceful and serene. All is extremely quiet and the individual is aware only of his mind and of the feeling of floating.

All at once, he becomes sensitive to, but does not see, a presence. The presence, who may be heard to speak or who may instead 'merely' induce thoughts into the individual's mind, stimulates him to review his life and asks him to decide whether he wants to live or die. This stock-taking may be facilitated by a rapid and vivid visual playback of episodes from the person's life. At this stage, he has no awareness of time or space, and the concepts themselves are meaningless. Neither is he any longer identified with his body. Only the mind is present and it is weighing – logically and rationally – the alternatives that confront him at this threshold separating life from death: to go further into this experience or to return to earthly life. Usually the individual decides to return on the basis, not of his own preference, but of the perceived needs of his loved ones, whom his death would necessarily leave behind. Once the decision is made, the experience tends to be abruptly terminated.

Sometimes, however, the decisional crisis occurs later or is altogether absent, and the individual undergoes further experiences. He may, for example, continue to float through the dark void toward a magnetic and brilliant golden light, from which emanates a 'world of light' and preternatural beauty, to be (temporarily) reunited with deceased loved ones, before being told, in effect, that it is not yet his time and that he has to return to life.

In any event, whether the individual chooses or is commanded to return to his earthly body and worldly commitments, he does return. Typically, however, he has no recollection how he has effected his 're-entry' for at this point he tends to lose all awareness. Very occasionally, however, the individual may remember 'returning to his body' with a jolt or an agonizing wrenching sensation. He may even suspect that he re-enters 'through the head'.

Afterward, when he is able to recount his experience, he finds that there are simply no words adequate to convey the feelings and quality of awareness he remembers. He may also be or become reticent about discussing it with others, either because he feels no one will really be able to understand it or because he fears he will be disbelieved or ridiculed.

From 'Heading Toward Omega' by Kenneth Ring.

Since the publication of 'Life at Death' in 1980 Kenneth Ring has found himself very much involved in near-death studies, helping found the International Association for Near Death Studies. His research seems to agree in most respects with the large study of the death bed observations of doctors and nurses carried out by Karlis Osis:

35,540 death-bed observations

The study was based on a large questionnaire survey; ten thousand questionnaires covering various aspects of death-bed observations were sent out, half of them to physicians and the other half to nurses. Detailed analyses were conducted on the 640 questionnaires that were returned. The respondents who returned these questionnaires claimed 35,540 death-bed observations.

Osis found that about 10% of dying patients appeared to be conscious in the hour preceding death. Surprisingly enough, fear was not the dominant emotion in these individuals, according to the physicians and nurses in the sample. They indicated that discomfort, pain and even indifference were more frequent. It was estimated that about one in twenty dying persons showed signs of elation. A surprising finding in this research was the high incidence of visions with a predominantly non-human content. They were approximately ten times more frequent than one would expect in a comparable group of persons in normal health. Some of these visions were more or less in accordance with traditional religious concepts and represented heaven, paradise, or the Eternal City; others were secular images of indescribable beauty, such as landscapes with gorgeous vegetation and exotic birds. According to the authors, more of these visions were characterised by brilliant colours and bore a close resemblance to psychedelic experiences induced by mescaline or LSD. Less frequent were horrifying visions of devils and hell or other frightening experiences, such as being buried alive.

From 'The Human Encounter with Death' by Stanislav Grof and Joan Halifax.

Music in NDEs

About 50% of people hear music during their NDE, and mostly 'music with a beautiful, floating sound', according to Dr Joel Funk, who is a professor of psychology at Plymouth

State College, New Hampshire, USA. Dr Funk played various kinds of music to 60 people who had had NDEs and found that they identified New Age style synthesised music as nearest to what they had heard during their NDE. 'Some people burst into tears when they recognise the music of their NDEs,' says Dr Funk.

Steve Roach of Tucson, Arizona, had an NDE after a bike crash and heard 'the most intensely beautiful music you could ever imagine' and decided 'to dedicate my life to re-creating the exact same sound.' The result is a record entitled 'Structures from Silence'. 'Many people contact me after hearing my recordings to tell me that they've heard the exact same music during their NDEs,' says Roach (see the Resources chapter, under Videos and Tapes).

Varieties of NDE

Karlis Osis and his colleague Erlendur Haraldsson examined whether NDEs varied between cultures. In their book 'At the Hour of Death' (published in 1977) they concluded that, although there were considerable similarities between Indian and American NDEs, the religious personages and symbols appearing in death-bed visions were different for each culture.

Although the majority of reports of NDEs describe the subject as having been in a state that could be likened to heavenly bliss, this is not universally the case. The myths on which many of us were reared, which conceivably may have their roots in experiences of the ancients akin to NDEs, are myths of both heaven and hell. As mentioned earlier, not all NDEs are sweetness and light. There may, for instance, be something in the Japanese culture that predisposes them to negative NDEs, at least according to one small study:

The Japanese find death a depressing experience

A study in Japan shows that even in death the Japanese have an original way of looking at things. Instead of seeing 'tunnels of light' or having 'out of body' experiences, near-dead patients in Japanese hospitals tend to see rather less romantic images, according to researchers at Kyorin University.

According to a report in the Mainichi newspaper, a group of doctors from Kyorin has spent the past year documenting the near-death experiences of 17 patients. They had all been resuscitated from comas caused by heart attacks, strokes, asthma or drug poisoning. All had shown minimal signs of life during the coma.

Yoshia Hata, who led the team, said that eight of the 17 recalled 'dreams', many featuring rivers or ponds. Five of those patients had dreams which involved fear, pain and suffering.

One 50-year-old asthmatic man said he had seen himself wade into a reservoir and do a handstand in the shallows. 'Then I walked out of the water and took some deep breaths. In the dream, I was repeating this over and over.'

Another patient, a 73-year-old woman with cardiac arrest, saw a cloud filled with dead people. 'It was a dark, gloomy day. I was chanting sutras. I believed they could be saved if they chanted sutras, so that is what I was telling them to do.'

Most of the group said they had never heard of Near-Death Experiences before. Perhaps the idea of dark, gloomy surroundings, ponds and reservoirs and pain and suffering appeared less like heaven to them and more like their experiences of Tokyo on a wet, winter Monday.

From an item by Peter Hadfield in the New Scientist (Nov. 30th 1991).

Margot Grey's investigations also uncovered a number, albeit a tiny minority, of unpleasant NDEs. Positive experiences, as we have seen, include a feeling of wholeness, joy and a lack of isolation; those who have negative experiences, while they only occasionally describe 'hell-like' scenes, nevertheless find themselves on the edge of something unpleasant, and unwilling to die:

Hanging on, in agony, to life

I felt like I was in a great black vacuum. All I could see were my arms hanging on to a set of parallel bars. I knew if I relaxed, my grip on life would cease. It was a complete sense of knowing that life had to be clung to. I knew without any question if I let go, I would die. The feeling of agony of hanging on only lasted a brief while.

From 'Return from Death' by Margot Grey.

From negative to positive

Yvonne Malik felt that she had to pass through 'humanity's fear and ignorance' during her NDE, and that in the end she was 'allowed' to return because she wanted to show others that life after death does exist:

I seemed to be in some outside place which was dark, or almost black, and I was going towards an even blacker area. I wasn't running but was moving; aiming to go up the side of a black mountain; in the dark going upwards.

Although it was so dark, I could 'see' that I was passing or being passed by a lot of men and women who were all rushing in the opposite direction away from me.

They were telling me in both an apathetic and angry way, not to go in the direction I was going because there was nothing there, that I was a fool, that it was useless and led nowhere.

Suddenly it was as if I were up on top of the mountain on a kind of plateau, it wasn't cold and there was no wind. I could see the tops of other mountain ranges and valleys, but was too high up to see people.

I was surrounded by light, it was golden yellow, very bright and seemed to become brighter and whiter. There was no need to squint as it was not painful.

Words are only useful when used to describe parallels – in this case words do not seem to work. The light itself had a personality, it *was* joy (an old-fashioned word). The air itself seemed to be full of love and joy.

Although I did not look around, I felt strongly aware that two 'guardians' were standing just behind me on my left. It seemed to be that I should not turn around to see them, but as I felt so sure of their presence, it did not seem important to try to do so. I had the definite feeling also, that they had great wisdom and compassion.

They seemed to 'tell' me that I could stay there in this absolutely wonderful place/experience if I wished. I do not know why on earth I said, No, and that I must go back to tell others just how wonderful it was and that it was untrue that there was nothing beyond the dark.

The essence of the NDE is the negative shock to consciousness that forces a transition to a higher level:

Confronting symbolic death

Confrontation with the issue of death is a pivotal part of the transformation process and an integral component of most spiritual emergencies. It is often part of a powerful death-rebirth cycle in which what is actually dying is old ways of being that are inhibiting an individual's growth. From this point of view, everyone dies in some form many times during the course of a lifetime. In many traditions, the notion of 'dying before dying' is essential to spiritual advancement. Coming to terms with the fact of death as part of the continuity of life is seen as tremendously liberating, releasing one from the fear of death and opening one to the experience of immortality. As the seventeenth-century Christian monk, Abraham a Santa Clara wrote: 'A man who dies before he dies does not die when he dies.'

From 'The Stormy Search for the Self' by Christina and Stanislav Grof, Mandula/Harper Collins, 1991, ISBN 1 85274 103 1.

Swami Muktananda described how he moved from terror of 'death' to a fearless rebirth:

From terror to fearlessness

I was terrified of death. My prana (breath, life force) ceased. My mind functioned no longer. I felt that my prana was passing out of my body. I lost all power over my body. Like a dying man, whose mouth is agape and arms outstretched, I emitted a strange noise and collapsed on the floor. I lost consciousness completely.

I got up after about an hour and a half and felt amused, saying to myself 'I died a short while ago, but I am alive again!' I stood up feeling deep calm, love, and joy. I realized that I had experienced death. Now that I knew what it meant to die, death ceased to have any more terror. I became completely fearless.

From 'Play of Consciousness' by Swami Muktananda.

The after-effects of NDEs

Not surprisingly, one of the results of these joyous and timeless experiences is that the great majority of subjects, whatever they may have believed before, become unassailably convinced that there is life after death. For many, this is simply a result of the conviction acquired during their NDE that their soul, or essence, can in effect be felt as separate from the body, and is a part of an infinite essence. Elisabeth Kübler-Ross tells a dramatic story of survival after death. A patient of hers, Mary Schwartz, appeared to her in fully materialised form ten and a half months after she had died:

Kübler-Ross visited by a dead patient

She said to Kübler-Ross, who has told this story to lecture audiences, 'Dr. Ross, I want to take two minutes of your time. Can we walk to your office?' Kübler-Ross began to conduct 'reality testing' on herself as they went to the office to assure herself that she wasn't hallucinating.

As they reached the office, Mary opened the door and entered. Kübler-Ross sat at her desk. Mary closed the door, walked over and stood in front of the desk. She said 'I came back to thank you and Rennie Gaines (a minister who was in attendance when Mary was dying) for helping me to die, but my major reason is to tell you not to stop this work now. The time is not right.' Kübler-Ross had been feeling frustrated and had considered stopping her work with the dying because of the opposition she had encountered among her colleagues. And now an apparition was telling her what was going on in her own mind. At that point, as Kübler-Ross described it to one audience, 'I did something shrewd in my desperation to obtain proof that this was real.' She lied to Mary Schwartz, saying she needed a note to send to Rennie Gaines. Actually, she planned to keep the note herself to compare signatures.

So she handed Mary a pencil and piece of paper, and asked if she would write a note for him. Mary appeared to be full of love, Kübler-Ross said, and she smiled as though she knew why her former doctor really wanted the note. She said 'Of course,' wrote the message, signed her name, moved back from the desk, looked at Kübler-Ross, and asked, 'You promise you'll not give up this work?' Kübler-Ross promised. Then Mary walked to the door, opened it, walked out and closed the door behind her. Kübler-Ross ran immediately to the door, opened it, but saw only an empty corridor. Nevertheless, this incident convinced Kübler-Ross of the reality of life after death.

From 'A Practical Guide to Death and Dying' by John White.

After this, Kübler-Ross resumed her work with the dying with renewed vigour.

Many of those who have had NDEs have found, upon recovery, that the spiritual side of their lives has become important to them, whether or not they had previously been conventionally religious. In some people this change was expressed modestly, casually almost – as related by this next woman whose NDE had been the result of a car crash which had actually killed her two young sons:

Letting the universe take charge

Without knowing the purpose, the boys died and were allowed to go on. And I died, but only symbolically – to my former way of life – and had to return. Does any of this make sense? When I revived, my life took on a different meaning, a commitment. I'm still a practical, level-headed person, but whereas before I was dogmatic and argumentative, now I let the universe take charge of my life. I don't have to be in charge, I just have to be.

From 'Acquainted with the Night' by Allegra Taylor.

Imbued with all the ardour of new converts, some have felt disappointed by what they have perceived to be the empty formalities of church services. Jayne Smith, in her NDE, felt that she had entered into a paradise of bright light and a flowery meadow saturated with colours she had never seen before. Afterwards she went consciously in search of religious fellowship:

God is about joy

When you've experienced total unconditional love, and then you are back in this world and can't find it anywhere, it leaves a kind of empty feeling. I was raised

Episcopalian. Before my experience, religion and God seemed such a long ago and far away thing; everything happened 2,000 years ago. But after my Near-Death Experience, I couldn't wait to go back to church.

So I went to church and heard a sermon on smoking and drinking. I found it a terrible let-down. I went other times, but the sermons weren't on anything that matters. I know God is about joy and I kept waiting for some minister to tap into love and joy and celebration, and to tell his congregation 'you are love'. Because that's what we are, I'm dead sure.

From 'Otherworld Journeys' by Carol Zaleski.

Even many of those who did not put any kind of religious label on their feelings after their NDE discovered that life as they knew it had been transformed for them. A decreased fear of death leads to feelings of enhanced health, well-being, tranquility and zest for life. The changes in life goals and values, which many view as a spiritual rebirth, include a renewed sense of individual purpose, an increase in compassion, an ability to be more loving, a desire for more wisdom, and the wish to develop their faculties and talents in order to be able to be of service to others. One woman, who took an overdose of anti-depressants, maintains that the significance of her NDE can be judged by its transforming after-effects:

NDE after a suicide attempt

The part of my story that's important is not so much the experience. What matters is how my life changed as a result. Just prior to the experience, I did my usual thing and ended up in a psychiatric hospital for about a month. And now I'm working in one. I'm the helper instead of the one being helped.

I don't drink or do drugs anymore. I just had my second year anniversary with AA. And I'm helping other people with their addictions and their feelings. And that's just amazing! If there's anything I didn't do, it was deal with my emotions. I didn't live in reality. I didn't accept life as it was. I didn't take responsibility for me. I was into blaming a lot of people.

So it's almost like my whole philosophy of life has changed.

Prior to the experience I didn't feel like I should be alive. After the experience I knew I was supposed to be alive. It was a vague feeling, but I knew.

I believe the experience was given to me to help me get on the right road, to help me see I am valuable and I should be helping people. And that's what I'm doing through my AA involvement and through my job. I'm reaching out a lot more than I did. I was really self-centered, and I'm growing out of that.

From 'Otherworld Journeys' by Carol Zaleski.

The following statements are also typical of this change:

Accepting others and showing feelings

Now I find that everyone I meet, I like. I very rarely meet someone I don't like. And that's because I accept them right away as someone I like. I don't judge people. And people respond to me in the same way and I think that they can feel this in me. I'm a very demonstrative person in showing my feelings. I haven't always been. I was with my children. But since I had that experience I kiss everyone I meet. It's just a natural thing, an expression of love.

One interviewee also stresses a more loving and healing relationship with others:

Insight into others

My joy comes from another's smile. I also notice that I reach out and touch people more, I seem to make people feel better. I know this - that when there's a family problem, everyone turns to me. I have more insight into other people. It's very difficult for me to lose my temper anymore. I can see the pain in other people's eyes. That's why they hurt other people because they really don't understand. The most important thing that we have are our relationships with other people. It all comes down to caring and compassion and love for your fellow man. Love is the answer. It's the answer to everything.

Both above extracts from 'Heading Toward Omega' by Kenneth Ring.

The president of the British branch of the International Association for Near-Death Experiences (see the Resources chapter), Dr Peter Fenwick, works as a consultant neuropsychiatrist at the Institute of Psychiatry at the Maudsley Hospital in London. The results of his survey of more than 300 Near-Death Experiences bore out much of the previous evidence. Of his sample, 38% felt more spiritual, 42% felt joy, 30% peace, 15% fear, and 10% a sense of loss. Half were convinced of survival after death; a third felt they had become more psychically sensitive; a third felt they had become better people; and a third felt they were more socially conscious. (Results reported in the Guardian, Oct. 12th 1990.)

We feel that people who have had positive NDEs would make very good recruits for any future midwifery service for the dying, since they have lost their own fear of death and in many cases report a strong urge to work with the dying, as described by another of Kenneth Ring's interviewees:

Everything went into place and I just knew what I had to do. It was as simple as that. And I had this urge – and I don't know where it came from – but I knew that I had to help people who were terminally ill. I read articles that just sort of came to me, and I said, 'That's it!' And it kept happening. And so it's been growing ever since. It's a nice feeling to work with them. You love them. I know sometimes when I go see someone, I go out of the room and I cry. I cry with them because you feel so bad, but you love them and you want to help them.

From 'Heading Toward Omega' by Kenneth Ring.

Mysticism and the NDE

The NDE seems to have a profound similarity to some varieties of mystical experience. The feeling of being at peace and blissfully unafraid can be compared to the joy of the mystic who manages to transcend himself or herself and be in union with God:

The necessity of ego death

An important way of experiencing symbolic death during transformation is the ego death. During the process of spiritual emergence, a person moves from a relatively limited way of being to a new, expanded condition. Often, in order to complete this shift, it is necessary for an old mode of existence to 'die' in order to make way for a new self; the ego must be destroyed before a larger self-definition becomes available. This is known as ego death. This is not the death of the ego that is necessary to handle daily reality; it is the death of old personality structures and unsuccessful ways of being in the world, which is necessary for the advent of a happier and freer existence. Ananda K. Coomaraswamy writes, 'No creature can attain a higher level of nature without ceasing to exist.'

Ego death can happen gradually, over a long period of time, or it may occur suddenly and with great force. Although it is one of the most beneficial, most healing events in spiritual evolution, it can seem disastrous. During this stage, the dying process can sometimes feel very real, as though it were no longer a symbolic experience but instead a true biological disaster. Usually, one cannot yet see that waiting on the other side of what feels like total destruction of the ego is a broader, more encompassing sense of self.

From 'The Stormy Search for the Self' by Christina and Stanislav Grof.

Because many of us are more accustomed to the outward trappings of formalised Christian religion, we often forget that the transcendent state is at its heart. Witness this description by a Christian, the Blessed Jan Van Ruysbroeck (1293-1381) who wrote:

Die to live in God

To comprehend and to understand God above all similitudes, as he is in himself, is to be God with God, without intermediary (but) whoever wishes to understand this must have died to himself, and must live in God, and must run his gaze to the eternal Light in the ground of his spirit, where the hidden truth reveals itself without means. This brightness is so great that the loving contemplative, in his ground wherein he rests, sees and feels nothing but an incomprehensible Light; and through that simple Nudity which enfolds all things, he finds himself, and feels himself, to be that same Light by which he sees, and nothing else.

Quoted in 'The Little Book of Life and Death' by Douglas Harding.

In this selfless state, a number of discoveries can be experienced. Martin Nathanael, who nearly drowned at the age of seven after falling out of a boat, believes that as a result he came to understand in later life:

All creatures one in essence

– that I am not this body; I inhabit a body which exists for my use;
– that my sense of personal identity is not dependent on the body;
– that I have subtle senses which bypass the brain and the physical sense-organs and whose modes of perception are more penetrating and versatile;
– that there is one consciousness, one life, which becomes differentiated through the various forms of life, which makes all creatures one in essence;
– that my essential nature is indestructible, invulnerable, immortal;
– that everything I do and how I respond to events is inwardly recorded;
– that there is a mighty, pure and loving Presence, for whom no words can do justice, who is available to me, especially in moments of crisis and danger.

From the New Humanity journal (subs. £14 from 51a York Mansions, Prince of Wales Drive, London SW11 4BP).

Walter Pahnke has made a comparative study of the transcendental experiences of mystics and religious teachers through the ages:

Characteristics of a mystical experience

Pahnke's mystical categories reflect the most important common denominators of transcendental states. The *sense of oneness or unity* with other people, nature, and the entire universe is a necessary condition of cosmic consciousness. *Ineffability* is another important characteristic; the ineffable quality of the experience can be due to its uniqueness, the intensity of the accompanying emotion, or the inadequacy of our language to describe it. The next typical aspect of mystical experiences is *transcendence of time and space*. This entails a feeling that the experience is outside of the usual space-time boundaries, beyond the past and future, in eternity and infinity, or in a completely different dimension. *Noetic quality* is another important feature; individuals are usually convinced that they are in touch with a deeper truth about reality and the nature of existence. Experiences of transcendence are always accompanied by a strong *positive affect*. This can range from peace, serenity, and tranquillity to an ecstatic rapture not dissimilar to a sexual orgasm of cosmic proportions. Accounts of mystical experiences are also characterized by striking *paradoxicality*. Many of the statements about such states appear to contradict each other and violate the basic rules of Aristotelian logic. One more aspect of these experiences deserves special notice, namely the sense of *objectivity and reality*. An individual tuned into cosmic consciousness usually has no doubt that he or she is confronted with the ultimate reality, which is in a way more real than the phenomenal world as it is experienced in a more usual state of consciousness.

From 'The Human Encounter with Death' by Stanislav Grof and Joan Halifax.

Many of these mystical features can be seen in the testimony of Claire Myers Owens, who began Zen training at the age of 74, and after six years had the following experience when meditating:

Zen meditation banishing fear of death

I slipped out of bed and placed the bed pillows on the floor to begin a meditation unlike any other I had know. My body immediately settled itself into a comfortable and proper posture, I sat with a 'sense of dignity and grandeur – like a mountain'.

I sat on and on – an hour? two hours? in full lotus position – motionless. Gradually my hands melted into each other. My knees were pierced by pain. My back was aching. All this was occurring at some far distance. Trivial matters like pain did not concern me.

As time passed my body grew heavier than heavy, like some great rock embedded in the earth, like some great tree strongly rooted in the deep, immovable – indestructible.

I wanted never again to move my body, never again to change anything. Any state into which I might move, a state of power – wealth – fame – love – passion – could not compare with the serene state of being I was in at this moment. It was peace – deep unutterable peace.

I seemed to have arrived at the end of a long journey, the end of a rough road that had offered many inspiring views along the way. It was a beautiful plateau on which I might rest indefinitely, at which I had arrived after years of striving on the path.

I felt no desire, no ambition, no regrets. No words can describe such perfection, such completeness, fulfilment and finality.

I was intensely aware of my body yet I felt suspended bodiless in a new height. Everything within me seemed to vibrate gently in a golden light. Then everything within me was in utter stillness – like an eternal stillness. Nothing anywhere except ineffable quietness and inexpressible stillness.

I did not feel the self fuse with the absolute. I felt that the whole universe – everything that is – the uncreated – changeless, beginningless – everlasting – was in me – was me – for a fleeting forever.

Everything was intangible, invisible, formless, and colourless – beyond the reach of the senses, above the grasp of conceptual thinking, beyond words – yet real as only reality can be. Everything was nothingness. Nothingness was everythingness.

Was it the end of everything or the beginning for me? Was it a glimpse of the bliss of life after death? All fear of death vanished right away – forever.

> *From 'Zen and the Lady' by Claire Myers Owens, Baratra Books, quoted in 'A Practical Guide to Death and Dying' by John White.*

Children's NDEs

Near-Death Experiences could perhaps be dismissed as people's conscious imaginations. This is less readily so in the case of children's NDEs. Melvin Morse has researched this subject – having himself once resuscitated a nine year old girl:

Morse first met Katie as a lifeless body in an intensive care unit. She had been found floating face down in a swimming pool a few hours earlier. Morse wondered whether she had been knocked into the water, or whether she had suffered an epileptic seizure.

Morse examined her carefully and reckoned that at best, Katie had a ten per cent chance of survival. She was one of the sickest children he ever cared for, and all the time he was looking after her he was convinced that she was going to die. However, she did not. After three days she made a full recovery, and when she was well enough, Morse summoned her for a follow-up examination:

A nine-year-old tours heaven

I marvelled at Katie when she came into the office. She was a pretty girl with long blond hair and a shy, frightened manner. Her eyes revealed an intelligence that hadn't been dimmed by the deprivation of oxygen to the brain that always accompanies drowning. There was nothing abnormal in her walk or mannerisms. She was just another nine-year-old kid.

Katie clearly remembered me. After introducing myself, she turned to her mother and said, 'That's the one with the beard. First there was this tall doctor who didn't have a beard, and then he came in.' Her statement was correct. The first into the emergency room was a tall, clean-shaven physician named Bill Longhurst.

Katie remembered more. 'First I was in the big room, and then they moved me to a smaller room where they did X-rays on me.' She accurately noted such details as having 'a tube down my nose', which was her description of nasal intubation. Most physicians intubate orally, and that is the most common way that it is represented on television.

She accurately described many other details of her experience. I remember being amazed at the events she recollected. Even though her eyes had been closed and she had been profoundly comatose during the entire experience, she still 'saw' what was going on.

I asked her an open-ended question: 'What do you remember about being in the swimming pool?'

'Do you mean when I visited the Heavenly Father?' she replied.

Whoa, I thought. 'That's a good place to start. Tell me about meeting the Heavenly Father.'

'I met Jesus and the Heavenly Father,' she said. Maybe it was the shocked look on my face or maybe it was shyness. But that was it for the day. She became very embarrassed and would speak no more.

I scheduled her for another appointment the following week.

What she told me during our next meeting changed my life. She remembered nothing about the drowning itself. Her first memory was of darkness and the feeling that she was so heavy she couldn't move. Then a tunnel opened and through that tunnel came 'Elizabeth'.

Elizabeth was 'tall and nice' with bright, golden hair. She accompanied Katie up the tunnel, where she saw her late grandfather and met several other people. Among her 'new friends' were two young boys – 'souls waiting to be born' – named Andy and Mark,who played with her and introduced her to many people.

At one point in the voyage, Katie was given a glimpse of her home. She was allowed to wander throughout the house, watching her brothers and sisters play with their toys in their rooms. One of her brothers was playing with a GI Joe, pushing him around the room in a jeep. One of her sisters was combing the hair of a Barbie doll and singing a popular rock song.

Finally, Elizabeth – who seemed to be a guardian angel to Katie – took her to meet the Heavenly Father and Jesus. The Heavenly Father asked if she wanted to go home. Katie cried. She said she wanted to stay with him. Then Jesus asked her if she wanted to see her mother again. 'Yes,' she replied. Then she awoke.

I didn't understand it. I began to investigate. I probed her family's religious beliefs. I wanted to see if she had been heavily indoctrinated with belief in guardian angels and tunnels to heaven.

The answer from her mother was an emphatic No.

My deepest instinct told me that nothing in Katie's experience was'taught' to her before the near drowning. Her experience was fresh, not recalled memory.

From 'Closer to the Light' by Melvin Morse.

Morse unearthed a number of other cases where he was convinced that the children's NDEs could not be explained by what they had previously read or heard – including this account by an 11-year-old:

Out of the body experience of an 11-year-old

I remember going to that hospital that day. My parents had gone into a room (the admitting office) when suddenly I heard a whooshing sound in my ears. I felt like you feel when you go over a bump in a car going real fast, and you feel your stomach drop out. I heard a buzzing sound in my ears.

The next thing I knew, I was in a room, crouched in a corner of the ceiling. I could see my body below me. It was real dark, you know. I could see my body because it was lit up with a light, like there was a light bulb inside me.

I could see the doctors and nurses working on me. My doctor was there and so was Sandy, one of the nurses. I heard Sandy say, 'I wish we didn't have to do this.'

I heard a doctor say 'Stand back' and then he pushed a button on one of the paddles. Suddenly, I was back inside my body. One minute I was looking down at my face. I could see the tops of the doctors' heads. After he pushed that button, I was suddenly looking into a doctor's face.

No, I have never heard of a Near-Death Experience. I don't watch TV much. If I read, I read mostly comic books. No, I didn't tell my parents about it. I don't know why not; I guess I didn't feel like talking about it. I have never heard of anybody having this happen to them. I would not tell my friends about it. They would probably think I was crazy.

From 'Closer to the Light' by Melvin Morse.

The sceptic's view of the NDE

While many people who have had NDEs are totally convinced about what has happened to them and the transformations that have occurred in their lives, many sceptics are convinced that the whole experience has nothing to do with life after death, or God, or infinity, but is explicable in simple mechanistic, that is, neurological terms.

Thus Dr Robert Buckman views the sense of peace and tranquility in an NDE as being caused by substances produced in the brain called endorphins, which are somewhat like painkillers. The nineteenth century explorer, David Livingstone, felt calm, peaceful and painless whilst being crushed across the chest in a lion's jaws. It led him to believe that 'death agonies' may appear so to the onlooker, but may be experienced differently by the patient, protected by a bodily defence mechanism switched on at the approach of death.

Dr Susan Blackmore, a Bristol University psychologist, explains the common NDE vision of a long tunnel with a bright light at the end, as the retina at the back of the eye becoming starved of oxygen, with nerve cells beginning to fire at random. There are more nerve cells in the most sensitive part, the fovea, so a bright spot that looks like the end of a tunnel is seen.

Her explanation is linked to the most common physiological explanation for NDEs, which is that the brain is in receipt of insufficient oxygen (cerebral anoxia). Or that NDEs are the result of temporal lobe seizure. This can produce similar effects to those of some NDEs, without necessarily accounting for the complete range of near-death phenomena. Whereas temporal lobe seizure causes distorted perceptions of the immediate environment, this is not always the case with NDEs.

Whatever the truth of the matter, to know that nature has evolved a way of allowing dying humans to feel blissful can only be reasssuring, even for the sceptic who dismisses the visions and feelings as delusionary. It is also reassuring to know that the term 'Near-Death Experience' is in some cases a misnomer – as we have seen, the same, or a seemingly almost identical, experience is accessed by people during 'peak' experiences, by mystics and by others who have not as yet suffered physical harm - such as those falling from a mountain or bridge, who have their NDE before even hitting the ground, when they have been no more damaged than a free-fall parachutist. The difference between the person falling from the mountain and the parachutist is one of expectation of harm and thus degree of shock; and this seems the essence of many experiences of heightened consciousness.

The trigger is any severe jolt to our normal consciousness, whether or not physically damaging, which brings about a complete change of perspective and releases us into a world of rich and strange magic.

In the end it comes down to a choice. Do you see consciousness as being contained and confined to the brain? For William James, Ferdinand Schiller and Henri Bergson, for instance, the brain was merely the transmitter of consciousness, necessary for our personal experiencing of consciousness but not its source, just as a radio set is necessary for the reception of programmes but is not their origin:

The brain a transmitter of consciousness not its source

James asked his audience what type of function the brain performed. Does it produce thought, or transmit it? Most, if not all, the major organs of the body are transmitters. The lung takes in air and transmits its nutrients to the rest of the body. There is, therefore, nothing unusual about organs that absorb and transmit; the difficulty would rather be to find an organ which, in any perfect sense, produces. The body neither manufactures the air it breathes nor the food it eats. If we do not manufacture what we eat or what we breathe, why assume that we manufacture, rather than regulate, what we think?

This transmission theory of the brain has the advantage that it solves problems, rather than creating them. The problem of the inrushes experienced in some mental illness, the problem of psychic phenomena and the problem of pure randomness in neo-Darwinism are real difficulties for the scientific world view.

This theory proposes a natural force of intelligence, which is perhaps received and transmitted by the brain, and also influences evolution in the direction of survival. That would restore purpose to nature, but it would also make possible, as James argued, the concept of human survival after death.

From an article by William Rees-Mogg in The Independent (July 29th 1991).

Of all the NDEs in this chapter, the one that most convincingly goes beyond a simply and solely neurological explanation is Professor Wren-Lewis's story of eating a poisoned sweet in Thailand. Among the more unusual elements in his NDE are that it is still continuing – he can switch back into it by mentally re-focusing on it at any time; that he used a dream-remembering technique – one that seems to help in recapturing the fullness of the NDE on first regaining consciousness; and lastly, that he experienced not the usual white light but rather a black darkness, albeit a radiant one. Here is his eloquent testimony:

The reluctant mystic – an NDE that didn't go away

I had spiritual consciousness thrust upon me in my sixtieth year without working for it, desiring it or even believing in it. The crucial event was a shattering, out-of-the-blue mystical experience in 1983 which, to the astonishment of everyone who knew me, and most of all myself, left me with a permanently changed consciousness, describable only in the kind of spiritual terms I had hitherto vehemently discounted as neurotic fantasy-language.

What happened in 1983 would nowadays be called a 'Near Death Experience', or NDE, though it differed in several notable ways from most of those I'd read about in the rapidly-growing literature on this topic (which I had, incidentally, dismissed as yet another manifestation of the mind's capacity for fantasy). In the first place, I had none of the dramatic visions which have hit the headlines in popular journalism and occupy a prominent place even in serious scholarly studies. As I lay in the hospital bed in Thailand after eating a poisoned sweet given me by a would-be-thief, I had no 'out-of-body' awareness of the doctors wondering if I was beyond saving, no review of my life, no passage down a dark tunnel to emerge into a heavenly light or landscape, and no encounter with angelic beings or deceased relatives telling me to go back because my work on earth wasn't yet finished.

I simply entered – or, rather, was – a timeless, spaceless void which in some indescribable way was total aliveness – an almost palpable blackness that was yet somehow radiant. Trying to find words for it afterwards, I recalled the mysterious line of Henry Vaughan's poem 'The Night':

'There is in God (some say) a deep but dazzling darkness.'

An even more marked difference from the general run of NDEs, however, was that I had absolutely no sense of regret or loss at the return into physical life. I lay on the bed, relaxed, and began to take myself back in imagination, in a series of steps, right to the point of coming round. 'Here I am, lying on this bed, with someone asking if I want supper; here I am, just before that, becoming aware of someone shaking my arm; here I am, before that again, with my eyes closed, and ...' Often this process brings back the dream one has forgotten, but what came back this time was nothing like a remembered dream. What came flooding back was an experience that in some extraordinary way *had been with me ever since I came around without my realising it*. It was if I'd come out of the deepest darkness I had ever known, *which was somehow still right there behind my eyes*.

What manifested was simply not the same 'me-experiencing-the-world' that I'd known before: it was 'Everything-that-is, experiencing itself through the bodymind called John lying in a hospital bed'. And the experience was indescribably wonderful. I now know exactly why the Book of Genesis says that God looked upon *all* that He had made – not just beautiful sunsets, but dreary hospital rooms and traumatised sixty-year-old bodies - and saw that it was very good.

What I am trying to describe is no vague feeling of 'good to be alive'. On the contrary, I no longer cared if John lived or ceased to be altogether, and the change of consciousness was so palpable that to begin with I repeatedly put my hand up to the back of my head, feeling exactly as if the doctors had removed the skull and exposed my brain somehow to the infinite blackness of space. Occasionally I still do so, for *the new consciousness has remained with me ever since* – which is the third and most significant difference from what happens in the general run of NDEs, and also from the 'altered states' experienced with psychedelics.

There is in no sense a high from which I can come down. The sense of aweful wonder has at the same time a feeling of utter obviousness and ordinariness, as if the marvel of 'everything-coming into being-continuously-from-the-Great-Dark' were no more and no less than 'just the way things are'. From this perspective, the term *altered* state of consciousness would be a complete misnomer, for the state is one of simple normality. It seems, rather, as if my earlier state, so-called 'ordinary' human consciousness, represents the real alteration – a deviation from the plain norm, a kind of artificially blinkered or clouded condition wherein the bodymind has the absurd illusion that it is somehow a separate individual entity over against everything else.

In fact I now understand why mystics of all religions have likened the enlightenment-process to waking up from a dream.

As I was walking in the hot sun to the police station to report the poisoned sweet crime I was struck by the sense of loss that the Dark was missing, and my first thought then was: 'Ah, well, you've had the Vision – I suppose now you'll have to join the ranks of all those Seekers who spend their lives trying to attain Higher Consciousness.' And then, to my amazement, I suddenly saw *it was all still there, just waiting, as it were, to be noticed* – the Dark behind my eyes and behind everything else, bringing again the perception that *of course* everything exists by emerging fresh-minted from the Dark now! and now! and now!, with a shout of joy yet also in absolute calm.

The NDE had evidently jerked me out of the so-called normal human state of chronic illusion-of-separateness, into a basic 'wakefulness', interrupted by spells of 'dozing off' – simply forgetting the Dark until the sense of something missing from life brings about instant re-awakening with no effort at all.

The key feature of God-consciousness as I know it from my own firsthand experience, is its quintessential ordinariness and obviousness – a feature actually emphasized by many mystics. I know from my own firsthand experience that God-consciousness doesn't abolish human appetites. When I'm in it I don't lose my taste for meat or wine or good company or humour or detective fiction – I actually enjoy them more than ever before. I don't cease to enjoy sexual feelings, nor do I see anything inherently dirty about money.

What the consciousness does bring is the cheerful equanimity of knowing that satisfaction doesn't depend on any of these special preferences of John's bodymind being met; it is inherent simply in being, in the Great Dark which is (in G.K. Chesterton's marvellous phrase) 'joy without a cause'.

Prof. John Wren-Lewis, 1/22 Cliffbrook Parade, Clovelly, NSW 2031, Australia. From a four page text in Social Inventions No. 23 – £3 from ISI, 20 Heber Road, London NW2 6AA.

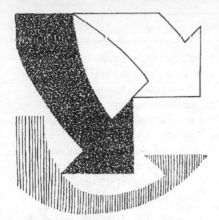

Chapter 4

TRAINING FOR
DYING

I am quite terrified of death. Not of dying, but of death itself.

I am a fit pensioner, in my seventies, and for about the last four years I have tried to get people to talk about the subject, with little success. It is very much a taboo subject.

I have spoken to many clergy and they seem uncomfortable about the subject, or else trot out the accepted teaching about the Resurrection. I am familiar with that as I have been a churchgoer all my life. My head accepts the doctrine but my heart is frightened.

There is much bereavement counselling but nothing to prepare one for death.

I am quite terrified and this fear spoils and destroys the quality of my life.
From a letter to The Natural Death Centre.

How can we ever be prepared, either for our own death or the deaths of those around us? How can we 'prepare'?

At first the idea may seem futile, or morbid. Yet most of us find ourselves responsible, at some stage in our lives, for meeting the needs of a dying friend, spouse or relative, and having to learn our way through the difficult process of helping someone who is dying. A wealth of revelations accompany this process, but, more often than not, time, practical considerations and our inability to come to terms with what is happening conspire to leave many things unfinished or unsaid. The same goes for our own death.

How do we want to be cared for? What will be our legacy to our loved ones? Will we have time to find out what needs to be done and then do it? And to what extent are our attitudes towards death and our anxiety about death affecting the quality of our lives now?

As a society we are not geared towards handling death as humanely as we could. The letter above expresses the fundamental problem: we don't want to deal with it until it is inevitable or has already happened. Talking about death, even thinking about it, does not come naturally to many of us. Our fear of death seems to prevent us from coping with it. Indeed, as another letter received by the Natural Death Centre points out:

Fear of living

What has struck me about the majority of people's attitudes towards death is not so much the fear of dying, as an all-consuming fear of actually living. It seems to me that people are not only afraid of life but also have tremendous difficulty accepting the concept of free choice. Why else would we struggle year after year to maintain dead relationships and unfulfilling jobs?

I was trained as a nurse twenty years ago and my initiation into the dying process at the age of eighteen with little to no experience of death was being told that I was never to mention the subject even if the patient asked, nor was I to speak to any relative no matter what the situation. I witnessed some appalling deaths. We were allowed to lay their bodies out, but we were not allowed to talk about it.

From a letter to The Natural Death Centre.

It is important to break the silence: we need to find ways to communicate and share thoughts, feelings and experience. Becoming more aware of the process of dying, and of the demands it makes on us and others, is a practical and valuable undertaking.

This chapter looks at ways of 'training' for dying. We begin with ways of acknowledging and exploring the reality of death, and overcoming our fears; and move on to practical considerations of making a will and making our wishes known.

Courses and workshops

A growing number of resources exist nowadays for taking care of the practical as well as the philosophical aspects of dying. In the UK two university courses have been launched recently, one run by the Open University, and one by St. David's University College, Lampeter. They differ greatly in approach:

The Open University – Death and Dying

In 1990 the Minister of Health announced a grant of £484,000 to make an Open University course on Death and Dying. Very few of the more than one million care workers in Britain, or the many family carers and volunteers, receive any serious education or training for working with dying or bereaved people. Existing courses, however good, reach only a handful of carers each year. At the same time, there is a rising awareness that the process of dying could be made more humane if lessons learned in recent years were shared with carers in hospital and community settings.

The primary studentship will be drawn from those who have regular, extensive contact with dying and bereaved people. It is anticipated that some carers and dying people themselves will study the course.

Key themes:
• The dying person's needs and strengths.
• Open communication and decision-making.
• Keeping everyone in the picture. Respecting confidentiality.
• The range of cultural and religious expectations and rituals concerning death and dying.
• The need for support for all those involved in terminal care.

From Open University preliminary course information.

While the OU concentrates upon practical considerations for carers, the one-year M.A. in 'Death and Immortality' at St. David's is philosophical in content:

Death and Immortality Course

The course focuses much of its attention on the paranormal so-called 'Near-Death Experience' and its possible implications for proving the existence of a life hereafter. All the students at Lampeter take a core course examining the philosophical arguments for and against a future life.

In the future it may well be that going on a course about preparations for dying will become as normal as learning first aid. The Natural Death Centre, for instance, offers workshops entitled 'Living with Dying' run by Christianne Heal. (Details of these evening and weekend sessions held around the country are available, for an SAE, from The Natural Death Centre.) On the whole death is not an easy or welcome subject for general, informal conversation, and so a setting in which death is discussed and explored is a welcome opportunity, as Christianne explains:

Living with Dying

Death is a crisis, but some view it as a crisis with a point to it. We complete exercises in the workshops that enable people to work out at what stage in the process towards death they are, and how they can feel more comfortable about it. It is the airing of the subject that is important to a lot of people: just being able to talk about it. Participants get a great deal out of it. Some simply want the opportunity to discuss their fears, worries and concerns without someone cutting them off because it is a difficult subject. Some people come because they are dying, others because they have been or are nursing someone who is dying and they don't know how to handle the issue, and others because they are old and near their own death experience. I even had a boy of thirteen come whose father had died before he was born. He needed to talk about this and we gave him the opportunity. I was surprised at just how positive the workshop was for him.
Christianne Heal, interviewed in Counselling News (Sept. 1991).

Linda and Martin, who attended Christianne's workshops, each describe the experience:

Christianne Heal created a safe atmosphere with her sensitive and grounded approach. We first examined our childhood beliefs and experiences of death, and then we sat in pairs, with eyes shut and we took it in turns to be each other's death. 'Hello Ruth, I am your death. I am like the dark side of the moon; you can't see me but you know I'm there. I have known you all your life and now it is time for you to know me, do not be scared, I am nothing to fear.' To hear my death speak was uncanny and this effect is heightened because in the silence you hear all the other deaths in the room quietly talking to their partners. I was amazed how the universality of death drew us closer as a group; we listened, and supported each other.

Linda.

Christianne asked us to draw a 'map' and to mark around us all the people who are important to us, living or dead. Then we worked in pairs, one partner listened, while the other had half an hour to say goodbye to all the people he or she had placed on the map. I found this very painful, I think everyone did. It is also beautiful to listen to your partner talking to their friends and family in such a loving and powerful way, expressing the very core of their feelings. Where else would we get the space to say these things to our loved ones, especially those who have died? Funerals only serve this function up to a point, and not at all when it comes to expressing the anger which often accompanies bereavement.

We danced a 'dance of death' to beautiful music with our eyes shut, improvising, imagining death, gently moving amongst each other. We painted death, fascinated by how different all the pictures were – some people started by drawing only black, but then realised that there had to be colour and light there too.

There was an exercise on 'what you would do if you only had six months to live'. Try it some time, take it seriously and you may be surprised at what you reveal to yourself.

We had the opportunity to write our own obituary and were given the freedom to fantasise about the life for which we would like to be remembered.

The difference in people's aspirations was quite lovely: from one person who had built his own chicken shed to another whose assassination at a political rally precipitated world revolution.

At the end one person said: 'I've never laughed so much in a weekend.'

Martin.

Anxiety about dying

Anxiety about dying can be experienced by people at any age. The Natural Death Centre has designed the scale below to help you to find out how likely you are to be anxious about death and dying when the time comes, if you were to remain as you are at present, and to help you to identify those specific high-scoring, high-anxiety areas that could suggest a focus for 'personal development' or other changes in your approach or lifestyle. There is no need to fake your scoring. There is no one to fool but yourself.

Death-Related Anxiety Scale

Give marks out of 4 to each of the following statements according to this scale:

Not true at all	Mainly not true	Not sure	Somewhat true	Very true
0	1	2	3	4

☐ I tend not to be very brave in crisis situations

☐ I am an unusually anxious person

☐ I am something of a hypochondriac and am perhaps obsessively worried about infections

☐ I have never had a semi-mystical, spiritual, out-of-the-body, near-death or 'peak experience'

☐ I tend to be unusually frightened in planes at take off and landing

☐ I do not have a particular religion or philosophy that helps me to face dying

☐ I do not believe in any form of survival of the soul after death

☐ Personally I would give a lot to be immortal in this body

☐ I am very much a city person and not really close to nature

☐ Anxiety about death spoils the quality of my life

☐ I am superstitious that preparing for dying might hasten my death

☐ I don't like the way some of my relatives died and fear that my death could be like theirs

My actual experience of friends dying has been undilutedly negative

I would feel easier being with a dying relative if they were not told they were dying

I have fears of dying alone without friends around me

I have fears of dying slowly

I have fears of dying suddenly

I have fears of dying before my time or whilst my children are still young

I have fears of dying before fulfilling my potential and fully using my talents

I have fears of dying without adequately having expressed my love to those I am close to

I have fears of dying before having really experienced much 'joie de vivre'

I have fears of what may or may not happen after death

I have fears of what could happen to my family after my death

I have fears of dying in hospital or an institution

I have fears of those caring for me feeling overwhelmed by the strain of it

I have fears of not getting help with euthanasia when the time comes

I have fears of being given unofficial and unwanted euthanasia

I have fears of getting insufficient pain control whilst dying

I have fears of being over-medicalised and unconscious whilst dying

I have fears of being declared dead when not really dead or being buried alive

I have fears of getting confused at death or not being able to follow my spiritual practices

I have fears of what may happen to my body after death

I have fears of an Alzheimer's type mental degeneration near death

Overall I would say that I am unusually anxious about death and dying

TOTAL

The extremely anxious (scoring over 65 or so) might consider the need for counselling or therapy; the unusually anxious (scoring over 40) might want to find a method of meditation, self-hypnotic autogenic training, chant, dance, co-counselling relationship, therapy workshop, philosophy, spiritual practice or similar that could help them to experience, explore and accept their feelings; the averagely anxious (scoring under 40) don't have to be too smug – in certain respects anxiety can correlate with intelligence; and once the shaman's advice to 'make friends with one's fear' has been absorbed, anxiety is free to transform into energy and ecstasy – perhaps there is a Zen Art of Being Anxious, just as there seems to be a Zen Art of everything else, from archery to flower arranging.

For the record, Nicholas Albery, one of the co-editors of this book, scored an anxiety rating of 45 – 'no doubt a need to face my anxiety on the subject is what attracted me to it in the first place,' he says.

The scale is perhaps more interesting for the questions it poses than for the number it produces. Most of us will recognise that it is possible to be 'over-anxious' about death, to the extent that it lessens our enjoyment of life; and indeed the possibility that we are so anxious about death that we deny any anxiety at all. It is to be hoped that people who do take the test do not become anxious about their anxiety rating!

Some people find that their anxiety about death becomes manageable in unexpected ways, as in these examples:

Da Free John

A contemporary American spiritual teacher Da Free John, reports in his autobiography, 'The Knee of Listening', how he overcame the fear of death by 'dying'. When his fear of death became almost overwhelming, he discovered the ancient wisdom of giving in (which is quite different from giving up) and cooperating with the process, flowing with the pressure, letting 'death' take its full and natural course. Here's what happened:

'I was lying home alone in the afternoon. It was as if all my life had constantly prevented this experience from going to its end. All my life I had been preventing my death.

'I lay on the floor, totally disarmed, unable to make a gesture that could prevent the rising fear. And thus it grew in me, but, for the first time, I allowed it to happen. I could not prevent it. The fear and the death rose and became my overwhelming experience. And I witnessed the crisis of that fear in a moment of conscious, voluntary death. I allowed the death to happen, and I saw it happen.

'When the moment of crisis passed I felt a marvellous relief. The death had occured, but I had observed it! I remained untouched by it. The body and the mind and the personality had died, but I remained as an essential and unqualified consciousness ... There was just an infinite bliss of being.'

> *Da Free John quoted in 'Practical Guide to Death and Dying' by*
> *John White.*

Birth, love, courage and death

It was getting pregnant with my first child ten years ago that started a process within me that revolted against the 'normal', expected, over-medicalised hospital birth. So I set about finding an alternative and by following my instinct (with some determination) I was able to have my first child at home. The experiences of that birth, and the following ones, brought me closer to death than I have ever been – and were comforting for that. I felt I was part of a process that was greater than me and that although it was terrifying in its unknown expectations, it responded to love and courage! I was acutely aware that I would have been unable to function had I not been given the quality of emotional support that I was given. And I thought that if I could die in the same way, I could accept it without too much fear.

I have been afraid of death since I was a very young child and I think the two things that have helped me are giving birth and being in therapy. I hope one day I will be able to welcome death without fear and I fiercely believe that people should die at home if they can and that we should all be able to talk about it.

From a letter by Jehane Markham to The Natural Death Centre.

Death without fear or pain

In our family there has been a strong taboo, or kind of a 'hush' on death as a subject even for mention, and we have had no education or experience. Deaths have occurred but somehow I have always been protected or just not there (when young) and now as an adult I'm all at sea about it.

When our son was on the way, I learned about 'birthing' (the theory) and went to relaxation classes. When he was born I had no fear, hardly any pain (merely discomfort) and he came along almost in record time. I wonder: if we could feel the same way about our deaths, mightn't it help the person involved and everyone else concerned? Perhaps the baby born to an unafraid and relaxed mother might feel better about being born than if the mother is all tense and hurting. Things may go a bit wrong afterwards, but at least she or he has had a fair start. The same could apply to dying.

From a letter to The Natural Death Centre.

The parallels between dying and giving birth are very strong. As Anya Foos-Graber in her book 'Deathing' urges us: 'Look at death's counterpart – fertilization, pregnancy and birth! Not knowing about the 'birds and the bees' doesn't ward off pregnancy! Knowing the process, whether of birth or death, means you can positively utilise it.'

Death Weeks

It seems probable that more anxiety is caused by ignorance and apprehension than by facing up to the fact of dying. A series of 'Death Weeks' were conducted by Peter Prunkl and Rebecca Berry, in which groups of young students were asked to simulate 'dying', to really imagine it intensely, over a period of seven or eight days. The organisers maintain that a remarkable degree of realism is obtained with a well-constructed simulation, and it is clear from the various participants' journals (excerpted below) that they were able to engage themselves fully in their roles as dying people. It is also apparent that the experience ultimately had a profoundly positive effect for them:

• To begin, let me share what I have learned from my experience of Death Week. I learned about myself. In fact, it was the first time in a great while that I took a very close look at what I am really like. I discovered that I am strong and persevering and that strength comes from a very deep faith in God. I learned about life. Not because I had 'only seven days to live' and wanted to cram every experience into that time that I could, but because as I was 'dying' I became more aware of the events happening around me. The very minute and trivial things of life seemed to become peak experiences for me, so much so that at times my senses were bombarded by stimuli which overwhelmed my mind to the point of great excitement, followed by confusion, and finally ending in total exhaustion. It was during these low points, these times of loneliness and depression, that I would come to an understanding of life. The understanding was not profound or shockingly new, but was remarkably simple. The simplicity gave me such a feeling of comfort and joy that as the week progressed, I became excited about my death. I was finally going home and that made me very happy.

• Yes, I no longer take life for granted. I have become aware of how precious every day is.

• It has made me more content about myself.

• The most significant effect is that I no longer fear the inevitable reality of death.

• The experience made me decide to tell my family how I wanted to be dealt with after death. I wanted to tell them what I wanted done. It is my last opportunity to take care of things for me. After all, it is my life and my death. I have talked to each of my children and husband about cremation and this is what I want done. Before Death Week, I just figured after I am dead what does it matter, but it does.

It seems to me that during that period after Death Week I became more comfortable with myself and expressed how I really felt to my friends and family. I gradually became less dependent on people for my own happiness and my relationships became more open, honest and mutual in their give-and-take aspects.

From 'Death Week' by Peter Prunkl and Rebecca Berry, Hemisphere (1101 Vermont Ave, NW # 200, Washington DC 20005. 1989, ISBN 0 89116 112 0, £14).

'Rehearsing death'

'Philosophy is a rehearsal for death,' says Plato. There is no reason why our everyday activities should not include such rehearsals. Alexander the Great's father, Philip of Macedonia, one of the most powerful men of his time, gave to one of his retenue a single, simple duty: regardless of how much the King protested, raged or grew violent, the man's only task was to approach him every day and say: 'Philip of Macedonia, thou too shall die.' This was a highly dangerous job, as the king often did rage and grow violent; yet he continued to keep the man in his employ. Fortunately for us there are less expensive (and safer) ways of 'rehearsing'.

One stimulating way is to write your own obituary – use a formal newspaper style if you wish, or imagine that you know you are to die within days and complete as many of the following sentences as you find suitably provocative:

D-i-y obituary

• Outside observers would probably say that my main achievements have been ...

• For myself, what I am most pleased with and proud of in my life, are ...

• One of the most important lessons that I have learnt in my lifetime is that ...

• During my life I have used my ... [list three positive personal characteristics, for example: imagination, sense of humour and intelligence] through my ... [list three activities, for example: writing, running groups and parenting] with the underlying vision, I now realise, of helping work towards a world in which, one day, ... [describe your long-term Utopia, for example: 'people are kind and sensitive to each other, nature is at ease and magic is alive'].

• The people I have felt closest to in my life have been ...

• One generalisation I could make about the quality of my relationships with others is that ...

• If I regret anything, it is that ...
• If I had known how short a time I had left to live, I would probably have ...

The purpose of this obituary, besides that of evaluating your achievements and failures, is to flush out whether a more acute awareness of your own mortality would lead you to want to make changes in your life, in case you might wish to make them now, rather than being filled with regrets on your deathbed.

Another way of preparing for death is just to imagine dying, which many of us must have done in our own way. Here is one version:

Meditating on dying

You close your eyes and imagine that you are on your deathbed.

You feel yourself drifting. You don't have any more energy to do anything. Your desk is piled high with unanswered letters, bills to be paid, unfinished projects. Either someone else will pick them up for you or they will remain undone. It doesn't matter much. No one will know that the idea you meant to work out never came to expression. No one will feel the poorer for it. Then there are the people in your life. If you loved them well, they will miss you and grieve for you. Over time the poignancy of your absence will fade and only a warm remembrance will be left. There will be those for whom you did not care enough, those you rejected, those with whom there is still some unfinished business. It doesn't matter now. There is nothing you can do about it.

There is only one thing you can do, and that is to let go. Let the tasks of the world slip away. Let your loved ones mourn a little while for you and then go on their way. Let go of everything, your home, your possessions, your feelings and your thoughts. Allow yourself to float. You begin to feel lighter. You have shed the heavy load you have been carrying. What was the heavy load? It was your sense of self-importance. It was your belief that everything you did had intrinsic importance, therefore you had to do it fully and perfectly no matter what the cost. Or, conversely, it was your belief that your work was so important that you couldn't possibly do it well enough, so the burden you carried was the unfulfilled responsibility. But, either way, don't you see how temporal it is, when you are facing your own death? This practice can help you to learn to do a little less, do it a bit more slowly, do it with care, and do it with love.

*From 'Seeing Through the Visible World: Jung, Gnosis and Chaos' by
June Singer, Mandala/Harper Collins, 1990.*

Many meditations on dying are to be found in Tibetan traditions, some charming ones as in the first passage below by Stephen Levine, inspired by 'The Tibetan Book of the Dead', and some at least superficially rather gruesome ones, as in the second extract below:

Shining true being

Imagine that your body no longer has the strength, the energy, to maintain its connection with the life-force, with the body of awareness within. And imagine now that you are beginning to experience the process of dissolving out of that body. Sensations from the body no longer so distinct, melting away, leaving just a spaciousness. Dissolving out of the body. Leaving that heavier form behind. Dissolving into consciousness itself.

My friend, listen now, for that which is called death has arrived. So let go gently, gently, of all that holds you back. Of all that pulls you away from this most precious moment. Know that now you have arrived at the transition called death. Open to it. Let go into it.

Recognise the changing experience of the mind as it separates from the body, dissolving.

Dissolving now into the realms of pure light. Your true nature shining everywhere before you.

My friend, maintain an open-heartedness, a spaciousness of being that does not grasp. Let things be as they are without the least attempt to interfere. Grasping at nothing.

Enter the essential nature of your own being shining there before you, a great luminosity. Rest in being. Knowing it for what it is. This light shining, luminous. Your true self.

Let go, gently, gently, without the least force. Before you shines your true being. It is without birth, without death.

Let go of all which distracts or confuses the mind, all that created density in life.

Go gently into it. Do not be frightened or bewildered. Do not pull back in fear from the immensity of your true being. Now is a moment for liberation.

Know that you are well guided by your compassion and love. You are the essence of all things. You are the light.

From 'Who Dies?' by Stephen Levine.

Visualising death

There are both external and internal ways of practice. An external technique is to dwell in a charnel ground and observe the stages of decomposition of the corpses in it, while keeping the mind fixed on the thought that these corpses represent the final destiny of one's own body.

An internal means is to visualise oneself as lying on one's death-bed awaiting the approach of death. Visualise that your parents, relatives and friends surround you, lamenting and upset. The radiance of your countenance has faded and your nostrils have sunk back. Your lips dry, slime begins to form on your teeth and all grace leaves your body. Bodily temperature drops, breathing becomes heavy, and you begin to exhale more deeply than you inhale. All the negative karmas [actions] generated during your life arise within your mind and you become filled with regret. You look to all sides for help, but help does not come.

From 'Tibetan Traditions of Death Meditation' by Ge-she Nga-wang
Dar-gye.

Allegra Taylor describes the way her wishes became clear and focused through participation in a group exercise:

The death bed imagined

... An impromptu drama in which we took it in turns to play the different characters in a death-bed scene: the distraught relative; the voluntary worker; the withdrawn child; the dying person.

As I lay there, my eyes closed, trying to visualise everything I love receding from me, I knew without a shadow of a doubt that what I most wanted was to be treated as I always had been, as me. I felt a need to finish relationships and say my goodbyes calmly. I saw myself as weak and frail but with a last great longing to pass on something of value. I wanted someone to put a baby in my arms for me to hold. A last connection with life – a symbol of love and renewal.

From my family I wanted only closeness, an easy honesty and assurances that they would be all right. From visitors I wanted to know that they would provide a support network for the family after my death. I did not want anyone to take heroic measures to save me or to save my soul. Anyone who spoke to me of spiritual things needed to be supportive of my own beliefs and not a representative of alien ones.

I did rather feel that it was my show, and that the most loving last thing people could do for me would be to set aside their own needs and help me have the kind of death I wanted.

From 'Acquainted with the Night' by Allegra Taylor.

It is through these rehearsals, these meditations, that we begin to develop our own understanding of death, beyond our received ideas. Our anxieties about social status and material possessions seem no longer as important, perhaps we even find death taking on new meanings for us. Relating realistically to impermanence is the essence of both the spiritual life and of living fully. The key point about death is that time runs out – there are no more chances to get it right. As Caroline Sherwood puts it: 'If I live my life "finishing business" by keeping myself up to date and clear in my relationships, living from the deepest truth of myself, working to dissolve the barriers to love in my life – how much more easy my death might be.'

Life is precious for the 'already-dead'

Once someone asked a well-known Thai meditation master: 'In this world where everything changes, where nothing remains the same, where loss and grief are inherent in our very coming into existence, how can there be any happiness?' The teacher, looking compassionately at this fellow, held up a drinking glass which had been given to him earlier in the morning and said, 'You see this goblet? For me, the glass is already broken. I enjoy it, I drink out of it. It holds my water admirably, sometimes even reflecting the sun in beautiful patterns. If I should tap it, it has a lovely ring to it. But when I put this glass on a shelf, and the wind knocks it over or my elbow brushes it off the table and it falls to the ground and shatters, I say, "Of course." But when I understand that this glass is already broken, every moment with it is precious. Every moment is just as it is and nothing need be otherwise.'

When we recognise that, just as that glass, our body is already broken, that indeed we are already dead, then life becomes precious and we open to it just as it is, in the moment it is occuring. When we understand that all our loved ones are already dead – our children, our mates, our friends – how precious they become. How little fear can interpose, how little doubt can estrange us. When you live your life as though you're already dead, life takes on a new meaning. Each moment becomes a whole lifetime, a universe unto itself.

From 'Who Dies?' by Stephen Levine.

Death in Mexico

Most of us Westerners are to an extent estranged from death. By contrast, the Nobel prize-winning writer Octavio Paz explains the Mexican attitude towards death:

Death as a favourite plaything

To the Modern Mexican death doesn't have any meaning. It has ceased to be the transition, the access to the other life which is more authentic than this one. But the unimportance of death has not taken it away from us and eliminated it from our daily lives. To the inhabitant of New York, Paris or London, death is a word that is never uttered because it burns the lips. The Mexican, on the other hand, frequents it, mocks it, caresses it, sleeps with it, entertains it; it is one of his favourite playthings and his most enduring love. It is true that in his attitude there is perhaps the same fear that others also have, but at least he does not hide this fear nor does he hide death; he contemplates her face-to-face with impatience, with contempt, with irony: 'If they're going to kill me tomorrow, let them kill me for once and for all.'

From 'The Labyrinth of Solitude' by Octavio Paz, Penguin, 1985.

Many of the exercises we have seen have been concerned with individual introspection. In the workshops and group exercises there is an added dimension of shared experience. Taking this one step further, the London-based City Dying Group organises candlelit vigils in cemeteries. Each of the participants brings a candle, which they light one by one, saying goodbye to somebody (or something). This relaxed ritual has been going since 1985; the group also organises picnics in cemeteries. Strange as this may seem, it is not unlike the Mexican festival called 'El Dia de los Muertes' (The Day of the Dead) when Mexicans celebrate the memory of lost loved ones with cemetery vigils, dancing and riotous parades, in the (loosely-held) belief that their loved ones return in spirit to join in. Mexico is like most of the world, in that infant mortality and adult illness are much more common than they are here. Death is more a part of life, and perhaps because of this, Mexicans treat it with a healthy mixture of respect and irreverence.

The Mexican Day of the Dead

That a festival to do with the dead should be a joyous occasion perhaps strikes those of us from other cultures with our different perceptions as something hard to come to terms with. The Day of the Dead is just that: a festival of welcome for the souls of the dead which the living prepare and delight in. The souls return each year to enjoy for a few brief hours the pleasures they once knew in life.

In the urban setting of Mexico City and other large towns the celebration is seen at its most exuberant, with figures of skulls and skeletons everywhere. These mimic the living and disport themselves in a mocking modern dance of death. It is not surprising that so colourful an event should have become a tourist event.

Not far away from the tourist routes there is, however, another Mexico. In the rural areas, in every village or small town, the Day of the Dead is celebrated beyond the glare of flashbulbs. Each household prepares its offering of food and drink for the dead to be set out on a table among flowers and candles. The blue smoke of burning copal incense sanctifies the ceremony, just as it has done for centuries. Outside the peace is shattered by the explosions of the rockets set off to mark the fulfilment of an obligation deeply felt. The whole company of the living and the dead share in the flowering and fruiting of the land which both have cultivated.

The Day of the Dead is essentially a private or family feast. It has a public aspect at community level, but the core of the celebration takes place within the family home. It is a time of family reunion not only for the living but also the dead, who, for a few brief hours each year, return to be with their relatives in this world.

From 'The Skeleton At The Feast' by Elizabeth Carmichael and Chloë Sayer,
British Museum Press (46 Bloomsbury St, London WC1B 3QQ), 1991,
ISBN 0 7141 2503 2, £12-95.

The Day of the Dead is celebrated on October 31st, the eve of All Saints' Day, on which day the same custom of visiting the dead in their last resting places used to be common throughout Christendom, and is still widely observed, in France for example. These practices enable us to commemorate and celebrate our loved ones, and keep our own sense of death in perspective, by giving death and the dead a time as well as a place.

The Natural Death Centre has inaugurated a smaller-scale English Day of the Dead, initially as a festival and exhibition, for the third Sunday in April of each year. Make contact with the Centre for the details, or if you have a suitable event to suggest.

Making your will

For those in good health there is one obvious and practical preparation for death. Make a will! Some of us avoid doing this because it is an admission that we are going to die. For that reason alone it is a valuable spiritual exercise as well as a highly practical and normalising procedure. Maybe we are not entirely comfortable with our death, maybe we have not fully joined the human race, until we have got hold of that document, filled it in, signed it and have got it witnessed.

In fact, as the Law Society has recently been campaigning to remind us, only about one in three adults in Britain has a will. This may not matter so much for single people without children, but it can lead to unnecessary financial hardship for many families. If you die without a will ('intestate'), the intestacy rules dictate who receives your estate (the total of your house and its contents, car, various insurance policies and savings accounts may well come to more than you realise). The rules will also decide who should manage the affairs of your estate, and who will be your legal representatives (and what their costs may be). It is important to realise that unmarried partners may have no claim on the estate (unless 'dependant', but this could be expensive to establish). Even a legal wife or husband may have to sell the home to pay the other automatic beneficiaries. Of particular importance in the case of divorced or separated parents, the rules will determine who the legal guardians of your children will be; with a will you can name the person you would like to act as your children's guardian.

The standard way to get a will drawn up is to consult a solicitor (this would be likely to cost between £15 and £400, with an average of £50 nationwide). It is worth familiarising yourself with the procedure before you visit a solicitor as this could save you time, money and possible confusion. There are six simple steps to take before you make a will:

(1) Before you see your solicitor, list all the items you have to leave – house and contents, car, savings accounts, etc, and their rough value.

(2) Consider who you would like to provide for and in what way.

(3) Consider whether you would like to leave money or property 'in trust' for

children or grandchildren until they are grown up and at what age you think they should inherit your gift.

(4) Decide who you would like to receive your sentimental belongings. These may be of little financial value but you can pass them on to someone you know will appreciate them.

(5) Consider whether you would like to leave some money to charity (bequests to charities are not liable to inheritance tax).

(6) Choose one or more executors to 'wind up your affairs'. The executors can be spouses or members of the family or friends, although it is as well to get their agreement in advance. If, in the event, they find the task too onerous, as they well may, they can always ask a solicitor to take over (solicitors tend to charge less than banks).

Adapted from 'The Granada Action Factsheet, Death: A Practical Guide'.

Here is an example of a will for a married man with two children who is concerned to minimise long-term liability to Inheritance Tax, and with several other unusual features:

Will for a married man and two children

WILL of Donald Roland Winterton of 26 Oxford Gardens, London W10, made this fourteenth day of April, one thousand nine hundred and ninety three.

I revoke all previous Wills and Codicils made by me. I appoint as my executors my brother Arthur Winterton of 48 Book Lane, London N8 (tel 081 286 2194) and my sister Alice Maples of 12 Montrose Road, London N4 (tel 081 937 4582) – or if either or both of them is unable or unwilling to act my friend Alan Beam of 12 Corry Close, London WC2 (tel 071 208 9432) is to be an executor.

I wish to be buried in a home-made coffin in my field in Speen in Buckinghamshire. I have notified the county council's environmental health department and planning department and they have no objections.

If my wife Rosemary dies before me or does not survive me for thirty days, I appoint my sister Alice Maples and her husband Michael Maples as the guardians to the age of eighteen of my son Arthur my daughter Mary and any other children I may have.

I give and bequeath as follows – with each gift and bequest throughout this will subject to the condition that the potential recipient survives me by thirty days.

I give the following bequests free from all taxes and duties payable on or by reference to my death. These bequests and legacies are to lapse automatically if the recipient is dead or if a total of six letters or telephone calls in any particular case fails to trace them within six months. No advertisements or other means need be used.

(a) my painting by Emily Young to my friend Amelia Hart of 88 Forge Terrace, Thornhill, Derby (tel 0437 3333)

(b) such motorbike as I may own at my death to my nephew Joseph Lawlor of 33 Warren Street, Church Stretton, Shropshire (tel 0331 3227).

I give the following legacies free from all taxes and duties payable on or by reference to my death:

(a) £500 to each of my executors who proves my will

(b) £1000 to my secretary Janet Simmonds of 51 Victoria Road, Chesterfield, Derbyshire (tel 0437 34282)

(c) £1000 to the Fourth World Educational and Research Association Trust, 20 Heber Road, London NW2 (tel 081 208 2853) Registered Charity Number 283040 for the benefit of their project The Natural Death Centre. I declare that the receipt of the charity's treasurer or other person professing to be the duly authorised officer shall be a full and sufficient discharge to my executors.

After the executors have paid my debts any taxes and duties payable on my death and the expenses of my funeral and of administering my estate I give to my wife the whole of the rest of my estate except for my interest in the property at 41 Baldwin Lane, Caversham, Reading but including its contents and furniture.

I give free from all taxes and duties payable on or by reference to my death all my interest in the property at 41 Baldwin Lane, Caversham, Reading to my executors as trustees. They are to sell everything not in the form of cash but they may postpone the sale of anything as long as they like. They are to invest or apply what is left in any type of property just as if it were their own money.

My trustees may give to the guardians of my children any percentage of what is left to enable them to acquire property as needed for my children or to apply for my children's benefit.

My trustees are to divide whatever is left from this 'trust for sale' (including any income from it) between such of my children as reach the age of eighteen – if more than one then in shares as near to equal as is reasonably practicable. My children are my son Arthur (born 3/1/76) my daughter Mary (born 28/7/78) and any other children I may have in future. The trustees may apply the actual assets rather than cash if they think fit without requiring the consent of any other person. All these children are to have a contingent rather than vested interest in my estate.

If any child of mine dies before me or dies under the age of eighteen leaving children who do reach that age then my trustees are to divide as equally as is reasonably practicable between these grandchildren the share of my estate which their parent would have received if that parent had lived long enough.

If my trustees think it proper they may at any time apply for the maintenance education or benefit of any beneficiary under the provisions of the two previous paragraphs any part of the capital of the property to which he or she would have become entitled on reaching eighteen.

The receipt of the guardian or any person professing to be the proper officer of any school college or other education establishment which any of the children are attending at that time shall be a full and sufficient discharge to my trustees in respect of that beneficiary.

Any person contesting this will or attempting to set aside any part of it before any court is to be denied any benefit from my estate.

Signed by Donald Roland Winterton
in our presence and then by us in his: Signature_____
First witness:
Signature_____Name_____
Address_____
Occupation_____
Second witness:
Signature_____Name_____
Address_____
Occupation_____

Some points about this will:

• On the whole a will can be written in plain English. Avoid any possible ambiguities of meaning.

• In the passages above where it descends into legal gobbledegook it is for a reason, so beware if you make significant changes in such wordings. Beware generally, and seek legal approval of your will if in any doubt. A very useful guide, used in designing the above will, is the 'Which?' book, 'Wills and Probate' edited by the Consumers' Association (for details see under Books in the Resources chapter).

• Revoke previous wills even if you have never made any.

• Note the absence of commas in the text, except in the addresses, an absence which lawyers think helps guard against fraudulent alteration of a will and against the need for judicial interpretation of the comma's meaning. If the will goes over one side of paper, continue on the back of the paper. If further pages are needed, these should be numbered and you and the witnesses should sign at the bottom of each page.

• Those appointed as guardians for children can also be executors of the will, unless you think there could be a conflict of interest – for instance the possibility of the trustees enriching themselves; or, on the contrary, of the trustees not taking enough, through being too diffident to recoup expenses.

• There is no Inheritance Tax payable when the spouse inherits, but when the spouse in turn dies, then the tax is payable on net assets over £150,000 (the current figure. which alters regularly). To avoid this in advance, the will (above) gives a house to the children, and the contents, furniture, cash, etc, to the wife. This would obviously only be practicable in a case where the children were to be trusted not to evict or harass the wife.

• Phone numbers and dates of birth are not normally put in a will, with all such details normally on separate sheets put with the will. But, as long as the details are correct, what harm can it do? Do not, however, fasten such sheets or anything else to the will itself, whether by pins, staples or paperclips.

• The reference to bequests lapsing if the beneficiaries are not readily traceable is to prevent the executors having to go to enormous lengths, including placing ads in the London Gazette, to find beneficiaries – as sometimes happens, especially when a person has lived to a grand old age and lost contact with those remembered in the will.

• A will such as this containing several vital technicalities and creating a 'trust for sale' for the children (which avoids various legal pitfalls and needs careful wording) should at the very least to be checked by a solicitor. One way we have done this for free in the past is through one of the house insurance free advice schemes – in this case Frizzell, tel 0202 292333 (who were, prior to the recent takeover, recommended by 'Which?', for providing good value house contents insurance in the London area). Frizzell offer 24 hour free medical, domestic and legal advice service to their clients. Faxing two prototype wills to them provoked a marvellous six page letter of comment from their solicitor in reply.

• The children have a 'contingent' interest – ie contingent in this case upon the youngest reaching the age of eighteen. If the child dies earlier then that gift will lapse (unless there are children of that child), and the gift will go to the other children. A vested interest on the other hand would have formed part of the child's estate.

• Denying any part of the estate to those contesting your will may not stand up in court, but it could put them off trying.

• The witnesses should be people who will not benefit from your will, or they will forfeit any provision made for them.

The following points are worth noting about wills in general:

• A will could be left in a safe place in the house, along with your other main papers, which would be simpler and quicker than leaving it with a solicitor or depositing it at the bank. Tell your executors where you have left it and consider giving them copies (note on the copies who has the original and where).

• A will is automatically negated by marriage, so make another one at this time. It is as well to make another one too if you divorce.

• Tax can sometimes be saved within two years after death by the beneficiaries of the will entering into a deed to vary its terms.

• To repeat: be careful in your use of words in your will. Do not write for instance 'I give all my money to ...' if what you really mean is 'I give everything I own to ...'.

• Avoid inadvertently giving your spouse a mere 'life interest' in your property (where the person is only able to get income from the house and no capital). You could make this mistake by specifying what is to happen to the property after the spouse's death. Such considerations should be left for the spouse's own will to deal with.

• In Scotland your spouse and children have rights to one third or more of your estate (other than lands or buildings) whatever your will may say to the contrary.

Many more such interesting points are raised in the 'Which?' book mentioned above.

Altering a will by codicil

Typing errors in a will are best avoided. If retained they must be signed with your signature and that of your witnesses in the margin. To make small changes in a will the normal procedure is to add a codicil, with two new witnesses signing at the end, using the same legal formula as in the main will ('signed by ... in our presence and then ...'). A sample codicil might read:

This is the first codicil to the will made the fourteenth day of April nineteen ninety three of me Donald Roland Winterton of 26 Oxford Gardens, London W10.

(1) I revoke the bequest of £1,000 to Janet Simmonds.

(2) In all other respects I confirm my will.

The Law Society has produced a series of fact sheets on will-making. For a free copy of the relevant one, state your circumstances (married, grandparent, divorced, etc) and send a stamped addressed envelope to The Law Society, 50 Chancery Lane, London, WC2A 1SX. They also have a leaflet 'Ten Steps to Make a Will' and a helpline on 071 274 7000. Homelife (formerly the Distressed Gentlefolk's Aid Association) have a free guide 'Where There's a Will There's a Way' available from Hilary Watt, Homelife, Vicarage Gate House, Vicarage Gate, London W8 4AQ. If you want to use a solicitor, you could phone around in the Yellow Pages for the cheapest.

The Will Registry offers a professional will-drafting service, based upon a detailed questionnaire, for around £20, or £30 for two mutual wills: write to The Will Registry, 357-361 Lewisham High Street, London SE13 6NZ.

The charity, Age Concern (see under Organisations in the Resources chapter), offers a will-making service, again based on a questionnaire, for £40.

The Camden Citizens Advice Bureau (tel 071 483 1860) has a list of solicitors who will draw up a will for a £30 minimum donation to the Bureau.

You may be able to get a will drafted at subsidised cost by a solicitor under the Legal Aid Green Form scheme if you are both over 70 years (or blind or partially blind or deaf or hard of hearing or handicapped by illness or injury) *and* of modest means with low savings.

Inheritance tax information is available from the Inland Revenue's Capital Taxes Office: Commerce Square, High Pavement, The Lace Market, Nottingham NG1 1HS (tel 0602 243939). For general information, ask for booklets IR 45 and IHT1. Or you can obtain a helpful and detailed free guide 'Planning for Inheritance Tax' from the financial advisers Chamberlain de Broe (tel 071 235 5999).

A final warning from the 'Which?' book:

Pitfalls of d-i-y wills

The one thing worse than not making a will at all is making a mess of making a will. Many lawyers would say that they can make more money out of poor home-made wills than they do out of drawing up wills for clients. There is probably some truth in this. There are many ways in which people who prepare and sign their own will can go wrong. This can, later, lead to long and expensive court cases to resolve the matter, with enormous legal costs for the lawyers. This can reduce by staggering amounts the size of the estate to which the beneficiaries are entitled.

A will is a technical legal document; it is not surprising that some laymen go astray when they try to make a will unaided. If you have any doubts, you should seek a solicitor's advice.

From 'Wills and Probate' edited by the Consumer's Association.

Enduring Power of Attorney

At the same time as making a will, it is a good idea to fill in a form entitled 'Enduring Power of Attorney' (available from Oyez Stationery Ltd, 49 Bedford Row, London WC1, tel 071 242 7132). This enables you to nominate one or more people to represent you at some future stage should you become mentally incapable of handling your affairs. Your form would only be officially registered with the Court of Protection if and when required. Filling in such a form in advance could save your relatives up to £1,000 a year, as otherwise a receiver would have to be appointed by the court.

A pre-death information dossier

In the same envelope as your will it is worth including a dossier of information that will be helpful for your survivors. For instance, you could leave them all the details they will need to register your death:

Registering a death – details needed

Address and phone number of the local registry office (under 'R' in the phone book); your full name (exactly as on birth or marriage certificate); maiden name if a married woman; date and place of birth; home address; (last) occupation; full name and occupation of the husband (and in Scotland, the names and occupations of the spouse, male or female, and of all previous spouses and of the deceased's father; and whether the parents are alive); your NHS number; date of birth of your spouse; information about state or war pensions and allowances. Your birth and marriage certificates and NHS medical card (or at least its number) should also if possible be in this dossier, for taking along to the Registry office in due course.

Other helpful information you could leave for your relatives after your death could include some of the following:

Addresses, telephone number, account numbers, etc for: your bank; building society; credit cards; hire purchase agreements; mortgage; house insurance; council rent department; local gas, electricity, water and telephone offices; life insurance; hire purchase agreements; debts or loans; car details; share certificate details (or the originals of these certificates); premium bonds; pension details; your doctor; your solicitor; your accountant; your stockbroker; your local inspector of taxes and your tax district and tax district reference number; your employers and professional associations; your main clients; your local priest or rabbi or British Humanist officiant or similar, depending on your religion or lack of it; those friends and relatives you would like invited to your funeral; which newspaper, if any, you would like your death announced in; what kind of funeral you would like; your preferred undertaker, if any; your burial rights if pre-bought.

Simplifying your affairs before death

Anyone who has looked into the complexities of probate (the administration of your estate after death) will know that you can greatly simplify matters, before death and especially if death is imminent, by dividing your assets among the relevant beneficiaries. It should be more enjoyable too, making these gifts whilst still alive. Assets given to the spouse are not liable to inheritance tax (although they may be when the spouse comes to die); nor are small gifts of up to £250 per recipient; nor are gifts up to £3,000 in total per year (you may also be allowed a further £3,000 if your previous year's allowance was not used; and a marriage gift can be up to £5,000 to your own child); nor are assets liable that are given away more than seven years before death (such assets attract a proportion of the tax between three and seven years).

If no precautions are taken, a spouse can be left with access to very little money after death freezes (non-joint) bank accounts: so if death is near it is as well either to take money out of the bank or to open joint bank or building society accounts. Probate on stocks and shares – sending forms to lots of firms and all the minute accounting involved – is excessively complicated: again, if death is imminent, it might be as well to cash them in, or to transfer them into the name of one's spouse (more complicated this – 'Con40' stock transfer forms are obtainable from Oyez Stationery Ltd – address above). In fact your executors may be able to avoid the whole problem of probate altogether if you leave behind you only cash and 'personal effects' (car, furniture, etc), having previously disposed of house, shares, bank accounts, pension arrears, etc. If you must maintain a personal store of money in your own name until your death, consider National Savings accounts at the post office, as these do not require a 'grant of probate or letters of administration'. Up to £5,000 in any of these can be handed over to the appropriate relative after death simply by that person filling in form DNS 904 from the post office and sending this in with a £1-50 death certificate copy and, if relevant, a photocopy of the marriage certificate. Building Society investments and Trustee Savings Bank investments may also be paid out if there is less than £5,000 in any one account.

If you can keep the total net worth of your estate (including any jointly owned property) at your death below £125,000 (the current figure, although this changes regularly), your executors can avoid the Inland Revenue rules demanding a full account of the estate.

A reminder: if your total estate after debts is likely to be worth over the inheritance tax limit (currently £150,000) then it may be worth taking measures to reduce this figure, such as dividing the house and other assets either before your death or in your will (see the section on wills above) between your children and spouse – so that your children will not be hit by the tax when your spouse dies.

Incidentally, if you are taking out life insurance, make sure that it is of a kind that enables your beneficiaries to get the money without waiting for probate.

Living Wills

Adapted from The Independent newspaper:

Among the most enduring of all horrors is the prospect of a slow, painful death. Those who witness the protracted terminal illness of a friend or relative often view the eventual death more as a relief than a tragedy.

But to make life-or-death decisions on behalf of a dying person unable to communicate his or her wishes is to enter a moral and legal minefield. Could a doctor be sued for withholding treatment and allowing someone to die – or for not allowing him or her to die? Could it ever be lawful to withhold food and water?

Legal moves are afoot which may settle these questions. Recently, the all-party parliamentary group on voluntary euthanasia proposed legislation to make documents known as 'Advance Directives', or Living Wills, legally binding.

An Advance Directive sets out the kind of medical treatment a person wishes to receive, or not receive, should he or she ever be in a condition that prevents them expressing those wishes. Such documents, much in vogue in the US and some Commonwealth countries, are becoming increasingly popular in Britain.

The proposed legislation is intended to clarify, not to change, the law. Doubts about the enforceability of Advance Directives arise from the lack of English case law on the issue. But a legal opinion sought recently from Alan Newman QC by the Voluntary Euthanasia Society suggests that its Advance Directive may, even without new legislation, be binding in an English court of law.

A clear distinction must be drawn between actions requested by an Advance Directive, and active euthanasia, or 'mercy killing'. A doctor who took a positive step – such as giving a lethal injection – to help a patient die would, as the law stands, be guilty of murder or aiding and abetting suicide, depending on the circumstances.

An Advance Directive, however, requests only passive euthanasia: the withholding of medical treatment aimed solely at sustaining the life of a patient who is terminally ill or a vegetable. The definition of medical treatment, in such circumstances, can include food and water.

In Mr Newman's opinion, the enforceability of the Advance Directive stems from the notion, long accepted in English law, that a person who is both old enough to make an informed decision and *compos mentis*, is entitled to refuse any medical treatment offered by a doctor, even if that refusal leads to the person's death. A doctor who forces treatment on a patient against his or her wishes is, therefore, guilty of an assault. Case law exists in the US and several Commonwealth countries that extends this right of autonomy over one's life to patients who write an Advance Directive refusing treatment and subsequently lose their reason. Mr Newman says there is no reason based on public policy or English case law, why an English court should treat previously made instructions any differently.

He concludes: 'Providing the declarant is informed at the time when he signs the Advance Directive, such Advance Directive is effective in English law and must be followed by a doctor administering treatment to a patient who has subsequently become incompetent.'

With or without the proposed legislation – which is being introduced as a Private Member's Bill – Mr Newman's opinion will bring reassurance to the thousands of people who have lodged Advance Directives with their GPs.

Douglas Harding, a retired headmaster, is 63 and physically fit and active. He has completed an Advance Directive out of the desire to avoid a drawn-out, painful death like that suffered by his wife, who contracted cancer during pregnancy.

'It was clear from the beginning that she was going to die. But she had an appalling and very protracted death. By the time she died, she had only one breast, she had a lump on her head the size of an ostrich egg, she was blind, and her spine was twisted. I never want to suffer the same way,' he says.

Equally important to Mr Harding is to maintain some control over the time and manner of his death. 'I'd like doctors always to treat me as a sensible being.'

Shane Snape, 31, is a nurse who completed an Advance Directive when he learnt he was dying of Aids. He says that by doing so, he hopes to free his doctors and his family from the burden of deciding whether or not to keep him alive.

'As a nurse, I've seen the difficult situations people get themselves into. The family and the hospital never know what to do. People are left wondering if they have made the right decision. This way, the onus falls on me,' he says.

Mr Snape has adapted the Voluntary Euthanasia Society's draft Advance Directive, specifying that he wishes never to be deprived of water, and that he should be included in discussions about his health for as long as he is able.

The document could be used to sue a doctor who disregards his wishes – but it could also protect medical staff, he says:

'The greatest difficulty for a care worker is to know what the patient's wishes are. Not knowing can work against them [in law]. The Advance Directive excludes doctors from guilt or liability.'

Nuala Scarisbrick, a member of the Committee Against Euthanasia, believes Advance Directives are unnecessary – there is an increasing number of hospices providing the means for people to die with dignity – and are vulnerable to abuse. 'Advance directives are really about killing people. They are open to the danger of relatives colluding with an unethical doctor. It all comes down to money,' she says.

The proposed legislation may prove to be the first step towards legalising active euthanasia. Its backers say that, with the support of more than 200 MPs and peers, it has a good chance of becoming law. If it does, a full voluntary euthanasia bill is likely before the middle of the decade.

From an article by Simon Denison in The Independent, July 1991.

In 1992 the courts established (in the case of a Jehovah Witness' daughter) that it is legal for doctors to disregard a patient's direct refusal of treatment when that treatment is considered life-saving and there is evidence that the patient has been 'influenced' in his or her decision.

As Shane Snape made clear, one of the purposes of living wills is to simplify the moral dilemmas of doctors and relatives, and indeed the British Medical Association (BMA) has recently supported the use of Living Wills (Advance Directives), stating, in part:

BMA Supports Living Wills

There are significant benefits to Advance Directives within the framework of continuing doctor-patient dialogue. It is highly recommended that patients discuss the specific terms of an Advance Directive with a doctor and that this be part of a continuing dialogue. Equally important is continuous dialogue with any nominated proxy decision maker.

The BMA suggests that patients who have drafted an Advance Directive carry a card [eds: see illustration later in this chapter] indicating that fact as well as lodging a copy with their doctor.

The Association recommends that any person making an Advance Directive updates it at regular intervals. Five years is suggested as an appropriate interval for patients to review their decisions.

Deborah Duda's examination of the religious considerations for the United States is equally relevant to the UK:

If you are Catholic, you may already be aware that the June 1980 Declaration of Euthanasia concluded: 'When inevitable death is imminent, it is permitted in conscience to take the decision to refuse forms of treatment that would only secure a precarious and burdensome prolongation of life.' The United Methodist Church says, 'We assert the right of every person to die in dignity without efforts to prolong terminal illnesses merely because the technology is available to do so.' The Central Conference of American Rabbis said, 'The conclusion from the spirit of Jewish Law is that while you may not do anything to hasten death, you may, under special circumstances of suffering and helplessness, allow death to come.'

She also reports a study carried out by an American educational council into the effect a Living Will might have on a life insurance policy:

They reported that signing a Living Will would not invalidate any life insurance policy and would not be construed as an intent to commit suicide. Insurance companies stand to save lots of money if people are not kept alive artificially for months or years in hospitals or nursing homes.

Reprinted with permission from 'Coming Home: A Guide to Dying at Home with Dignity', © 1987 Deborah Duda, Aurora Press, PO Box 573, Santa Fe, NM 87504, USA.

In the United States, Congress has passed a bill whereby anyone going into hospital can fill in a Living Will – some of the States now issue very long six page versions. The following Living Will has been adapted by the Natural Death Centre from those put out by the Voluntary Euthanasia Society, the Terence Higgins Trust and others. You would be well advised however to discuss your Living Will with your GP, or with another doctor if necessary; and to lodge a copy with a doctor (it might be best to change doctor if necessary, if yours is particularly hostile to the Living Will concept) and with your relatives. If you go into hospital for any serious reason, you can show it to your doctors there and have a copy put in your notes. You may also want to update the form every few years, even if just to sign and have witnessed the statement (at the end) to the effect that it still represents your wishes. Strike out any parts which you do not wish to apply to your case – or write your own version entirely.

Living Will (The Natural Death Centre's adaptation)

TO MY FAMILY, MY PHYSICIAN AND ALL OTHER PERSONS CON-CERNED. THIS DIRECTIVE is made by me at a time when I am of sound mind and after careful consideration.

I wish to be fully informed about any illness I may have, about treatment alternatives and likely outcomes.

I DECLARE that if at any time the following circumstances exist, namely:

(1) I suffer from one or more of the conditions mentioned in the schedule below; and

(2) I have become unable to participate effectively in decisions about my medical care; and

(3) two independent physicians (one a consultant) are of the opinion that I am unlikely to recover from illness or impairment involving severe distress or incapacity for rational existence,

THEN AND IN THOSE CIRCUMSTANCES my directions are as follows:

(1) that I am not to be subjected to any medical intervention or treatment aimed at prolonging or sustaining my life;

(2) that any distressing symptoms (including any caused by lack of food) are to be fully controlled by appropriate analgesic or other treatment, even though that treatment may shorten my life.

(3) that I am not to be force fed (although I wish to be given water to drink).

(4) that I wish to be allowed to spend my last days at home if at all possible.

I consent to anything proposed to be done or omitted in compliance with the directions expressed above and absolve my medical attendants from any civil liability arising out of such acts or omissions.

I wish to be as conscious as my circumstances permit (allowing for adequate pain control) as death approaches. I ask my medical attendants to bear this statement in mind when considering what my intentions would be in any uncertain situation.

I RESERVE the right to revoke this DIRECTIVE at any time, but unless I do so it should be taken to represent my continuing directions.

SCHEDULE

A Advanced disseminated malignant disease.

B Severe immune deficiency.

C Advanced degenerative disease of the nervous system.

D Severe and lasting brain damage due to injury, stroke, disease or other cause.

E Senile or pre-senile dementia, whether Alzheimer's, multi-infarct or other.

F Any other condition of comparable gravity.

I have lodged a copy of this Living Will with the following doctor, who is/is not my GP, with whom I have/have not discussed its contents :

(Name)_____

(Address)_____

_____(Tel No)_____

Should I become unable to communicate my wishes as stated above and should amplification be required, I appoint the following person to represent these wishes on my behalf and I want this person to be consulted by those caring for me and for this person's representation of my views to be respected:

(Name)_____

(Address)_____

_____(Tel No)_____

If this person named above is unable to act in my behalf, I authorise the following person to do so:

(Name)_____

(Address)_____

_____(Tel No)_____

MY SIGNATURE_____**Date**_____

My name_____

My address_____

WE TESTIFY that the above-named signed this Directive in our presence, and made it clear to us that he/she understood what it meant. We do not know of any pressure being brought on him/her to make such a directive and we believe it was made by his/her own wish. We are over 18, we are not relatives of the above-named, nor do we stand to gain from his/her death.

Witnessed by:

Signature:_____	Signature:_____
Name:_____	Name:_____
Address:_____	Address:_____
_____	_____
_____	_____

FOR RENEWING WILL IN LATER YEARS:

I reaffirm the contents of my Living Will above.

MY SIGNATURE_____Date_____

Witnessed by:

Signature:_____	Signature:_____
Name:_____	Name:_____
Address:_____	Address:_____
_____	_____
_____	_____

If you fill in the part above appointing a person to represent your wishes on your behalf, it should be someone whom you trust absolutely, especially if they stand to inherit under your will.

If you would like to see the 'Advance Declaration' on which this Living Will is largely based, contact the Voluntary Euthanasia Society (VES), 13 Prince of Wales Terrace, London W8 5PG (tel 071 937 7770). (The form for Scotland produced by the independent VES there is different from that used in the rest of Britain, but can be obtained from the London VES. In Scotland a 'tutor dative', a legally enforceable proxy can be appointed by the court; and witnesses are not needed, it is sufficient to sign writing above your signature the words 'adopted as holograph'. Incidentally, there is less legal risk in Scotland attached to the publishing of books detailing how to practise active euthanasia.) The Terrence Higgins Trust version is available from 52-54 Gray's Inn Road, London WC1X 8JU (tel 071 831 0330). For a copy of this present Will please send one SAE plus one first class stamp to cover expenses to: The Natural Death Centre, 20 Heber Road, London NW2 6AA (tel 081 208 2853; fax 081 452 6434).

> **LIVING WILL:** I have made a Living Will stating, inter alia, that, if terminally ill, I do not wish to have my life prolonged by medical interventions. This Living Will is lodged with Dr...
> Tel.. and with
> my proxy ....
> Tel...

Living Will summary to carry around with your credit cards

Alongside or instead of the legally-worded version above, you may like to write your own informal Natural Death Instructions. Here, for instance, is a wonderfully idiosyncratic version written by Scott Nearing (and honoured in the event by his wife – see the chapter on 'Brave and Conscious Deaths').

Natural Death Instructions

This memorandum is written in order to place on record the following requests:

1. When it comes to my last illness I wish the death process to follow its natural course; consequently:

a. I wish to be at home not in a hospital.

b. I prefer that no doctor should officiate. The medics seem to know little about life, and next to nothing about death.

c. If at all possible, I wish to be outside near the end; in the open, not under a roof.

d. I wish to die fasting; therefore, as death approaches I would prefer to abstain from food.

2. I wish to be keenly aware of the death process; therefore, no sedatives, painkillers, or anaesthetics.

3. I wish to go quickly, and as quietly as possible. Therefore:

a. No injections, heart stimulants, forced feeding, no oxygen, and especially no blood transfusions.

b. No expressions of regret or sorrow, but rather, in the hearts and actions of those who may be present, calmness, dignity, understanding, joy, and peaceful sharing of the death experience.

c. Manifestation is a vast field of experience. As I have lived eagerly and fully, to the extent of my powers, so I pass on gladly and hopefully. Death is either a transition or an awakening. In either case it is to be welcomed, like every other aspect of the life process.

4. The funeral and other incidental details:

a. Unless the law requires, I direct that no undertaker, mortician, or other professional manipulator of corpses be consulted, be called in, or participate in any way in the disposal of my body.

b. I direct that as soon as convenient after my death my friends place my body in a plain wooden box made of spruce or pine boards; the body to be dressed in working clothes, and to be laid on my sleeping bag. There is to be no ornament or decoration of any kind in or on the box.

c. The body so dressed and laid out to be taken to the Auburn, Maine crematorium of which I am a paid member, and there cremated privately.

d. No funeral services are to be held. Under no circumstances is any preacher, priest, or other professional religionist to officiate at any time or in any way between death and the disposal of the ashes.

e. As soon as convenient after cremation, I request my wife, Helen K. Nearing, or if she predecease me or not be able to, some other friend to take the ashes and scatter them under some tree on our property facing Spirit Cove.

5. I make all these requests in full consciousness and the hope that they will be respected by those nearest to me who may survive me.

Excerpted from 'Loving and Leaving the Good Life', © 1992 by Helen Nearing, with the permission of Chelsea Green Publishing Company, Post Mills, VT 05058, USA.

Choosing the attitude

Most people die at the end of a period of illness. Someone who is going to die has the right, so far as possible, to choose the circumstances, particularly where it will take place. But even when we can no longer control the circumstances of our living and dying, we can still decide on our attitude, as Deborah Duda writes:

Choice of attitude – the ultimate freedom

When we can no longer control the circumstances of our lives, we can still control our attitude about them. We can choose our attitude about dying. We can choose to see it as a tragedy, teacher, adventure, or simply as an experience to be lived. Our attitude will determine the nature of our experience.

When we choose to surrender to life, we are free; and when we are free, we are in control. This paradox lies at the heart of our human existence.

To surrender and to be free we have to accept life as it is instead of holding on to how we think it should be. We can't change something we don't first accept. Surrender and acceptance are not to be confused with resignation and succumbing. Resignation and succumbing are passive – something just overpowered or overcame us and we had no choice but to give up. Resignation is self-pity and believing the illusion that we're powerless. Acceptance and surrender, on the other hand, are positive acts. 'I choose to let go, to give up control and accept life as it is. And there will be things I can change and things I can't.'

If we deny dying and death, we're prisoners to them. When we accept them, we're free and regain the power lost in resisting them. We let go of our resistance by letting go. It's easy to do and can be hard to get ready to do. The choice to let go must be made in the heart. A choice made only in the head, unsupported by the body, feelings and soul, is unlikely to be carried out.

If we remember that choice of attitude, the ultimate freedom, is always available, we make a spacious place in which to experience dying. We can be free whether we are dying ourselves or sharing in the dying of someone we love. We can be free whether we die at home or in a hospital. Choosing our attitude is easier at home than in an atmosphere that unconsciously says dying should be isolated from life and is, therefore, not OK.

Reprinted with permission from 'Coming Home: A Guide to Dying at Home with Dignity', © 1987 Deborah Duda, Aurora Press, PO Box 573, Santa Fe, NM 87504, USA.

More specifically, you can discuss with your family and friends how you would like to die. Henry Tennant, an Aids patient, made up a list of simple demands for how he wanted to die. Some of these he was able to arrange himself, for some he needed his friends and helpers to be aware of his wishes. Allegra Taylor reports his reflections:

A death plan

As I become iller, AIDS becomes my life. I long to take a holiday from it – from waking every morning feeling so lousy. But you have to accept the reality of your life and then create maximum value out of what you've got. I'm so much helped by my Buddhism because it gives me a strong and vibrant focal point which is not AIDS.

I want to die in a state of true happiness. I want to die chanting. I want to be in control of my death and have people with me who know what kind of spiritual atmosphere I would like around me.

It's a pity that society's current taboo about death, particularily untimely death, is denying us all an invaluable source of learning and personal development. We need death to savour life. Do what you can in the time you have. You can't expect to be 'normal' again once you're diagnosed with AIDS, but accept the fact that you can be changed by it.

From 'Acquainted with the Night' by Allegra Taylor.

Your wishes may take more specific, personal or light-hearted forms. How would you like to spend your last few weeks? Would you go on one final holiday? Would you take up smoking right at the end? Would you write rude letters to your bank manager? Would you want a bench in your memory? What would you want to say to your family and friends? Is some of it worth saying now? What would your loved ones have to remember you by? A tape of your voice, a home movie? If it enabled you to be utterly decadent for just one month or one week or one day, what would you want to do? Eat at an expensive restaurant? Swim with dolphins? Meet your hero(-ine)?

Dying wishes

It is worth remembering that 'dying wishes' or messages can assume extreme importance for those you leave behind. It gives them a way of giving to you when you are no longer there. It may be a focus for meaningful or constructive activity when everything is falling to pieces. It can be a creative and humorous act of warmth which proves long-enduring. Death has an uncanny way of freezing certain memories and moments; if they are happy and loving they will prove repeated comfort for the people who mourn you. A difficult request ('I want to be buried in Bolivia') or prohibition ('Don't marry that ghastly man') will stick too!

Your family will have to make certain decisions as to your funeral arrangements: should you be buried or cremated or buried at sea? What sort of casket should they use? What sort of service? What should be the tone of the wake, if there is one? If your spouse, partner or family is aware of your wishes, at least in general, it could save them considerable distress about 'getting it right'.

In her workshops Christianne Heal encourages people to consider the art of funeral preparation.

Imaginative send-offs

Everyone knew it wasn't the done thing to plan your own funeral, but, said Christianne, most of us put plenty of effort into organising weddings and christening parties, so why did funeral parties have to be such thrown-together, dismal affairs?

Thus prompted, ideas for imaginative send-offs flowed thick and fast. Bridget wanted a pub crawl for all her friends, followed by a short service at a harbour during which her body would be thrown into the sea. Peter wanted a funeral *al fresco*, preferably on a hillside, with a ragtime band playing his favourite melodies. Monica said she would like a 'Green' funeral, with her body buried in a biodegradable bag rather than a tree-wasting coffin. Christianne suggested that anyone with ideas of how they'd want their funeral to be conducted ought to write them down and leave them with a close family member. 'Families have enough to think about after a death without spending hours trying to imagine what the dead person would or wouldn't have wanted at their funeral.'

From an article by Joanna Moorhead, Weekend Guardian (Aug. 25th 1990).

Liz has gone further, and has taped her own funeral service in advance:

Taping my own funeral

A little of myself: I am a nurse (well-qualified) of 33 years standing and have personally experienced the death of countless people in the last few years while working full-time with terminally ill patients in their own homes and in nursing homes. This has made a lasting impression on me and always raised the question within myself of how I would cope with all the eventualities that certain death, at whatever age, would entail.

It wasn't until I found myself comparatively recently in the throes of emphysema and kidney failure (it chokes me to write the words) with a considerably shortened life expectancy that I had to look at my exit from this world and what I wanted for friends and loved ones.

It has been, and still is, a painful and saddening thought, but there is so much I have, and can still do. I have my will organised, my personal wealth (that's a laugh!) and treasured belongings all listed and named for the beneficiaries. As regards the funeral service I have chosen what means the most to me and I am sure in many ways my friends and those regular worshippers on a Sunday will no doubt raise an eyebrow. The easiest part was my choice of music: a recording of Lloyd-Webber's 'Pie Jesu' because the beauty of clarity and pureness exudes from this work and provides vital uplifting of the soul. Secondly, a hymn sung by the congregation 'Crimond – The Lord's My Shepherd'(hopefully with descant). As a finale, a recording of 'Now is the Hour' sung by the Maoris of New Zealand. I would like to share how these pieces in particular, and music in general, have often enabled me to transcend severe physical pain. Having made a positive decision on this and the readings I want I sat back – it was something else marked off the agenda.

Some time later whilst listening to music and in pain, I reflected again on those that I would leave behind. It eased the pain, my belief that this life is only a stage, a platform, and that each step takes us into a different realm, and from each of these, lessons are learnt in betterment of the soul and spirit. At this point it became of vital importance that I left messages of love and hope and thanks to those who had greatly influenced my life. For this, the obvious way was by incorporating into the service my own voice on tape, for however good, nobody can convey the uniqueness of the human voice, the intonation and inflection and the vocal mannerisms that we associate with a particular person. It was also important to me that my voice be known not clouded by analgesics – the clarity should be unmistakable, so that at my farewell my friends will experience the love and sincerity I feel for them. It will be a service of joy not sadness: after all, I will be hovering above and over-seeing all! God help them!

To end this letter, I recognise how painful saying goodbye will be, and many will find it hard – I can hear it now: 'Don't talk about it,' 'Some cure may be found,' or 'I don't want to hear.' I understand, I've used those words myself. My way, of speaking to everybody and to some personally, in my final farewell, and offering my favourite music, will perhaps ease the heartbreak and the tears and help my friends, who have known me in this life, to begin to see me as – I hope – a celestial being! Still Liz, saying, 'Talk to me – say goodbye now. I love you always. I'll be waiting to meet you again later on, and God bless you all.'

My tears have flowed in the writing of this as they have flowed in making the arrangements for my funeral and death.

From a letter to The Natural Death Centre.

Nevertheless, a simple note left with your will may be all you wish to leave to express your funeral wishes, or even to state that funeral arrangements are not important to you, that there is no 'right way'. Funeral arrangements are discussed in detail in two later chapters.

Widow's budget

Some people choose to leave informal 'instructions' which go beyond funeral arrangements. When Stan Chisman learned that he had cancer, writes his wife Margaret,

His first thought was to draw up a 'Widow's Budget' to see if I would have to sell this house, but with economy and no really bad inflation we found it would be possible for me to continue to live here.

From 'Interim' by Margaret Chisman.

A will covers the legal allocation of your property and the legal guardianship of your children. A Living Will covers your wishes in case of debilitating, intractable illness. There is a wealth of other matters in which you might like a say, or to leave guidance for your family and friends:

Do you have an organ donor card? Does anybody know? (See the Good Funeral Guide chapter on how to offer your body after death.) By contrast, is the idea against your wishes?

Do you want to leave a message for your spouse, family or friends? Letting go of their loss will be a slow and painful process. Is there a simple way of telling them that it's O.K. to let go?

Are there any obvious conflicts which could be avoided? You will not be able to tell someone how much you love them, to forgive them, or let them know that in fact you weren't as angry with them as you made out. Are you willing to relax some of the views for which you are known after your death? Carrying on with life after losing someone is hard enough, without having to try not to step on their toes!

Can you make it easier for your partner or spouse eventually to move on to a new phase in their life, perhaps changing their job, interests, home or town? Do they know that you don't mind their eventually finding someone else, if that's the case? Compassion exercised from beyond the grave could be a last loving act which spares your circle of loved ones a great deal of distress.

Christianne Heal includes in her workshops exercises to help people focus on what they would want to say.

Rehearsing last goodbyes

Alison, a student in her early twenties, was trying to voice the words she knew she should speak to her mother. They had never been close, she explained. Her mother always seemed distant, more interested in her younger brother than in her. 'I don't know how to begin – we've just never had that kind of conversation,' she said haltingly. Her partner nodded sagely. 'Do it,' she said. 'However hard it is, try to talk to her. My mother and I didn't get on very well, but now she's dead there's so much I wish I'd ...' 'That's it,' said Christianne triumphantly. 'The end of the exercise. Please stop talking straight away. Death, when it comes, won't allow you to finish your sentence.'

From an article by Joanna Moorhead, Weekend Guardian (Aug. 25th 1990).

'I didn't know what to say...'

So far we have looked at ways of 'preparing' ourselves for death, our own training for dying. What do you say when someone tells you that a loved one of theirs is dying – or that they themselves are dying? Many of us find ourselves caught between the feeling that there's nothing we can really do to help and the fear of upsetting the person by touching their pain, so instead we just gloss over the subject. In the chapter on 'Improving Grieving', we quote Jean Baker explaining how other people's reactions to her husband's death were often to 'cross the road if they saw me coming'. Her advice for how to relate to the recently-bereaved is equally relevant for supporting the dying person and the family: 'The most helpful thing people can do is listen, just let you talk and be compassionate. People think it will hurt you to talk. Or they fear they will be reminding you – as if you had forgotten.' If you are not someone's close friend or relative, there is a tendency to think that the dying or bereaved person is best looked after by that close network of support, and that it is best not to interfere. There is also perhaps even the fear of being 'landed' with someone else's grief. However, people in such circumstances can experience this as being ostracised. At the time when most they need to be connected to their community, they are hermetically sealed within a bubble of pain, along with the few friends who have the courage to step inside it with them. They may, of course, have chosen to isolate themselves. Either way, the gentle reassurance that you are still there, that you can tolerate their talking about their grief, even that you are not afraid of them, made through words or a gesture, will make a difference and gives them a choice. If you are stuck for words, would a hug not do?

Our wider community

Training for dying is not just about ourselves. We have still a long way to go as a society. It is not hard to see that we accord many of the same prejudices, fears and apprehensions to the issues of illness in general, and ageing, that we do to dying. Why is it that so many people assume the role of the 'elderly' when their minds and bodies are fit enough to allow them to expect so much more from life? Why do people hide the terrible suffering of long illness? Why, as a society, do we contract our caring for, and management of, illness and dying out to other people, and then refuse to become involved ourselves? Why is it that some of us deal with the problems of hundreds of dying people, and the rest of us barely see death?

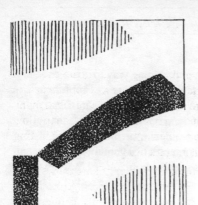

Chapter 5

PRACTICAL CARE FOR THE DYING

Facts and figures

In a recent study, approximately 70% of patients died in hospital, 20% died at home and 10% died in hospices and elsewhere. The percentage dying in hospital has gone up over the years – in 1960 it was less than 50%. According to Pam Williams, from whose nurse's dissertation these figures are taken:

> As a result of changes in family structure – smaller families, more mobile society, women working, unemployment and poverty – it is harder for families to cope with caring for the dying at home, even though it is generally accepted that most people wish to die in a familiar surrounding, and that the home environment (even with limitations) is the 'ideal' place to die.

The same study cites the aim of the World Health Organisation's 'Global Strategy of Health for All by the Year 2000', that

> Everyone should be afforded Dignity and Comfort at the time of Death. By the year 2000, all those dying who are in contact with health and social services should be able to choose where they spend their last days, and, wherever that is, they should be able to expect optimal pain relief, physical comfort and psychological support from professionals.

It needs pointing out, to put these matters in perspective, that 50% of deaths in Britain are sudden. Here we are concerned with slow deaths, the dying process. Studies show that hospital nurses have more difficulty managing slow than quick dying.

The hospice movement offers great expertise in the care of the terminally ill, 'both inside their walls, and through staff such as Macmillan nurses going out into the community to give support to patients and relatives at home. But since the modern hospice owes its being and related service development to major cancer charities, the emphasis is on support for patients dying of cancer. Yet 75% of people who die do not have cancer.'

That home for many is the preferred place to die is confirmed by a study of home care services as an alternative to hospices:

> Information provided by the carers three months after the patient's death indicated that patients who died at home preferred this, while half the patients who died in a hospice or hospital would have preferred to have been at home.
>
> From 'Home Care Services – an Alternative to Hospices?' by
> Audrey W. M. Ward, in Community Medicine Vol. 9 No. 1.

Hospital attitudes

It is generally accepted that 'in the past many nurses and doctors viewed death as a failure of their skills, and rejected the dying person as a reminder of the limitations of their ability to sustain life' (Pam Williams). Much has been done to improve hospital care of the dying in recent years – for instance with the introduction of hospital palliative care teams and hospital-based Macmillan nurses – and attitudes have dramatically improved; but institutional change can take a long time to show its benefits in practice.

In 1961, 90% of doctors indicated a preference for not telling patients they had cancer, but in 1979 this was reversed, with 97% indicating a preference for passing on the diagnosis. Yet even today, many nurses are frequently being put on the spot by patients who have been told something ambiguous by the doctor and want more information.

Pam Williams.

Doctors and nurses have testified to the difficulty of coming close to the dying patient in hospital surroundings (although the small community cottage hospitals have a better reputation). Here are three such accounts, the first by Dr Sean Spence:

Television in hospital

One night in cubicle number one there was a child dying of a rare tumour. She was three years old with her hair short, as if shaven, as a result of chemotherapy. In the corner of the room the television eavesdropped. It played shadows of blue, white and red across the room, silhouetting the bars at the end of the bed, the forms of the parents waiting, its light enough to reflect them in the window opposite me. I could see their tears in that window. It became a mirror in the night. The emotions playing across the room did so without me, carried on around me. My presence was superfluous. No medical intervention would save her now. Curing is easy, but not curing is so hard, an impotence in the soul.

The gathered relatives, extended family, filled the rest of the room. Middle-aged men in suits crouched, sitting on plastic chairs, with tabloid newspapers open before them. They appeared to read the inane headlines by the glow of the artificial light, so that other agencies' realities flooded theirs. Their own state of reality must have been so great – a grandchild about to die – yet they chose to ruminate on external symbols, signs, secrets, intrigues, consumer durables which would not sustain them. When our own internal, subjective world becomes too real, when our own consciousness is too connected, do we then retreat into the external, the objective, the unreal?

From 'Television and the Retreat from Consciousness', by Dr Sean Spence,
in Beshara magazine.

A dying nurse

I am a student nurse. I am dying. I write this to you who are, and will become, nurses in the hope that by sharing my feelings with you, you may someday be better able to help those who share my experience.

We're taught not to be overly cheery now, to omit the 'everything's fine' routine, and we have done pretty well. But now one is left in a lonely silent void.

With the protective 'fine, fine' gone, the staff is left with only their vulnerability and fear. The dying patient is not yet seen as a person and thus cannot be communicated with as such.

I know you feel insecure, don't know what to say, don't know what to do. But please believe me, if you care, you can't go wrong. Just admit that you care.

Anon, American Journal of Nursing, 1970.

Doctors withdrawing from the dying

I have recently completed a dissertation, related to how much information terminal patients are offered regarding their diagnosis and prognosis. The results of the study have convinced me that death and dying are over-medicalised, the disease process assuming primacy over the person. Patients within the study firmly located the fear of cancer and dying within their doctors; rather than within themselves. They reported having to 'fight for their diagnosis and prognosis' with very little, if any, information offered voluntarily.

The most disturbing (for me) feature of the study was the reporting by patients that doctors and nurses 'withdrew' from the patient once the patient knew their prognosis. This was despite patients feeling that this was the time they most needed emotional support from their doctors and nurses.

Keith Ward, c/o Wakefield and Pontefract College of Health Studies,
Pontefract General Infirmary, West Yorkshire (tel 0977 600 600, ext 6663).

In spite of these testimonies, modern hospitals are not soulless machines; doctors and nurses are not ogres.

Their fears and withdrawals cannot be wholly blamed on the hospital environment; they are part of the wider 'alienation from death in our age':

Orderly death

The kind of death one would hope for today – that is, to die in one's sleep, ignorant of the event, was, in the Middle Ages and the Renaissance, only wished upon one's enemies.

An orderly kind of death was part of an orderly life, and a number of ceremonies were an intrinsic part of dying. A will was written, psalms were chosen, and the speeches to be held were well prepared: these tasks were well in order long before death actually occurred.

If one fearfully retreats from the new and unknown in life, one will also attempt to flee from death. The need constantly to seek out continuity (non-change) is, in itself, an expression of fear of death.

From 'The Anxiety of the Unknown' by Jorn Beckmann and Henrik Olesen,
Odense University Hospital, Denmark, 1988.

Nurses are human too (like the rest of us!) as testified in the next letter from a nurse to The Natural Death Centre, which is followed by an account by a priest of visiting an old friend dying in hospital.

Nurses too busy

I do understand the need for a dying patient to be holding someone's hand and for nurses to communicate with them, but most of the time we cannot spare the nurses. Also, some people die quickly and others live for a long time – for one of our patients it was three weeks before he passed on. Many a time I just wanted to sit with patients who are dying for all of my shift, and give them tender loving care – to talk to them, hold their hand and give them the knowledge that someone cares.

From a letter to The Natural Death Centre.

Dedication despite distractions

There was a pulsating machine behind the bed with a digital reading of 30, and which progressively crept up to 35 over the period of my visits. I supposed this to be an oxygen regulator to the pair of tubes which had been inserted into her nostrils. There was another tube emerging from under the bedclothes which was draining off some body fluid and on her wrist a plastic valve had been fitted to enable her to be given subcutaneous injections of antibiotics. On my last visit the nostril tubes had been replaced by a transparent plastic oxygen face mask. There was a perpetual background noise of radio from one of the adjoining beds, so pervasive as to make it difficult to locate its precise origin, and so persistent as to madden one with its inescapably inconsequential form of distraction.

However one might interpret its labours there was no mistaking the sheer dedication of the nursing staff to the well-being of the patients. One evening the old black lady was visited by a young, fresh-faced nurse. She chatted with the patient for a few moments and then said, 'Well, good night Amy, I am going off duty now.' And proceeded to plant a firm kiss on the old lady's withered cheek. 'Now give me a kiss,' she continued, 'and have a good night's sleep. Oh no, that's not a proper kiss; now give me a real one. Come on now.' She bent lower over the bed and duly received her benefit. 'That was lovely,' she said, holding the patient's hand, 'Goodnight now, see you in the morning.'

Rev John Papworth, Editor, Fourth World Review, 24 Abercorn Place, London NW8 9XP (tel 071 286 4366).

Hospice facilities

Like every institutional movement, the hospice system is shaped by its source of funding and forms of administration. In the United States the first hospice was founded by Elisabeth Kübler-Ross. Since then, all hospice funding in the States has been done through the medical hospital system, with a few independent exceptions. The UK hospice movement has been going since the mid-nineteenth century, and there are approximately seventy hospices currently operating. As noted previously, the source of funding is mainly cancer charities and the emphasis on patients dying of cancer. However, much current energy and thought is devoted to extending the hospice philosophy to hospitals and people's own homes and to providing community facilities, as described in this extract from a letter to The Natural Death Centre from a hospice home-care volunteers' co-ordinator:

The Cancer Relief Macmillan Fund has moved away from the idea of raising money to build bedded hospices because of the vast running costs. It now feels it is more economic to encourage the building of day centres where people can be given both specialised care – eg assisted baths, physiotherapy, aromatherapy, massage – and social activities that keep them in the community and also give their carers a break from looking after them. In this way, people can stay at home longer, taking pressure off scarce hospital and hospice beds. The provision of twenty-four hour care at home is still out of reach in most places, but some people do see that as the ideal. Marie Curie nurses are available in some areas to stay with patients all night. Or there may be Iain Rennie Hospice At Home services who will provide twenty-four hour nursing care if necessary.

From a letter to The Natural Death Centre by Christine Mills.

The Hospice Information Service, at St Christopher's Hospice, puts out a regular newsletter giving the latest developments on the domestic and international scene, and information about local hospices, etc, may be obtained from them (see under Organisations in the Resources chapter).

The Buddhist Hospice Trust have volunteers in their Ananda Network who are prepared to sit with and befriend the terminally ill, whether the latter are Buddhists or not (again, see the Resources chapter for details).

Dying at home – the legal situation

The first resource worth acquiring by any family contemplating looking after a dying person at home is Deborah Duda's previously mentioned book 'Coming Home'. This present chapter is very much imbued with her advice and approach, adapted to the UK situation as necessary. For instance, Duda advises that it is our basic legal right to leave a hospital or hospice and to return home whenever we please, with or without a doctor's approval. An important consequence of this is that if a person is unable to make or express their own decisions (in legal terms 'incompetent'), their family (or next-of-kin) has the legal right to make decisions for them. This includes the decision to remove the person from hospital to go either to a hospice or back home. You may have to sign a form which states that the patient has been checked out against medical advice. Even if this is the case, it is worthwhile discussing your decision in detail with the relevant doctors and staff. They will be able to advise you about the future or back-up role which the hospital will play in the care of your relative, and can put you in touch with relevant local support services.

This is the basic enabling right that helps us to bring a dying person home. There are other important legal rights, and in each case the issue is one that requires deep thought and consideration. The Voluntary Euthanasia Society of Scotland has published 'guidelines for the relatives of patients nearing eighty or more who are faced with a major operation, setting out medical factors to be considered before consenting on the patient's behalf'. It needs to be stressed that all such patients who are mentally competent should make such decisions for themselves and that the factor of chronological age is an irrelevance, it is more a question of biological age and mental and physical frailty. But the Society does make an important point:

Very elderly patients facing major operations

No operation is undertaken without the expectation of the patient's survival and the policy of treatment is therefore one of 'maximum recovery', even if it involves resuscitation, the use of artificial breathing apparatus, etc.

In general, before consenting on a very elderly patient's behalf, be sure that he or she has a genuine zest for life and will be content to suffer the stresses and struggles of 'maximum recovery'.

For a Declaration of Rights that a person dying at home should have, see our Manifesto for the Dying, chapter nine.

Making the decision

It has been said many times that 'we die alone', but there are degrees of loneliness, and the feeling of being unwanted at the end of life may be the most poignant of all human emotions:

Mother Teresa on being 'wanted'

I have come more and more to realize that it is being unwanted that is the worst disease that any human being can ever experience. For all kinds of diseases there are medicines and cures. But for being unwanted, unless there are willing hands to serve and a loving heart to love, I don't think this terrible disease can ever be cured.

Mother Teresa, quoted in 'Coming Home' by Deborah Duda.

Deborah Duda summarises some of the arguments for 'coming home', both for the dying person and for the carer:

Easier to adjust at home

Bringing dying people home reassures them they're wanted and won't be deserted. Dying people fear losing control over their lives. In the hospital, the staff takes over and largely dictates what the patient can and must do, when you can see them, etc. You and the dying person don't have time to adjust gradually to loss of control. At home, on the other hand, you can take a few steps at a time toward giving up control, which makes dying easier.

The feeling of being totally wrenched by an unnatural catastrophe, common in sudden deaths and many hospital deaths, is less likely to occur at home. You know you're doing all you can do. If the thought comes up afterward, 'Maybe I could have done more,' you're likely to let go of it much more quickly than if you'd been isolated from a loved one in a hospital. After caring for someone who dies at home most people report feeling peace as well as loss - a feeling of appropriateness and completion and a greater openness to the new life ahead.

Reprinted with permission from 'Coming Home: A Guide to Dying at Home with Dignity', © 1987 Deborah Duda, Aurora Press, PO Box 573, Santa Fe, NM 87504, USA.

The patient who is unconscious may already have expressed a desire to be home. It may still be possible to elicit a response through signals where the level of consciousness is uncertain: 'Do you want to go home? Squeeze my hand for Yes - blink for No.'

Determining the best interests of a person who cannot express his or her own wishes, or who wishes to go home against the advice of the doctor, may be difficult. It is worth being clear as to who in the family has to make the decision, and how each person might be affected by it. A family discussion to decide, or to talk about the decision once made, may be appropriate. You may want to work out how you might share some of the tasks, and to make others aware of the sort of changes that will be happening. As Deborah Duda points out, 'Once you've made the decision for home, keep in mind that your focus shifts from curing to making comfortable.'

There will be circumstances where dying at home would not be appropriate – for instance if the person wanted to donate organs after death; or if there would be insufficient carers to look after the patient; or if it would involve the carers in overmuch difficulty, anxiety and pure physical exhaustion (especially if there were young children also needing care). Almost everyone asked blandly 'do you want to go home?' would say Yes, but all the factors need to be carefully considered, and it is important that those carers who decide that they cannot cope at home for whatever reason should not be made to feel guilty.

Likewise, the decision to bring or to keep the dying person at home may sometimes be made in circumstances that place an initial burden on the person making the decision. Here is a moving account of such a case, where a woman in Scotland found there was more support for her decision than she had imagined, in spite of official unhelpfulness.

Sharing the bed at home

My husband had had a pain below his chest for several weeks and finally went to see his GP. At first the doctor thought that he had pulled a muscle, but on a second visit took a blood test. The doctor then decided that my husband should go to a specialist at our local hospital and he was subsequently taken in for a biopsy.

The specialist then told my husband that he had liver cancer and nothing could be done for him. He died ten weeks later. I regret that the specialist told my husband without first telling me or asking me to be present and that he was so blunt about it. I also felt it negative to give no treatment of any kind as I feel there are many alternative treatments that could have been tried and that might have given hope. Soon after my husband told me the result of his biopsy, a friend advised me to get in touch with Macmillan nurses. I went and asked my GP how to contact them and he told me they would not be needed yet and did not seem to know where they were based. I then rang a cancer charity in Edinburgh who told me that they were in the same hospital where the specialist was based and had a part-time cancer doctor working with them.

I got in touch and from that time their support was invaluable. They are in fact not just nurses but specialists in the treatment of cancer and also counsellors. The nurse who called at the house regularly soon realised that my husband was in far more pain than he would admit to the doctor and arranged for him to have increased painkillers. When later he was given drugs to combat sickness, constipation, etc, she was able to tell me whether the way he reacted to them was normal. She gave me her telephone number and I was able to ring her at home any time I needed advice. I find it sad to think that the specialist does not send his patients along the passage to see the Macmillan nurses as soon as he has had to tell them that they have terminal cancer. The doctors appear not to want to recognise that these nurses can help the patients and families more than they can.

We had the choice whether to keep my husband at home or whether he should go to hospital. He was always very attached to his house and family and although we never talked to him about it, I was sure he would wish to stay at home, as we were able to carry on as if he had an illness from which he might recover. I was able to sleep in the same bed with him right until the day he died.

I was lucky enough to have a friend, who had been a nursing nun, with me during the last days, as well as my daughter. It was particularly nice to have somebody whom we all knew and who was a Catholic as we were. However I could have had a Marie Curie nurse daily or nightly if she had not been there. My husband did not need much nursing until the last week. Although he might have been a little more comfortable with a special bed, bed pans, etc, in a hospital, and also have had more confidence in a nurse giving him the pills regularly, I am sure the fact that we could be with him most of the time in a normal way, and not as a hospital visit, made up for that.

While my husband was dying we were all able to pray together and I tried to see death as Christianity teaches us. I do feel however that the Church still tends to regard death as a tragedy and not as God's plan. The world makes us feel that dying is unacceptable. Those who live to a great age are congratulated so that conversely those who do not are almost regarded as failures. I have a great belief in another life and also that those who have died are still around in spirit. Both my daughter who is not a practising Catholic and I feel that my husband is still looking after us. He was a particularly caring person and, as she said, he has more power to help others now. The book that has helped me more than any Catholic book is 'Who Dies?' by Stephen Levine. I came across it accidentally about a year after my husband died, and it made a great difference to me. I understand that it is not even on the reading list for those training as CRUSE counsellors and I feel that it should be more widely known.

From a letter to The Natural Death Centre.

Elizabeth Lawlor in Cheshire has written to the Natural Death Centre about her decision to bring her husband home to die. She has no regrets about doing this, despite the lack of support from outside agencies:

Dying amidst familiar chaos

My husband Peter died on New Year's Eve 1991. He had been diagnosed with lung cancer in February 1990 and I think surprised everyone by living so long. He had pneumonia and was admitted to hospital in November. The consultant was not able to face what we realised – that Peter was dying. So at the beginning of December, when our local hospice opened beds for the first time, it was thought to be a good idea for Peter to go there. The doctors were still talking about curing the pneumonia!

Probably because the unit was so new, our experience of the hospice was *not* good and after ten days I 'kidnapped' Peter – they would not organise transport, so I managed to get him into the car somehow. And home into his own bed, with intrusive cats, kid's music reverberating and cobwebs that threaten to garotte the unwary!

The day before he died, the drains blocked and Dyno-Rod spent an unbelievably noisy afternoon. I think that Peter was unconscious, but if there was even a flicker, he would have loved the chaos.

District nurses did their best but were rather limited. The Macmillan nurse never showed up – she was on holiday over Christmas and New Year. We had a Marie Curie nurse for one night – ie 11.30 pm to 5 am – which was disastrous. But I did have my wonderful doctor friend, who bullied GPs and made sure that Peter had enough heroin at the end.

She and I were with Peter when he died. Brain death had been at about 7.30 in the morning, I think. I was in bed with him – as I had been throughout – and I got a sense that his soul (or whatever one calls it) had detached itself. And at 11am, he quietly stopped breathing.

Mary and I washed him and laid him out, to the disapproval of the funeral director. It was very real, very loving, and I was able to keep literally in touch with Peter. Then I kept him at home, in our bed, until ten minutes before the funeral. We live near the church and the local Coastal Forces veterans' association put the coffin onto the bier (usually used for transport from the church to the grave) and wheeled him round to the church - no hearse.

Now I am again being perhaps a bit difficult and organising the headstone I want and think Peter would have wanted, with the help of Harriet Frazer's Memorials by Artists [eds: see the Good Funeral Guide chapter]. Mottled black marble wasn't Peter's 'thing'! And it is taking time, and I am working through the grieving process in my own time, my own way, with the erecting of the headstone after a year or more as a symbol of letting go.

Elizabeth Lawlor, Furnival Cottage, Acton, Nantwich, Cheshire CW5 8LD.

Support structures and outside help

Where cost of medication is an important factor the patient may be entitled to assistance on the grounds of age. Otherwise the patient should apply for exemption from payment because of a 'continuing physical disability'. Free prescription forms (FP91) are available from post offices or doctors' surgeries.

Un-means-tested attendance allowances, currently £43-35 per week for day-and-night carers, are available from local Social Security offices. The terminally ill person or carer completes a claim form and obtains a simple medical report (DS1500) from the doctor. These allowances are designed to help terminally ill people to be cared for at home by relatives and friends, but can be spent any way you like. No assessment is required (although one would be required if for a routine attendance allowance).

NHS facilities provided by local authorities include nursing care at home and advice on the care of ill persons at home. Other services vary in different regions and are sometimes provided in conjunction with voluntary bodies. These include domestic help, delivery of meals at home and special laundry services for bed linen. The Social Security may grant special financial allowances in certain circumstances. In some areas, as already mentioned, night nurses or night attendants may be available.

It is particularly worth exploring the help available from local societies and local voluntary agencies which are experienced in this form of care and may offer technical help and services as well as emotional support.

Individual circumstances vary, and the most crucial area of support in a particular case may be found in a list ranging from the official to the highly informal. Here is a useful checklist:

Checklist of possible assistance locally
- NHS provisions
- Social Services
- Macmillan Nurse
- Marie Curie Nurse
- Home Help

- Occupational therapists (for some equipment loan – or try Red Cross)
- Physiotherapists (for walking sticks, frames, etc)
- District nurse
- Meals on Wheels
- Laundry Service
- Night Sitters
- Local support groups and societies
- General Practitioner
- Hospital specialist
- Priest/Vicar/Minister
- Friends and Relations
- Neighbours

If you do not know how to contact any of the services on the list, ask those you can contact. See also the list of Organisations in our Resources chapter. It is worth writing down a list of your needs, so that you can ask each source for more information (as well as being a good way of getting them in perspective for yourself). The Marie Curie nurse is perhaps the key figure in the natural death movement at the present time. She (or a team of such nurses) can be available to give support for up to seven nights a week. This is an enormous factor in preventing unnecessary hospital admissions. Otherwise relatives can reach the end of their tether and allow the relative to be admitted to hospital because they know no alternative. Most advisors stress that the carer should not become isolated in the task of looking after the dying person. One recommends that 'there be at least two people at home to take turns supporting the dying person'. This may not always be feasible. If necessary, ask the local priest or doctor to mobilise potentially helpful neighbours on your behalf. Care of the dying should be shared with friends and relatives, and with neighbours too. This is good not just for the health and well-being of the caring person, but, as Ruth I. Johns points out, for the health of society as a whole:

We need the dying in our neighbourhoods and lives

At best death is very peaceful, quick; at worst, long, protracted and accompanied by illness, pain and suffering. But it is happening to a person and that person matters. The neighbourhood needs – for its own health – to help its members in death and not pass them on to impersonal 'helpers'. In this kind of discussion some people are always quick to say that they know someone whose life 'was ruined' because of 'having to' care for an elderly person for whom they did not feel any particular affection. To have to appear to care for someone purely out of a sense of duty is never easy and can even be injurious to all concerned: yet this is exactly the way our social systems are designed. Perhaps we have never bothered sufficiently to recognise the immense difference between pseudo personal care and affectionate personal care? Maybe it is the people who have been 'saddled' with 'caring' for those they did not really care for who have precipitated the increase of the same blight within the formal social helping systems? The people who quietly get on with their affectionate personal care accept it, and, hard work though it may be, feel enhanced by it.

I would venture the suggestion that some of the young people who play with violence are only seeking a substitute for a suppressed and unrealised natural need to be involved in the whole process of life. We protect them (and ourselves) from real death, which is, thereby, devastatingly lonely for the dying.

Perhaps we actually need the inclusion of dying in our lives to use up energies which otherwise can pop up as actual or fantasised aggression?

Being part of the dying of a loved relative or friend makes life more livable and death a reality. The more we push it into the back of our minds, the more it will bounce back to haunt us with substitute fantasies and impersonal aggression.

It is only by becoming deeply personally involved with family, friends and neighbours, that we can demonstrate that they mean something to us: thereby we become more at home in ourselves. If we feel 'whole' we can more easily see ourselves as having a niche in the continuing affections of others: beyond our own death. Life certainly becomes more tenable once we accept some personal responsibility for death.

> *From 'Life Goes On - Self-help philosophy and practice based on ten years'*
> *pioneering work with Family First Trust, Nottingham' by Ruth I. Johns, 1982*
> *(£6 from 'Unknown Publisher', PO Box 66, Warwick CV 4XE).*

Of all the people around you, some will want to help 'somehow'. Others will be overwhelmed by the thought of having to 'deal' with it all. Take the statement, 'If there's anything I can do to help, let me know,' at face value, and give them a concrete practical task: walking the dog, making a meal or participating in a round of bridge. These would be manageable favours for them, and it allows them to visit with a specific purpose, rather than just mouthe the empty question 'how are you feeling?'

Within the family, how is the responsiblity shared? Often it is concentrated in one person, even when the decision has been made to share it. The family's help can be organised along similar lines as the ones above. 'Responsibility' can be split into three components: tasks; time spent in the role of chief carer (shifts); and the feeling of responsibility. The latter is automatically shared if the first two are shared successfully.

The needs of children may have to be taken into account:

Guilt feelings in children

Guilt feelings can be particularly strong in children. They may believe that by some misdemeanour they caused the death of the loved one. Some children will then misbehave more in order to earn the punishment they believe they deserve. It is vital that such feelings are discovered, in order that the child does not go through life burdened and emotionally crippled by such beliefs.

> *From 'Dying at Home' by Harriet Copperman.*

Generally it is believed that it is healthier for children to be involved. Most authorities advise that throughout any terminal illness and following the death, the children should remain an integral part of the family. Children will regard death as abnormal if they are kept away from the scene, and prevented from contact with their relative either just before or just after death. How to tell a child of an approaching death in the family may be discussed with whatever support persons are available. It may be useful to consider how much worse a sudden unexpected death would be for the children than one for which they had been prepared. There are many good books available for children too – some are on the booklist in the Resources chapter or contact The Compassionate Friends (also in the Resources chapter) for their specialist children's book list (they have a postal lending library too).

Finally, support may be forthcoming from unexpected quarters. It may come from people who step out of their formal roles as 'vicar' or 'GP' or 'neighbour' and become especially supportive individuals. Help for the dying is an emotional business. Not everyone can handle it but some leap into it with enthusiasm, like the four-legged friend in the following example!

Comfort for the dying from a dog

A four-legged therapist named Inky works every day giving the most precious love of all. She comforts the dying. In her own small way the ten-pound Chihuahua-mix dog is as much a hero as the valiant animals who save victims from blazing buildings or raging rivers.

'Some of the most impressive emotional healing I've seen is brought about by Inky,' says Rose Griffith, nursing director at the Hospice of Saint John in Lakewood, Colorado. 'Inky brings back life and humour to the terminally ill - whose existence has been dulled by pain, fear and loneliness.'

And Pam Currier, former hospice director, says: 'In many cases Inky is more effective than any two-legged therapist.'

Says hospice spokesman Peter Wellish: 'One of the greatest tragedies is how many patients die without loved ones by their side. For these patients, Inky's presence is a true blessing. Dying patients don't seem to demand much. All the riches and money in the world are no longer important. Quality time is what matters most.

'For those patients who really need her, Inky will spend the entire night. If there are two who need her, Inky intuitively will divide her time between them.'

Getting and training a canine therapist to help the dying was the idea of volunteer Sister Helen Reynolds of the Sisters of Loreto. She found Inky in a humane society shelter. 'I wanted a dog who wouldn't hesitate to jump into people's laps, to spread love instinctively and impartially,' she explains. 'When Inky first leaped into a patient's arms, she jumped into the hearts of all!'

From the National Examiner (USA) October 8, 1991.
In the UK contact P.A.T. Dog (see Organisations in the Resources chapter).

Carer's needs

The best advice to carers is to remember that 'we also serve by respecting our own needs'. It is sensible to be aware in advance of the burden that supporting a seriously ill person places on the care-giver, and to anticipate some of the difficult feelings such as resentment and hostility that may arise. This needs to be said more than once.

Carer's resentment...

Your life-style may be affected as much as (or even more than) the patient's. You may be spending your time doing things you don't really want to do. You resent that the burden of the relationship may have fallen on your shoulders.

You cannot but help feel resentment. But you can help (both yourself and the patient) by recognising that you do feel some resentment and by not pretending that it does not exist. If you understand that you are feeling this way, you can respond to the patient by saying something like, 'This is really tough and I'm getting very bad tempered' (which is a way of describing your feelings) rather than 'You never do anything except lie there and grumble,' (which is a way of exhibiting your feelings, and quite likely to lead to an argument).

From 'I Don't Know What To Say' by Dr Robert Buckman.

...and anger

The most usual and, for many people, the most frightening feeling is anger. If you have very high expectations of being patient and loving every second of the day, it can be upsetting to feel angry and frustrated. But feeling guilty about it will not help – that simply turns the anger on yourself and sooner or later you will start to feel depressed.

Carers have every reason to feel angry and resentful if they are left to cope alone. You may feel tied and trapped by caring, and angry at the opportunities you have missed.

Anger may also be a reaction to loss – witnessing the suffering of someone you are close at hand to can make you feel angry at the injustice of it all. Or it may be a reaction to the anger expressed by the person you look after: carers often bear the brunt of that anger and frustration.

From 'Help at Hand – the Home Carer's Survival Guide' by Jane Brotchie.

Jane Brotchie's book, 'Help at Hand – the Home Carer's Survival Guide' is recommended (see the Resources chapter for publishing details). It is a useful and sensitive book which helps carers through the practical and emotional difficulties with clarity, and is in itself a source of moral support.

The emotional ups and downs of the situation can cause conflict. The dying person and their family may be going through necessary stages of denial, or experiencing a lot of anger and confusion. Dying does not give one an obvious target for one's anger, and so it is easy to lash out at those nearest to you instead. It can also feel safer to express overwhelming anger in terms of mundane things: a cup of tea which is too hot, or someone else's forgetfulness.

If you can, as Deborah Duda advises, stop before entering the room, and arrest your own 'down' feelings, just for a moment. Relax, breathe in deeply and centre yourself. Touch a place of receptive stillness within that allows the process to unfold as it must. Focus on that aspect of being that is larger than the sick body and the distressing symptoms.

Perhaps a smile is all that is needed to make the difference: the negative side of things is there already, and doesn't need reinforcing. Balancing sadness with cheerfulness and humour can be tricky – if your words are taken the wrong way, stand by what you know you meant. If you feel that the other person is playing emotional games, sidestep them rather than joining in. The oldest technique of them all, and one to use when really riled, is to breathe deeply and count to ten.

Stress can result from many 'side issues', apart from the obvious, especially if you do not allow yourself 'selfish' feelings. If you can recognise the causes of stress, you are more able to deal with its effects. Jane Brotchie provides the following list of common causes:

My source of stress is...

• not knowing for how long I am going to be giving home care.
• having had the decision of caring forced on me rather than having freely chosen it.
• being of advanced age or having ill-health myself.
• not having the training or information I need to provide care.

• lack of free time for myself.
• loss of freedom.
• changes in family life.
• family conflicts.
• competing demands between my role as a carer and other roles in my life.
• loss of social contacts and social life.
• feelings of guilt.
• financial losses or difficulties.
• having to carry out tasks I find unpleasant or embarrassing.
• changes in the personality of the person I care for.
• lack of sleep.
• needing a complete break from caring.
    From 'Help at Hand - the Home Carer's Survival Guide' by Jane Brotchie.

Most importantly, try not to become too locked into the roles of 'carer' and 'patient'. Remember that you also exist for each other outside those roles, and that sometimes you can reverse the roles: the carer may need looking after, and the patient may be able to offer support. Coping is not the care-giver's sole responsibility, and an active role for the patient is recommended where possible. It may be worth gently reminding each other of this from time to time: 'Can I speak to John my husband, not John the patient? Just for a minute.'

At times the care-giver will need to escape. Whether this means sharing a worry-free activity with the ill person or getting out of the house to go to the cinema, don't feel guilty about it. Don't feel surprised if at times you resent the other person, just ensure that you get some space and time to yourself.

Enjoy yourself

DO what YOU want and what you think the person you are looking after would want. Then you feel as if you are still in control of your own life, and the person dying is in control of theirs. Everyone is different, so every death is different. There are no 'right' or 'wrong' ways of doing anything within the process.

Ask for what you want or need. You may not get it but there is quite a lot of help around. Conversely, don't accept 'well-meaning' help that makes you feel in any way uncomfortable.

Make sure you (as carer) continue to be as normal as possible. Eat/drink/laugh/ take the dog for a walk.

Tell people how you feel if it helps you – 'I'm fine' is probably not true!

For me, Peter's dying was very intense emotionally. You can't ever do it again, so GO FOR IT!
    From a letter by Elizabeth Lawlor to The Natural Death Centre.

The carer may feel extremely lonely, isolated both from the non care-giving world and from the relative or partner as they knew them. A support group can go some of the way towards filling that gap – who better to talk to than people in your own position? If you need someone to help you find a way through complex problems, you may benefit from seeing a trained counsellor. In the wake of public disasters in recent years, counselling is gradually becoming widely recognised as an important way of coping with life crises. Counselling is completely confidential, and counsellors are trained to help you to clarify and resolve tangled emotions and problems. Contact the British Association for Counselling (see under Organisations in the Resources chapter), or ask your GP or friends who may be able to recommend particular counsellors.

Most carers begin their roles with little experience and inadequate information. Even if we do eventually become near perfect carers, it is only reasonable to assume that on the way we will have made many mistakes. Over the whole period of time, we will on average have been only half perfect! What now follows is a practical guide to looking after someone who is dying at home. If you are reading it in advance of any need to apply it you may get a clearer idea of what dying at home involves and whether you can provide for it. If you are caring for someone it will serve as a primer and resource for the whole process, to be supplemented by local nursing help and expertise. If you are in a rushed situation you may find in places that some advice needs to be discarded as impractical for a short period, and you may find that other advice makes all the difference.

Preparation and equipment

Physical comfort is regarded as the number one priority for the dying patient. Certain needs clearly have to be met before worrying about emotional requirements. If the bed is wet, the sheets must be changed. If the patient is in an awkward position, he or she should be helped to move. If the sheets are tangled, they need rearranging. If the patient is unwashed, he or she will be uncomfortable. Pain and toilet requirements must be dealt with immediately. Here common sense prevails. Physical comfort is basic to a person's dignity and clarity of thought, and is the mainstay of the care which must be provided. Paying close attention to the patient's physical environment and needs is itself a form of emotional care.

A bed downstairs?

Location of the bed may require considerable thought and analysis of the available conditions. Elizabeth Lawlor's sensitive advice is again based upon her own experience of looking after her husband Peter:

> Keep everything as 'normal' as possible. If the cat/dog usually sleeps on the bed, let it. And if the bed can stay in its usual place, all the better. It is a way of maintaining a feeling of reality which is comforting when someone is drifting in and out of consciousness. The bed should be accessible on both sides to facilitate moving and turning the patient and the making of the bed, as well as bed-bathing, etc. If possible, a chair by the bed that is easy to transfer into is initially good for morale – the patient can spend the periodic half-hour sitting – which is also useful for the bedmaker. Later on the chair is good for visiting family, etc, and is an accepted piece of furniture in that location.

Other important considerations can be taken into account. If the bedroom is upstairs, the staircase may become an increasingly awkward and frustrating barrier to the rest of the house as the patient becomes less mobile. The experience of negotiating a flight of stairs with little or no strength of one's own is for some an unbearable reminder of their condition, and so the stairs can become a symbol for feelings of isolation and impotence, both for the patient and the carer.

If the patient is moved downstairs then calling for the carer may be less hit-and-miss, and just popping one's head around the door to check may be less tiring. In some cases the same energy expended on coping with stairs could instead be used to get some fresh air outside. This must be balanced with the feasibility of nursing the patient downstairs.

Ideally there will be room for a bed and for creating a space which the patient feels is suitably self-contained and private. If this is the living room, the patient may feel invaded by visiting relatives unless there is another room in which they can be greeted and entertained. Are the sleeping arrangements suitable for both partners? Temporary compromises, such as a sofa for the patient, can be quite practical, as long as change will not upset everyone's routine or sense of place. Washing and toilet requirements are also very important.

Ultimately some form of compromise will have to be made. It is important for the carer not to feel guilty that arrangements are not perfect (few people choose a home with all this in mind), just as it is important to make sure that the carer's needs are taken into account. It is easier to be selfless when you have had a few hours' sleep.

Often the sense of what 'feels right' is most important. The care-giver may find unbearable the idea of eventually having to sleep alone in the bed in which their partner spent their last few weeks. Alternatively they may feel that any other way is wrong. The patient may have strong opinions or an obvious need one way or the other: whether to keep everything as normal as possible, or deliberately to create a 'special environment' in which the patient is 'spoiled rotten'. As conditions change a new set-up may be required.

Having said all this, what will very probably happen is that events take over and these decisions are made by circumstance! Wherever the bed is, a bedside table is useful for bottles, tissues, flowers and a constant supply of water and juices.

Other practical equipment needed might include the following, which is an extended list based upon suggestions from 'Who Dies?' by Stephen Levine:

Practical equipment list

A rope and a bell by the bed so the patient feels in contact and can summon help; a stand-up bed tray if appropriate; two hot water bottles, one for the feet and one for easing the pain; an ice bucket; a thermos; possibly a hot plate in the room.

A bedpan, slipper bedpan or urinal bottle may be essential, as well as incontinence pads and plastic sheets. Plastic bedpans are less cold to the touch than metal. A plastic washing-up bowl for bed baths may also be useful.

TV, video recorder, radio, walkman according to requirements. With telephone arrangements, bear in mind both the needs of both patient and carer for privacy.

Extra nightgowns or pyjamas that are easy to put on and take off, socks and a safe pair of non-slip slippers.

Paper towels and tissues, cotton towels, drinking straws that bend, favourite picures and photos, a potted plant or bunches of flowers! Bring nature from outdoors indoors as much as possible.

Consult with your nurse, doctor, or your local physiotherapist to find out about the provision of walking sticks, walking frames and wheelchairs. These can sometimes be borrowed from the Red Cross (see the Resources chapter). Some local councils can provide handrails for toilets, bathrooms and stairs, as well as access ramps for wheelchairs – contact the Social Services department. A shower seat and non-slip bath mats help with bathing. A step-up stool is useful for relatively mobile people.

Bed and bedding

A hospital bed may be preferred (and may be better for the carers if lifting is involved – low divans can wreck lifters' backs) although some patients may be upset at having to give up their own bed. Again, Stephen Levine makes a useful comment:

A hospital bed

A hospital bed with side rails is often quite useful for comfort, because it can be adjusted in so many ways. And the side rails can act as protection during the night so that one does not restlessly or absent-mindedly fall from the bed. Though a hospital bed is very useful, many prefer to die in their own bed and would rather use a foam wedge for support and a few extra pillows than have the up-and-down movement of a strange bed.

From 'Who Dies?' by Stephen Levine.

Special bedding can give extra comfort and prevent bedsores. Sheepskins and pillows are helpful in this respect.

Bedding and comfort

A Spenco mattress helps with preventing sores, as does a fleece. The district nurse should provide that. There should also be a fleece under the heels which should be washed, dried and rubbed regularily to prevent sores.

A wedge of foam under the head of the mattress gives a firmer base than pillows for a half-upright position. The triangular, orthopaedic pillows are also good.

From a letter by Elizabeth Lawlor to The Natural Death Centre.

Special mattresses are available depending on patient requirement. A large-cell ripple mattress offers protection to pressure areas in cases of severe need. However, this is a highly specialised piece of equipment requiring advice and consultation. A bed cradle, V-shaped pillow, sponge or air rings for sitting on, sheepskin squares for sitting or lying on, and sheepskin pads or booties for the feet provide additional comfort. Fresh clean sheets are important, perhaps helped by a rubberised flannel undersheet with a duvet as a comfortable underblanket. You should consult with your nurses or local hospital as to which combination of equipment is best, as well as for details of how to get hold of them (they may themselves be able to provide you with some items). Hospital suppliers are listed in the Yellow pages, although they normally want large orders. There are specialist chemists, such as John Bell & Croyden (see the Resources chapter) – their sheepskin rug, for instance, costs £35. And the Red Cross, as mentioned, can lend equipment (again see the Resources chapter).

A supply of soft pillows and towels is useful for extra comfort – between or under the knees, behind the back, underneath the patient's book, or at the foot of the bed to lift the top sheet – all according to need. Experts emphasise the need for prevention in dealing with bedsores – see below.

Moving

If you need to help the person to move in bed or out of bed, advice and perhaps demonstrations of certain standard moves can be given by your district nurse. Several of these are demonstrated in the excellent, if out-of-date video, 'Caring for your relative at home', which is available from the Marie Curie Memorial Foundation (see under Videos and Tapes in the Resources Chapter). Alternatively, use the instructions which follow, which are based on the video. Practise these complicated instructions on a friend who is well first, rather than on a patient in pain. Of course, as mentioned earlier, in an ideal world there would always be at least two carers at any one time, able to share the strain of moving the patient, and assisted by mechanical hoists where necessary. Try asking for such aids if needed – they are going to become much more common. Indeed a new EC Directive on 'manual handling of loads' came into force in 1993, whereby employees such as nurses would not normally be expected to lift a patient weighing 8 stone or more without a 'mechanical handling device'. Why should unpaid carers be less well equipped?

But in case you find yourself on your own, here are a few basic general guidelines:

• Make sure that the patient understands what you are doing;

• Allow the patient as much independent movement as possible;

• Make sure that you have a firm footing, and remove any bedclothes that will get in the way;

• Keep the person warm; cover her or him with a towel or dressing gown if necessary;

• Take the manoeuvre one step at a time, agreeing or explaining each step before you carry it out together;

• Take tricky steps, where you have to co-ordinate moving together, on the count of three;

• If you find that you are 'lugging' the person, or that she or he is experiencing discomfort, you may need to break the move down into simpler steps;

• If you are lifting the person, make sure that your back is straight and that your knees are bent;

• Don't overdo it! You may just have to wait until you can find someone to help you.

Turning in bed

Frequent changes of position are important for comfort, to avoid bedsores, and to facilitate washing. These steps are used to turn people onto their side from their back. The basic idea is that you turn first the legs, then the arms and shoulders, and then the back.

• Stand at the side of the bed towards which the person wants to turn;

• Remove covers and excess pillows;

• Take hold of the person's far leg (at the knee and ankle), and cross it over the other leg towards you;

• Take hold of the person's far arm (at the elbow and wrist), and cross it over their chest towards you;

• Place one hand on the person's hips and the other on their uppermost shoulder, and gently pull their torso towards you.

Sitting upright

These steps are used to help someone sit upright from lying down. The basic idea is that you lift the person, and then help them move caterpillar-style back along the bed.

• Stand at either side of the bed and remove the covers if necessary. Take your shoes off;

• Help the person sit up: face the person and hook your near arm under theirs, asking them to hold your shoulder and lift themselves up, pushing against the bed with their free arm;

• Still supporting the person, remove the pillows with your free hand;

• Still supporting the person, get onto the bed and kneel behind them;

• Hold the person around the waist like this: slide your arms under their arms, ask them to fold their arms across their chest, and take hold of their wrists;

• Ask the person to bring up their knees, and to push backwards with their feet at the same time as you lift and pull them backwards;

• Still supporting the person, replace the pillows.

Moving to a chair or commode

These steps are used to help someone move to a chair from lying down in bed. The basic idea is that you help the person to sit on the edge of the bed, to get up and to shuffle round to a chair behind you.

• Position the chair or commode a few feet from the side of the bed;

• Remove the covers and stand by the bed in front of the chair;

• Help the person to turn towards you (see 'Turning in bed', above);

• Put one arm under the person's lower knee, and the other under the lower ankle. Lift the person's legs and gently pull them towards you, over the side of the bed;

• Put one arm under the person's shoulders, and the other hand on their hips;

• Ask the person to push up with their lower arm, at the same time as you lift them up by pulling their shoulders and pressing lightly down on the hips. Have a breather.

• Facing the person, place your feet firmly beside the other person's so that you 'sandwich' their feet;

• Bend your knees and keep your back straight;

• Ask the person to put their arms around your shoulders, as you put your arms around their waist;

• Lift the person to their feet by straightening your knees;

• Stay holding each other and shuffle round slowly to the chair;

• Support the person as they sit down. If using a commode, you may have to help the person lift their nightdress/nightshirt or lower their pyjamas as they sit.

Changing sheets with the person in bed

The basic idea here is that you unmake and make half of the bed at a time.

• Remove the covers. Leave one pillow;

• Help the person to roll onto one side, facing away from the centre of the bed (see 'Turning in bed' above);

• Untuck the free side of the sheet, and roll it up as far as you can towards the person;

• Tuck in the fresh sheet on the same side, and fold up the rest close to the dirty sheet;

• Gently help the person roll over the rolled sheet and the folded part of the fresh sheet onto the clean side of the bed;

• Remove the dirty sheet; tuck in the rest of the clean sheet;

• Change the pillowcases and help the person roll back to the middle of the bed;

• Put on a fresh top sheet and replace the covers.

If many changes of sheets are required, a single sheet lengthwise on a double bed can be changed more easily than a double sheet.

Accidents

If the person falls to the floor, check for obvious signs of injury. If he or she can't move fingers or toes, if tentative movement produces sharp pain, or if you are unsure, assume that there are injuries. Call a doctor or ambulance. Make sure that the person moves as little as possible before examination. Make the person comfortable with pillows and blankets. Give reassurance that the situation is being dealt with as well as possible.

Eating

Peter stopped wanting to eat or drink when he had pneumonia. The hospice tried to bully him into eating which upset him. Once he was home, I would ensure that something that he could manage was always available, but didn't make an issue of eating or drinking. Hence, I think that the actual cause of death was kidney failure. But it meant he didn't need to pass urine very often, and he could have a bit if he wanted. On Christmas Day he managed two sips of whisky!

From a letter by Elizabeth Lawlor to The Natural Death Centre.

It will probably be necessary to find alternatives to 'three meals a day'. The person is likely to find their appetite waning, and may be too weak to eat more than a small amount at a time anyway. It is important to consult your nurse or doctor about nutrition, but the basic idea is this: offer small and more frequent helpings, and try to make food available to fit the person's sporadic hunger. Liquid food is easier and less tiring to take in: try soups, milk shakes (with a beaten egg for extra nourishment), yoghourt, and so on. Available from chemists, or with a prescription, are a range of nourishing drinks (some very sickly and sweet!), such as Complan, Build Up, Fortison and Ensure (they do a savoury version of this), which are acceptable if the person is only able to take in small amounts of food, although some are constipating if no bran-type roughage is added. Your doctor can prescribe food supplements, which are taste-free powders that can be sprinkled on food.

Help the person to sit up as much as possible before they eat and immediately after, if possible in a chair. Not being completely flat can help prevent nausea. If they feel dizzy or weak from the movement, they may need a calm moment to recover before eating. If the person feels nauseous, try smaller snacks, a boiled sweet, mineral water or a fizzy soft drink, or dry toast in the morning, or try waiting to give liquids for an hour or two after meals and avoid fried or fatty foods. If the nausea is preventing them from eating, contact your GP for advice.

IVs and dehydration

Intravenous drips (IVs) are used when a person is too weak to take in enough food or liquids to stay alive. Your doctor will be able to explain the medical implications of using an IV, although in the vast majority of cases the effect is simply to prolong life artificially. Wherever possible, the patient's decision should be respected: many people find IVs cumbersome, uncomfortable and alienating, and some people react angrily to their use. On the other hand, if a dying person needs to feel that everything possible is being done to keep them alive, this may include intravenous feeding.

If the decision is made to use an IV, the doctor or nurse will be able to explain how it works and what to check for. It is worth clearing with them any worries you may have about the operation of the IV. A nurse will either stay with the patient, or come to check the equipment at least several times a day. IVs are not themselves dangerous, but the needle can be painful and can cause inflammation.

The alternative is to accept that death is imminent, and to concentrate upon making the dying person's remaining time more comfortable and dignified, rather than longer. Someone who does not take in enough liquid becomes dehydrated. The effect of dehydration is often a sense of mild euphoria, accompanied by thirst and a dry mouth. This can be alleviated by applying a wet cloth to the lips, filling a drinking straw with water to drip into the mouth, or giving the person crushed ice. Ice can be made with juices or cordials and crushed; or the patient may suck chewing gum or boiled sweets or tinned or fresh pineapple chunks (this last contains an enzyme that makes it a wonderful mouth freshener); or a chemist can prepare 'artificial saliva' concentrate (Luborant or Glandosane in various flavours), which can be diluted and taken in small and frequent doses. Swallowing is easier in general with a slightly raised head.

Washing and hygiene

Bathing

Regular washing is best not skimped, as not washing soon leads to discomfort, sores and infection. It is well worth establishing a routine: ideally a full wash once a day, with either another full wash in the day, or a hands-and-face wash when needed. Where possible, help the person with a bath or shower (a shower seat makes this easier). Be sensitive as to whether they would enjoy being 'pampered', or whether it is best to allow them to wash themselves as much as possible. The best way to cope with getting a frail patient out of the bath is to get in yourself, stand at her head, put your arms under hers, ask her to bend her knees and then lift her up and forward.

If mobility makes going to the bathroom difficult, then help the person with a bed-bath. Wash all areas of the body in turn: help the person move into the most appropriate position each time, and keep the rest of the body warmly covered. Pay special attention to 'hidden' areas: the back, underarms, buttocks, groin and between the legs, feet, under the breasts and/or folds of skin. As you wash, check for signs of redness or sores. Change the water in the bowl several times during the wash. Make sure that the soap is rinsed off thoroughly and, especially important, that the skin is dried completely. If the skin is too dry in patches, apply an effective moisturising cream such as Atrixo.

Mouth care

It is very important to maintain a regimen of oral hygiene, as this can be a source of considerable discomfort. If normal teeth brushing, twice a day, is difficult, then a soft toothbrush or cotton wool buds can be used. Failing that, a mouth rinse from the chemist can be used. After eating, a pinch of bicarbonate of soda in a glass of water used as a mouth rinse keeps the mouth clean and fresh. False teeth should be soaked daily in denture-cleansing solution, and brushed with a soft toothbrush. There may come a point when false teeth no longer fit – in which case they should not be used, as they may cause ulcers.

It is important to examine the mouth periodically for ulcers and to watch for the symptoms of thrush. Thrush is a very common fungal infection which shows up as very sore white patches on the tongue, gum and inside the cheek. You should report thrush to your GP.

Hair care

It is possible to wash hair in bed. You can buy Dry Shampoo powder (Aero) and liquid No-rinse Shampoo (La Professionelle) from your chemist and use in the same way as normal shampoo, but without water: apply sparingly and then towel off. For wet washing, your district nurse may be able to supply you with a special bowl with 'splash' attachment. You can use an ordinary plastic bowl: support the person's neck with a rolled towel, and lay plastic sheets or plastic sheeting (a bin liner will do) underneath. Or have the person hang his or her head over the foot of the bed.

Trim finger and toe nails regularly. Men may of course need help with shaving.

Bedsores and skincare

Prevention of bedsores may be achieved by a regime of turning the person in bed regularly:

> This takes the form of strict attention to regular turning at four-hourly intervals, or two-hourly if necessary and possible. A certain amount of hectoring the patient about changing his position is justified because it can prevent so many future problems. Following an explanation, these problems will usually be appreciated by the patient.
>
> *From 'Dying at Home' by Harriet Copperman.*

Careful positioning and avoiding pressure also help. Where two parts of the body touch, such as the thighs or the knees, prolonged pressure leads to impaired circulation which leads to skin breakdown which leads to bedsores. It is important to protect the bones, particularly if the person is very thin. See the 'Beds and bedding' section above. This can also be done with thick cushions, towels and pillows, when seated. The most common 'pressure points', areas prone to sores, are: the back of the head, shoulder blades, elbows, spine and coccyx (tailbone), hips and heels. These should be checked for signs of redness daily. An obvious time to do this is during washing.

Special dressings are available to prevent bedsores and skin-toughening substances can be used. If the skin does redden and break down, a doctor or nurse should be consulted for suggestions. Massage may be used as a regular method of keeping the blood circulating in sensitive areas, as well as to enhance the patient's well-being generally (see below).

Infected wounds can be very smelly. Cancerlink, in their booklet 'Caring for the Very Sick Person At Home', say that the doctor may be able to prescribe special tablets to reduce the smell and they advise that 'concentrated lemon spirit, from the chemists, mixed with a little water' will mask most other smells. Or use joss sticks, scented candles or spray deodorisers; and give the patient a handkerchief dabbed with their favourite scent.

Bowel management

Aspects of bowel management such as constipation or diarrhoea may arise. Some of these may be managed by comforting and attention to diet. Others may involve help and advice from a nurse or doctor.

Constipation

A blockage in the bowels can cause discomfort and pain and eventually may be life threatening. Constipation is generally caused by inactivity, insufficient fibre in the diet or as a side-effect with certain pain-relieving drugs. It can usually be eased with a combination of the following dietary measures: bran and other fibre foods, fresh vegetables, prunes and fruit in general, live yoghourt, coffee, herbal tea and plenty of fluid. Cut out white bread and rice, cheese and meat if possible. Enquire at health food shops for natural and homoeopathic remedies.

Incontinence

The occasional soiling of bedclothes may be inevitable, is unpleasant, and can be alarming for the patient. It is obviously important to change the sheets and help the person wash immediately; it is also important to be sensitive to what reassurance and affection she or he may need. Ask your district nurse about obtaining disposable incontinence pads from the Incontinence Laundry Service in your area; or the nurse may recommend a catheter (a hollow, flexible tube that drains urine from the bladder into a bag; and that works best if the patient remains unconstipated and drinks plenty of fluids).

Insomnia

The cares and concerns of a dying person may cause sleeplessness. If your patient has difficulty sleeping, see if you can help without sleeping pills and barbiturates.

Addiction is not a real concern with the dying, but why interfere more with delicate body balances? Some possibilities are to take, before bedtime: calcium tablets (two grams), camomile tea, valerian with B-vitamin complex, a warm glass of milk, or tryptophan. Tryptophan is an amino acid in meat, milk and cheese. Turkey is high in tryptophan. Try a warm bath, hot foot bath, a back rub or foot massage, or a guided meditation.

Stroke the hair and scalp and encourage the person to let all thoughts float away and to let the head feel spacious and empty, clouds drifting in and out. When I can't sleep I use the Bach Flower Remedy, Sweet Chestnut. Avoid coffee, black tea and all dark coloured colas before bedtime. They contain eye-opening caffeine. It's also OK not to go to sleep even when someone else thinks it's time. Encourage the person to read, write, watch TV, listen to soothing music or think for a while. If not sleeping continues to trouble the patient, ask a doctor about sleeping medications.

Reprinted with permission from 'Coming Home: A Guide to Dying at Home with Dignity', © 1987 Deborah Duda, Aurora Press, PO Box 573, Santa Fe, NM 87504, USA.

Depression/anxiety

Anxiety will probably be experienced to a greater or lesser degree by most patients.

Some may become mildly anxious on reaching such a significant point in their lives. Others have always been so anxious with any new event or change of circumstance, however minor, that the advance of debilitating illness and the approach of death, fills them with a terror which is sad to behold. The main treatment is listening, and honest discussion with the patient of the many causes of his anxiety.

Depression, like anxiety, usually involves taking the time to listen to the patient or encouraging him to talk. He may understandably be depressed for many reasons, but if this is the result of boredom or inactivity it should be possible to find a remedy.

From 'Dying at Home' by Harriet Copperman.

Consult your doctor, of course, if you feel medication for anxiety or depression may be called for.

Relaxation

A cassette recorder may be particularly useful:

The person may listen to the wide variety of music and guided meditation tapes available that might encourage investigation and letting go [eds: see under Tapes in the Resources chapter]. Speaking of the process of letting go at two in the afternoon when the patient feels relatively well and is not particularly open to investigating dying may not seem appropriate or even be well received. But a tape about working with pain or preparing for the moment of death, left at the bedside, may be appreciatively absorbed when the patient feels it is the right moment. Perhaps at four in the morning when sleep has become impossible and the pain in the body has intensified, that individual may then feel prepared, open to hearing what earlier in the day may have seemed beside the point or frightening.

From 'Who Dies?' by Stephen Levine.

Richard Boerstler advocates a meditative Tibetan-inspired breathing technique. The carer copies the patient's breathing pattern, making the sound 'Ah' on the outbreath, strung out as 'Aaaaaaaaaaahhhhhhhh'. The patient may like to make the same sound at least for the first ten breaths or so, or may prefer just to listen. This simplest of exercises can greatly enhance the patient's sense of physical comfort and well-being. (See under Videos in the Resources chapter – also for Joanna Gilpin's details; she runs seminars in the UK on Boerstler's method.)

Massage

Massage in its various forms is useful in decreasing tension and anxiety whilst deepening personal contact. Simple touching, aromatherapy, foot massage can all be relaxing and encouraging. (Be careful about massaging or applying lotions to skin damaged by radiotherapy.) A personal account of giving scalp massage shows that it can offer many benefits to the dying patient:

Scalp massage

Last year a friend of mine died of cancer. She found it very difficult to open up or to ask for much. I offered to give her scalp massage. She loved it. She said it made her feel wonderful and I did it for her for many of her last days. It made her feel relaxed and cared for and sometimes she talked easily and personally – although I never pushed her to. It was wonderful for me to have something to offer which she really wanted.

This massage offers an easy way to loving physical contact. It gives the patient a relaxing time and I suspect that many will find it a good time to talk: relaxed, loved, but not always looked at. (Some people, as a parallel example, will talk on a car journey where they have company but are not looked at.) It is easy to do once explained: you use your finger tips to move the scalp over the skull. Ask the person you massage to tell you what they like and don't like, and if you are doing it too hard or soft. They should sit or lie comfortably and not 'help' by holding their head in a 'good' position – they should just relax. You move their head gently if necessary. (Try also gentle face massage, as well as neck and shoulders, all places where tension accumulates.) Feedback is the key to getting it right.

I have seen people sitting next to a dying person having run out of things to do, say or offer. I felt that this idea might mean a lot to many people.

From a letter by Margaret Ryder to The Natural Death Centre.

Contact

Simpler than massage is a hug. A spontaneous hug, or ritual 'good morning' hug, may seem out of place for whatever reason. If there is something in the way, you can either offer a hug, which gives the other person the chance to say No, or just surprise them!

Having people going about ordinary activities in the same room is another way of keeping close. While you read a book, eat dinner or watch television, you can just be with your relative. Make sure that everyone in the family is aware of when it would be a good idea to leave the person in privacy.

Making contact can involve simple but valuable actions:

Even when someone is apparently unconscious, do keep talking to them. On a very deep level it is reassuring, and apparently hearing is the last sense to go. Touch and smell are also important.

When my husband was in hospital I started putting a notepad by his bed. Every time I visited, before I left I would write down when I would be back, where I was going, etc – and that I *had* been.Once home, I kept it up so he had a memory prompt. And when he died, I had a record of the last weeks.

From a letter by Elizabeth Lawlor to The Natural Death Centre.

Small gestures mean a lot.

Pain management

Natural pain relief may be useful in addition to any medication the patient is taking.

Breathing and visualisation techniques can be very useful in working with pain. If there's delay in getting a pain reliever, you might try them. In some cases, they may preclude your needing drugs at all. Breathing can be as useful for dying as it is for birthing. When we feel pain, we tense up and tend to stop breathing fully. Our cells don't get the oxygen they need to clean out toxins and keep the nerve signals straight, and the pain gets worse.

One of the first things to do for pain is to keep breathing. Unless someone has had previous experience with breathing consciously, he or she may focus on the pain and fear and forget to breathe. As the helper, encourage the person to breathe deeply, to breathe into the area that hurts, and then down into the toes. Ask the person to relax, to 'soften' around the area that hurts, and open him or herself to the sensation of pain. As the person surrenders, gives up resistance, more oxygen enters the area and the pain may lessen. The body senses that its message is received and relaxes. Keep repeating, 'soften, relax, open'.

Paying attention to pain helps relieve it if we don't judge it as bad! It just is.

I find it helpful to combine breathing techniques with hot water bottles and foot massages. While the person is breathing into the area that hurts, partially fill two hot water bottles with hot, not boiling, water. Cover the bottles with a towel so you don't burn the person's skin and place them under the feet and on the area that hurts. If you don't have hot water bottles, put the person's feet into a bucket of medium-hot tap water. Put a hot washcloth on the forehead. Together these seem to keep energy moving through the body so pain is lessened or eliminated. Some people prefer ice packs and cold water. Either is OK. (If the pain is severe and you're unprepared, call a doctor.) If it feels right to you, add a foot massage to further relax the person and to stimulate increased circulation.

Breathing and foot massage are useful techniques for calming anyone in a stressful situation. You might want to take time for them yourself.

I sometimes hear talk in New Age circles that taking drugs for pain is somehow not spiritual. That's baloney. Again, physical pain is a message that something's not working right in the body. The dying get the message loud and clear only this time there's nothing they can do about it. The body can't be fixed. Taking drugs is useful to free us to experience dying on other levels and not to fixate on one level – the body. If we're in pain, the body has our undivided attention. And if dying teaches us anything, it teaches us that we're more than just a body.

If, as many New Age people believe, our essential identity is God, why torture God's body – or anyone else's – by not taking pain medication? That's cruelty. If we truly believe that everything is equally sacred, morphine is just as sacred as the herb from which it's derived.

Reprinted with permission from 'Coming Home: A Guide to Dying at Home with Dignity', © 1987 Deborah Duda, Aurora Press, PO Box 573, Santa Fe, NM 87504, USA.

It is advisable to keep your GP informed about the person's changing pain relief needs. The Beecham Manual of Family Practice advises doctors that many patients 'are given too little analgesia too late'. Patients dying at home can often have better pain relief than in hospitals, where doctors are loathe to use drugs, especially the opiates, appropriately – mainly through ignorance, or fear of legal consequences. In her letter to The Natural Death Centre Elizabeth Lawlor says that she kept a chart of the medication which her husband received, 'partly to see if there was a pattern of when it was most needed, and partly for the doctor to see what was going on'. In this way it may be possible both to pre-empt pain and to establish clear communication about the person's needs. Pain is made worse by fear, loneliness and anticipation of pain to come.

Here is a pain meditation, for the patient to read or that can be read aloud very slowly by a friend. You could record it on a tape – leave up to ten second gaps between each direction, the reason being that the body responds at a much slower rate than the mind. This is a considerably reduced version – see Stephen Levine's book for the text in full and for other equally helpful meditations. (See also under Videos and Tapes in the final chapter.)

Guided pain meditation:

Sit or lie down in a position you find comfortable. Allow yourself to settle into this position so that the whole body feels fully present where it sits or lies.

Bring your attention to the area of sensation that has been uncomfortable.

Let your attention come wholly to that area. Let the awareness be present, moment to moment, to receive the sensations generated there.

Allow the discomfort to be felt.

Moment to moment new sensations seem to arise.

Does the flesh cramp against the pain? Feel how the body tends to grasp it in a fist, tries to close it off.

Begin to allow the body to open all around that sensation.

Feel the tension and resistance that comes to wall off the sensation.

Don't push away the pain. Just let it be there. Feel how the body tries to isolate it. Tries to close it off. Picture that fist. Feel how the body is clenched in resistance.

Feel how the body holds each new sensation.

Begin gradually to open that closedness around sensation. The least resistance can be so painful. Open. Soften. All around the sensation. Allow the fist, moment to moment, to open. To give space to the sensation.

Let go of the pain. Why hold on a moment longer?

Like grasping a burning ember, the flesh of the closed fist is seared in its holding. Open. Soften all around the sensation. Let the fist of resistance begin to loosen. To open.

The palm of that fist softening. The fingers beginning to loosen their grip. Opening. All around the sensation.

The fist loosening. Gradually opening. Moment to moment, letting go of the pain. Release the fear that surrounds it.

Notice any fear that has accumulated around the pain. Allow the fear to melt. Let tension dissolve, so that the sensations can softly radiate out as they will. Don't try to capture the pain. Let it float free. No longer held in the grasp of resistance. Softening. Opening all around the sensation.

The fist opening. The fingers, one by one, loosening their grip.

The sensation no longer encapsulated in resistance. Opening.

Let the pain soften. Let the pain be. Let go of the resistance that tries to smother the experience. Allow each sensation to come fully into consciousness. No holding. No pushing away. The pain beginning to float free in the body.

All grasping relinquished. Just awareness and sensation meeting moment to moment. Received gently by the softening flesh.

The fist opened into a soft, spacious palm. The fingers loose. The fist dissolved back into the soft, open flesh. No tension. No holding.

Let the body be soft and open. Let the sensation float free. Easy. Gently.

Softening, opening all around the pain.

Just sensation. Floating free in the soft, open body.

From 'Who Dies?' by Stephen Levine.

It may become necessary to relieve pain by means of intravenous or intramuscular injections. The latter can be given by the carer once instructed by a doctor or nurse. Better still might be for your medical helper to obtain a subcutaneous syringe driver – this has revolutionised pain control at home. It provides a continuous infusion of painkiller, so that there is no need for injections, and is thus very practical for home use.

Music

The astounding power of music to soothe the dying person has been most dramatically demonstrated by the work of Therese Schroeder-Sheker in the United States, who runs the Chalice of Repose project and is bringing harp music, Gregorian chants and other spiritual music into hospice and other settings. Here she describes the beginnings of her work:

Musical midwifery for the dying

The first time that I was ever actually present and alone with someone who was in fact dying is the first time that I ever really experienced silence, and an indescribably delicate kind of light. The man was struggling, frightened, unable to breathe. No more respirators, dilators, tracheotomies or medicines could resolve his disintegrated lungs. He could take no more in, could swallow no more, and in his complete weariness, there was almost nothing he could return to the world. I climbed into his hospital bed and propped myself behind him in midwifery position, my head and heart lined up behind his, my legs folded near his waist, and I held his frail body by the elbows and suspended his weight. At first I held us both in interior prayer, but soon began leaning down to his left ear and singing Gregorian chant in an almost pianissimo.

He immediately nestled in my arms and began to breathe regularly, and we, as a team, breathed together. The chants seemed to bring him balance, dissolving fears, and compensating for those issues still full of sting. When his heart ceased to beat, I stayed still for long moments. Almost twenty years later, the silence that replaced his struggle and that was present in his room has continued to penetrate the core of my life.

People ask if a midwife knows fear or sorrow: none of that exists if you are with the dying person. It's their time, not yours. Any burden or sorrow or wounds of your own disappear.

From 'The Luminous Wound' by Therese Schroeder-Sheker. The Chalice of Repose is at 554 West Broadway, Missoula, USA (tel 0101 406 0001 ext 2810).

Arts

A family doctor in Kent, Dr David McGavin, gave over the top floor of his surgery to three therapists who treated terminally and seriously ill patients with music, singing, movement and art:

He hired them out of his own salary four years ago to help patients who had reached the end of the NHS road.

Above Dr McGavin's surgery, Alan Baker and Ellen Bishop, both in their fifties, are exploring the use of colour on a wet canvas under the guidance of an art therapist, Hazel Adams. The walls are decorated with the artwork of other patients and the quiet concentration of Alan and Ellen produces a tranquil atmosphere.

Alan was diagnosed as having Parkinson's Disease seven years ago. He says he is no artist, but the weekly sessions have a deeply relaxing effect. He also had nine months' intensive eurhythmics – rhythmic movement to music – which helped him recover balance and flexibility lost through the disease.

Dr McGavin believes much of the success of the therapies lies in the co-operation of the patient. 'The problem in general practice occurs when you just see the body as a complex machine, and call in the doctor to fix the part that goes wrong,' he said. This merely encourages the patient to wait passively for the doctor to make him or her better. 'I ask the patients if they would like to have a go.'

Therapist John Logan treats patients in the last stages of cancer. He said: 'Cancer patients suffer tremendous fear and anxiety. The music and movement helps that, putting something healthy and life-giving in the face of the illness.'

From The Independent (Feb. 12th 1988).

Hospice Arts is an organisation which promotes the arts as 'an essential component of the hospice philosophy of ensuring that people really experience as much as life can offer right up to the very moment they die':

Hospice Arts

Taking part in creative arts activity can be a vital component of whole-person care, and can be therapeutic in a number of ways. By making something worthwhile, you can restore a feeling of self-esteem and a sense of purpose at a time when life may seem confusing and of little value. The piece created can become a treasured memento for family and friends, charged with important emotions. The arts may encourage communication, and stimulate mobility and concentration. The act of creativity, incorporating both mind and spirit, can be a means of exploring and resolving strong and difficult emotions, and those who care for terminally ill patients can also benefit in this way.

For some hospice patients, it may be a case of reviving a long-ignored skill or enthusiasm which had been forced into the background by the business of day-to-day living. For others, the creative arts may be a new experience, yet they too can enjoy making their own works of art, discovering hidden talents and abilities.

From the Hospice Information Service Bulletin, May 1990 – for contact details see the Resources chapter.

Yvonne Malik suggests the creation of Memory Box personal museums by the elderly or the terminally ill, and has made a beautiful prototype of her own, shoe-box size. She writes:

Memory Boxes

Many of us have keepsakes – nostalgic mementoes which stimulate our memories, such as old photos, letters, trinkets, holiday souvenirs, scarves, medals. Individually they may seem small or insignificant, but put together in a display, these same objects could become a decorative and pleasing Personal Museum.

The arrangements could be displayed inexpensively in, for instance, sewing boxes, tool boxes, circular tea trays or shallow suitcases.

Memory Boxes leave something precious behind for our relatives and children. They are the opportunity to communicate in non-verbal ways that 'I was here; I did this; I learnt that,' or personal letters can be placed there.

See final chapter for Malik's address, under Organisations and Individuals.

Chapter 6

GREEN, CHEAP & 'D-I-Y' FUNERALS

Almost everyone who has tried it advocates wherever possible looking after at least some aspects of the funeral of friends and relatives oneself, with the assistance of family and neighbours, without depending entirely on funeral directors. This chapter, parts of which are not for the squeamish, aims to help you find the courage to organise and design such a funeral, by arming you with the essential information and with tales from some pioneers. The next chapter, however, gives advice about particular undertakers, cemeteries, crematoria and other services. The suggested advantages for a 'd-i-y' funeral are that:

• Participating in this way, according to psychotherapists, helps people to begin to come to terms with their loss;

• You have the option of trying for a Greener funeral if you so wish;

• It can be a great deal cheaper – potentially free if the body is buried in a shroud on your own land, or from about £200 if cremation is used (whereas a recent Chosen Heritage survey found the average cost of a funeral in the South of England to be £1,025);

• You have more control over every aspect of the funeral, which can as a consequence be a much more personal and less 'assembly-line' affair.

Below are some of the stories from the front line, with a discussion of the points they raise; first, a letter that appeared in The Times from the Reverend Canon Raymond Wilkinson of Warwick, who looks back nostalgically to the past and urges relatives not to hand over funerals entirely to the trade:

Personal involvement in funerals

Two of the ancient parish churches where I served as incumbent (one of them as recently as 1970) still possessed the parish bier, whereon in past days parishioners had themselves placed the body of the deceased member of their family, in a coffin made by the local joiner, before pushing it solemnly to their church. They were then met by the parson at the lych-gate before the service in church and the subsequent burial in the churchyard, again performed by friends and relatives.

Undertakers were – and are – neither necessary nor obligatory; but we in this country increasingly divorce ourselves from this last service to our relatives by handing everything over to the professionals – often to the choice of sadly over-used hymns.

One of the most memorable funerals I have conducted (from a total of about 5,000) involved no undertakers. The relatives laid out the body; the coffin was made by friends; the family bore it from their own car; after the chuch service, they lowered the coffin into the grave which they had dug.

A few weeks ago (without, of course, the grave) I conducted just such a funeral at the local crematorium. Could it be that an uncommon but godly sense of what funerals are about is returning? Personal involvement may be painful, but it represents reality and personal accountability – as well as a proper reminder of our own mortality.

The dramatic increase in crematorium disposal of the dead in this century is said to be largely in the interests of convenience, cleanliness and conservation. Where convenience is an over-riding factor that may well be so. But ashes are useless to growing plants, and I have yet to read of a health risk proven regarding burials.

Churchyards remained relatively small until the 19th century because the usual small wooden memorials decayed, families died out, bones discovered were placed in the charnel-houses built in churchyards, and God's Acre was re-used. On the Continent today, such economy of land is general. Grave space there is re-used, unless further leases are paid for.

It seems to me that journeys to distant, and often somewhat ugly, crematoria have added expense and detachment where death is concerned. Any enquiry into spiralling costs of undertaking needs to be linked to our increasing detachment from involvement domestically and parochially with our departed friends and relatives.

From a letter to The Times (April 25th 1991) from the Reverend Canon Raymond Wilkinson, 42 Coten End, Warwick.

The recycled coffin

The parish burials of the past that Wilkinson refers to were originally ecologically sound affairs: back in the 15th Century, the body was hygienically wrapped in a shroud and the parish coffin, stored in the church, would be re-used time and again – in some parts of the country, indeed, town councils decreed that funerals should be 'shroud only' with coffins for the privileged few who could obtain special permission (see the fascinating account in 'The English Way of Death' by Julian Litten, pages 123 to 129). The Natural Death Centre has visions of a similar Green funeral service in the future, where the coffin could be re-used (and often delivered directly to the next family needing it) with a biodegradable body bag preventing any 'leakages' into the coffin.

Wilkinson questions whether crematoria are environmentally friendly. So which is better for the environment, being buried or cremated?

Which is Greener, burial or cremation?

In the UK cremation was originally presented as the environment-friendly option, with the anti-burial slogan of 'keeping the land for the living'. Nowadays cemeteries and church-yards help protect the land *from* the living, preventing land being used for development and often acting as a refuge for wildlife. (Some of the few bits of green space left in Tokyo are graveyards – although some bodies in Tokyo now have to be kept in special warehouses close to the railway stations until burial space can be found in country graveyards.) In some countries, in the early days of cremation, the body was taken out of its coffin before being incinerated; nowadays, however, the coffins are all wastefully burnt and we are in the realms of European regulations concerning the pollution of the atmosphere and ground water from the glues used, and from the heavy metals, hydrochrolic acid, carbon dioxide, sulphur dioxide and hydrofluoric acid emitted in the burning process.

More forests are planted if more wood can be sold, so as long as these forests are not entirely monoculture ones, it could be argued that wooden coffins are to the benefit of the planet's tree cover. Furthermore, in the case of burial, they help prevent the greenhouse effect by locking up and burying the carbon in the timber. Thus at present burial seems to be a Greener option than cremation, at least for the time being, particularly if the idea of cemeteries as nature reserves, discussed later in this chapter, catches on.

Jane Spottiswoode, who lives near Bala in North Wales, shares similar doubts to those of Raymond Wilkinson about the encroachments of the funeral industry, and has written a spirited book, 'Undertaken with Love', describing the funeral of her husband:

Undertaken with Love

When Jane Spottiswoode's husband Nigel was diagnosed as having lung cancer in December 1986, she began to put into operation a plan they had made long before (when both were in perfect health) which was to be buried as cheaply as possible. Indeed her husband had said he would happily be consigned to the compost heap, any funeral money being put towards a slap-up party.

Jane set about arranging Nigel's funeral during his second period in hospital. Immediately, she came across the first of numerous hurdles – that of purchasing a coffin. Armed with the Yellow Pages, she settled down to try to find one but was soon met with much hostility. No manufacturer would supply her with one; she was told they only supplied to funeral directors. So she turned to the undertakers themselves, but the results were the same. They would only supply a coffin as part of their full service.

Jane grew cunning. She was, she said, a theatrical producer, intending to tour village halls with an amateur production of 'A Scent of Flowers' by James Saunders, a play she knew well and one which had a coffin on the stage throughout. 'Oh no we couldn't possibly supply one of our coffins for that sort of thing!' said the lady on the telephone. 'Why not?' asked Jane. 'It might offend our customers,' came the prim reply. Surely not the audience in distant village halls? 'They are all our potential customers,' said the lady, but before putting down the receiver on this incontrovertible truth, she revealed the name of a firm which Jane will always hold in great regard – that of S S Joinery, Stoke on Trent, who would supply a coffin in veneer chipboard for £34-50 plus VAT as long as she could collect it herself.

At a total cost of £197-97 against the £700 or so charged by the Co-op, Nigel Spottiswoode's funeral was certainly cheap. But that wasn't the main point. From start to finish she regarded it as an act of affectionate respect, as did his pall-bearing friends. 'My husband was merely taken to the crematorium by his friends, instead of employing a stranger to do it. That was all it amounted to, really, and if more people realised how comparatively easy it can be with a little forethought, they might like to consider it for themselves.'

Although in excellent health, Jane Spottiswoode has already purchased her own coffin which she keeps in the loft, tucked away in the shadows behind the water tank to avoid alarming the plumber.

From publicity material for 'Undertaken with Love' by Jane Spottiswoode.

Incidentally, Jane Spottiswoode subsequently discovered that SS Joinery denied all knowledge of having supplied a coffin to her. In China, many elderly share her desire to have a coffin ready in advance (they get the children to buy one for them). And as for putting the body on the compost heap, a letter writer to The Independent quoted with approval an advertisement in James Joyce's 'Ulysses': 'Well preserved fat corpse, gentleman, epicure, invaluable for fruit garden. A bargain £3-13-6.' Andrew Kerr has suggested further research into how body composting could work:

Composting bodies

I suggest compost funerals. Animal wastes (and the human body belongs to the animal kingdom) are an integral part of the process by which the vegetable kingdom is sustained. If animal remains are mixed with vegetable wastes to the proportion of one in four, in a controlled system, turned and dampened correctly, the result will be a perfect product to be fed to any kind of plant. Most dangerous pathogens are dealt with in the process.

The corpse could be taken to the Compostorium and placed in a specially constructed autoclave or pressure cooker. The corpse would have already been disembowelled and that material placed into a methane digester; this would have averted the potential danger of pathogens. The gas so generated would contribute to the slow and steady heat required to render the remains to a condition ready to be ground up to a kind of slurry to be 'intimately mixed' with straw and other vegetable wastes.

The whole process would be completed in about twelve weeks or so: a decent time for mourning. The finished compost could then be incorporated into the family memorial garden.

This would be far better than burial which is too deep for aerobic processes, or wasteful incineration which is damaging to the environment.

From a letter from Andrew Kerr, Oak Tree Cottage, 89 Netherton Road, Appleton, Abingdon, Oxon OX13 5LA (tel 0865 862237).

Keeping the body at home

Jane Spottiswoode's book about her husband's funeral came in for criticism in the journal of the National Association of Funeral Directors, and it was in this journal that Don Moar commented: 'She found that when she needed a mortuary in which to leave her husband until the time of the cremation, she was forced to resort to hijacking the municipal mortuary. Luckily for her she lives in a quiet rural area and as a consequence that facility was otherwise not in use. However, in a busy urban area the use of the municipal mortuary would neither be possible nor desirable.'

Keeping the body cool

So how is the city dweller to manage without the municipal mortuary? If the person has died in hospital, the mortuary there might be willing to look after the body for a few days, most probably without charge; or a funeral director might be willing to provide just this facility without the complete package (certainly many of those listed in the next chapter are willing to do this). If the person has died at home, the body could be kept in a room with the window open, in the coldest room in the house or in the cellar if necessary. In rural France a special refrigeration plate is often placed under the body so as to make it possible for the body to remain in the house while relatives come to pay their respects. Wrapped ice cubes could be placed by the body. Or dry ice (which gradually sublimates to a carbon dioxide mist without leaving a wet puddle) could be used – it has been used on occasion by mortuaries, when their equipment breaks down; and is widely used in Japan in hot weather to allow the body to be remain on a futon at home before the funeral. One supplier in London for dry ice in pellet form is BOC Ltd Hackney, 59 Eastway, London E9 5NS (tel 081 985 5544), where 10kg, approximately three days' supply, can be collected 8am to 5pm daily (Saturdays 8am to 1pm) for £25-03 including VAT, or it can be sent to you express by TNT for a grand total of £33-28.

Why keep the body at home?

In some religions, such as Tibetan Buddhism, it is argued that it is best to leave the body undisturbed for several days after death, to allow the complete departure of the soul. And in the West, there are many who emphasise the importance of allowing family members and relatives to see the body – and of giving even young children this opportunity, although not insisting if they prefer to stay away.

Bereaved parents denied the opportunity to see and touch the bodies of their dead children often deeply regret this. The purpose of concealing grief seems to be to protect other people, not the griever.

The need to hold one's dead child

My child was killed in a road accident. He was 17.

We arrived at the hospital just after 10.15 pm: no one was expecting us. 'Everybody has gone and I should have gone too by now,' a social worker said. My friend and I were put in a small anteroom and the door was closed. We had been put into a box with the lid closed to spare us the sight of panicky people rushing to and fro, telephone calls being made, while the system was reassembled for us.

Apparently there was great rushing about preparing Timothy for viewing. Putting a piece of gauze over a graze on his head was regarded as important so that I should not be offended or frightened or disgusted. We walked along a corridor. We arrived at a door. It was opened. No more hope; no more thinking it might not be Timothy. Incredibly, it was my Timothy, my lovely boy.

He was lying on an altar covered by a purple cloth edged with gold braid and tassles. Only his head was visible. Such was the atmosphere of constraint I either asked or was given permission to enter. I can't remember. I entered alone. The others watched through the open door. I stroked his cheek. He was cold.

Timothy had not ceased to be my child. I deperately needed to hold him, to look at him, to find out where he was hurting. These instincts don't die immediately with the child. The instinct to comfort and cuddle, to examine the wounds, to try to understand, most of all to hold. But I had been told not to do 'anything silly'. They were watching to see that I didn't. So I couldn't move the purple cloth. I couldn't find his hand. I couldn't do anything. I betrayed my instincts and my son by standing there 'not doing anything silly'. I knew that if I did my watchers would immediately constrain me and lead me away.

Why? No doubt they thought they were acting for the best. We, as a society, have lost contact with our most basic instincts. We marvel at cats washing and caring for their kittens. We admire the protection an elephant gives her sick calf and are tearful and sympathetic when she refuses to leave her offspring when he dies, when she examines and nuzzles him and wills him to breathe. This is exactly what the human mother's most basic instinct tells her to do. And we deny her. She is being denied her motherhood when in extremis.

We have come to think we are protecting her when we are really protecting ourselves. We have forgotten that this is the mother who has cleaned up the vomit, washed his nappies, cleaned the blood from his wounds, kissed him better and held him in his distress. She has done all this since the day he was born. If he has been in hospital she has possibly fed him by tube, she may have changed his dressings and given injections. She will certainly have washed him, helped him to dress and combed his hair. She will have held him. Who are we protecting when we deny her this last service which she can do for her child? We are not protecting the child. We are not protecting her. The fact of her child's death is not altered by the denial of her instincts.

Having nursed my mother through her last illness, I was privileged to bathe her after death, put clean dressings on her wounds, remove her catheter. It was a tearful and loving last service that my sister and I were privileged to perform for her. It helped to heal our grief. But my lovely boy was draped on an altar, covered with a robe, and all expressions of love and care I had were denied to me. And I don't know when that wound will heal. The caring services should think again about how we serve the bereaved. A cup of tea and an aseptic look at the body does not serve. If it is our wish and instinct to hold and wash the body and to talk to the dead loved one, we should be helped to do this. We will be distressed and may frequently need to stop and wipe the tears, but we will be helped in our healing.

From an article by Sheila Awoonor-Renner in The Guardian (Mar. 15th '91).

From a more academic perspective, one researcher, Therese Rando, has written, with reference to adult deaths as well as children's:

Seeing and touching the body

Give the bereaved adequate private time to be with, touch, caress and hold the body, as time with the deceased may be very critical in helping them finish unfinished business and accept the reality of loss.

Those who did not view the body or had arranged for immediate disposition of the remains (excluding the normal Jewish custom of not viewing the body) reported the greatest hostility following the death, the greatest increase in consumption of alcohol, tranquilisers and sedatives, the greatest increase in tension and anxiety, the lowest positive recall of the deceased and greater problems in adjustment to the death, particularly among male respondents.

From 'Grief, Dying and Death' by Therese Rando (Champaign, USA; Research Press Co., 1984) quoted in 'Caring For Your Own Dead' by Lisa Carlson.

Fear of being buried alive

A surprising number of people are frightened that they will be buried alive. Indeed this has occasionally happened. Back in 1912, the Funeral Service Journal reported:

In Galicia, the body of George Masug, a rich landowner, was being interred, and the last prayers were being said by the officiating priests at the open grave amid weeping, when, as the bereaved relatives were dropping earth on the coffin, ghastly sounds were heard to proceeed from it. The cover was lifted and a panic arose among members of the family when the supposed-dead man was found to be alive. He was at once freed from his terrible position. Masug, who was supposed to have died from apoplexy, soon recovered and was able to walk home with the mourners.

A recent newspaper report from China tells of a Chinese teenager who was buried in his coffin having been unconscious for ten hours from drinking too much alcohol. When the body was later exhumed, it was apparent that the boy had died trying to claw his way out of the coffin. And one perhaps over-suspicious correspondent has complained to The Natural Death Centre about 'the unsavoury practice of removing people from nursing homes to undertakers' parlours before being certified or seen by a doctor, even though a qualified nurse may have expressed an opinion that the person was dead. The reason why it is unsatisfactory is that most undertakers either embalm, sew the gums together or refrigerate the person immediately they arrive on the premises. The consequences of a person not being actually dead are horrific.'

These may well be very unrealistic fears in Western society today – although in a study of 150,000 exhumed American war-dead from World War II in Europe it was revealed that no less than 6,000 (4%) showed signs of having been buried alive. In any case, keeping the body at home for several days can reassure all concerned that the person is truly dead. It has also been argued that doctors should use tests like the Ether test and the Icard test that are completely reliable indicators of death.

Laying out the body

If you have a nurse helping you, she or he will normally help with laying out the body. Traditionally whoever is attending to the body closes the eyes after death – and coins on the eyelids can help with this. The chin is propped up with a pillow to keep the mouth closed, or a piece of cloth can be tied under the chin and over the head. To prevent seepages from the body, it may be prudent (depending on the risk of infection, the likely rate of decomposition and the aesthetics of the situation) to plug the natural orifices (rectum, nasal passages, throat). This is simply done with cotton wool using disposable gloves and some lubrication such as soap or KY jelly if required. It is not essential that nappies be put on the body. The correct procedure when laying out is to press upon the lower abdomen thus ensuring that the bladder is drained. A waterproof dressing should be put on any body ulcers or leaking wounds. As soon as the doctor has certified the cause of death, the body can be washed and dressed, as this is easier in the first six hours or so after death, before the body stiffens. The head is left raised on a pillow – as the embalmers put it, 'this helps prevent the expanding internal contents from purging.'

One correspondent wrote to The Natural Death Centre that she felt 'somewhat un-nerved' when washing the body of her husband an hour after he had died, 'to see the purple/bluish state of his back and buttocks, due to the blood draining into it, once circulation stopped'.

For some religious communities, such as Sikhs and Muslims, preparing the body for burial by gently washing the body is an act of devotion that family members insist on, even if they have to go to do it in the undertaker's premises. For many Jews, the body should remain untouched for twenty minutes after death, with all washing and preparation the prerogative of the Jewish community.

Forms and procedures

Death is a surprisingly form-filled obstacle course facing the newly-bereaved relative who is arranging the funeral, and even more so later when looking after 'probate' of the estate. The Consumers Association devotes two excellent books to the subject ('What To Do When Someone Dies' and 'Wills and Probate'); and a free Social Security pamphlet 'What To Do After A Death' is available (see the Resources chapter). We can help the survivors before our own deaths by following the advice in this present book in the 'Training for Dying' chapter: by leaving a will, telling people where to find it, and putting in the same place all our financial and other details, and with it the information and documents that will be needed for the registration of death (again listed in that chapter); and by simplifying our affairs.

When the person is dying at home, it is as well to ensure that the doctor (not just the nurses) sees the patient within 14 days of the death (28 days in Northern Ireland). This will normally avoid the death being referred to the coroner. After the person has died, the doctor will (without charge) fill in a medical certificate as to the cause of death. (If cremation is wanted, the doctor charges for the relevant form – and will need to know about any operations in the past year – and the doctor gets another doctor to fill in a similar form, for a total charge of £57, known in the trade as 'ash cash'; the forms are issued by crematoria and also stocked by funeral directors.)

If the person dies in hospital, you can refuse permission for a post-mortem (to learn more about the cause of death) if you wish. The coroner will have to issue a certificate as to the cause of death (and may insist on a post-mortem) if there were unusual circumstances surrounding the death. But the coroner can issue an interim certificate to allow the executors to begin work on sorting out the deceased's affairs.

Going to the Registry Office

As the next-of-kin or the person arranging the funeral you then take the medical certificate (if the doctor does not send it for you) to the Registrar of Births and Deaths. You have to do this within five days (eight days in Scotland) or within 42 days in the case of a stillborn child. Find out which registrar covers your area by looking up under 'R' in the phone book, 'Registration of Births, Deaths and Marriages', and checking by phone with whichever seems to be the nearest office to you and asking whether or not they have an appointments system. In Scotland the registrar will want to know the time of death as well as the date and place of death.

Make certain the registrar has correctly recorded all the details in the registry as it is very complicated getting them altered once it has all been signed.

Take with you also information about the deceased's banks, friendly societies, life insurance and so on, and then the Registrar should be able to estimate how many copies of the various types of death certificate you will need to be able to claim these assets. It is easier and cheaper to obtain as many copies as you may need and an extra one in case, at the time (or soon after), for £1-50 to £2 each (£3-50 Scotland), rather than later when it can cost £5 or more (£6 Scotland).

The basic white certificate that you will also be given is free and contains a social security form for claiming benefit arrears and widow's benefit.

You may need to give a registrar three clear working days' notice before a burial can take place. A 'Notice of Interment' form must be completed and this, together with the necessary Disposal Certificate (either the registrar's or the coroner's), may be required by a cemetery at least 24 hours before a burial. Likewise, the forms permitting cremation may be required by a crematorium at least 24 hours in advance of cremation.

Moving the body

Jane Spottiswoode had problems moving her husband Nigel's body after he died:

> There was no way that Nigel in his coffin and with the coffin in a horizontal position, could be carried out of the room and around all the corners and down the stairs to where the Volvo was waiting. Since then I have learned that the way it is done by the professionals is in a body bag, which is much easier to handle, and then transferred to a coffin either in the pick-up vehicle or at the undertakers.
>
> *From 'Undertaken with Love' by Jane Spottiswoode.*

A wide range of body bags can be bought from Lear of London (for details see the listings in the next chapter for the London region) who have a minimum order of £30. You can also go through Green Undertakings (see the next chapter for the North East region).

If you do not have access to a suitable estate car or van for transport, and cannot find a friend with one, it may be possible to persuade your local undertaker to help. See the section on undertakers in the next chapter – the best quote we had for this service was £25 (or £100 if a hearse and bearers were wanted). Or a transit van can be hired through the Yellow Pages for a few hours from about £20 to £50.

Burial on private land

Most of the accounts of d-i-y burials come from the United States. Land there is not in such short supply as it is in the UK and knowledge that burial on the family's own land is possible seems more widespread. Lisa Carlson there has published a book 'Caring for Your Own Dead' in which her husband Steve describes the funeral of his mother Mary Jane. He admits that 'when the time came for funeral arrangements, we were not well prepared. We had to learn and plan quickly at a time of great stress.'

Mary Jane's funeral

Although none of us had experience with funeral arrangements, it didn't occur to us to delegate our final acts of love to outsiders.

In retrospect, that may have been partly because of our experiences when she was bedridden. Ma had preferred that her sheets be changed by family members, for example, even though trained nurses were far more skilled at replacing sheets on an occupied bed. That was because we took the time to rub her feet. She remarked more than once she needed her feet rubbed more than she needed the sheets changed. Yet nurses always seemed too busy to provide that extra attention.

When it came time for burial and tributes, the qualities of thoughtfulness, consideration, and love seemed far more important than professional expertise. Those qualities were abundant among Ma's family and friends.

The family had been inclined toward cremation, but Ma had specifically requested burial, so two of my brothers built a simple pine casket and brought it to the apartment. Another brother spent an hour with Ma, quietly saying goodbye. Then each of us joined him, lifting a corner of the sheet to place Ma's body in the box.

The burial site my mother had requested was unavailable, so we chose what we guessed would be an equally desirable location for her: a hilltop owned by her brother where she had spent many happy years.

We needed approval from the municipal clerks of the city where Ma died and the town where she was to be buried. Neither clerk was very familiar with the tasks, since the forms are usually filled out by funeral directors who are deputised for that purpose. Both clerks, however, were extremely responsive and helpful. After checking with health officers and other officials, they performed their duties with a minimum of delay.

My brothers and I transported the coffin in my pick-up truck, and spent the next eight hours digging the grave by hand. It was hard work, in clay soil with many large rocks.

This task culminated weeks of shared work and shared emotions which brought the four of us closer together than anything else we could have possibly done. For many years we had been separated by distance, careers and individual commitments. By working together at a time of great need we renewed and strengthened our family bonds. For my brothers and me, the private burial was the best way to say goodbye to our mother.

But others also needed a chance to pay their respects. (Although Ma was deeply religious, she was not a church member, so we had no prescribed procedure for honouring her.) We took the easiest route we could think of. We announced a memorial gathering a week after burial, brought a few jugs of cider, accepted offers by others to provide additional refreshments, and played it by ear.

Scores of people showed up, including some who drove great distances. None of us knew everybody else. The only thing we had in common was that Mary Jane had touched each of our lives in profound ways. But that was actually a lot to have in common, and gathering together, at least this one time, was important.

Lacking any formal rituals, we sat around the hillside grave site, saying and doing whatever seemed appropriate. Some spoke words of tribute, some recalled meaningful incidents and experiences, some sang songs, some planted flowers.

As far as I know, nobody felt uncomfortable, out of place or unfulfilled. There were many comments about what a moving, special experience it was. Some of us remained long after the anticipated two or three hours, conversing and recalling our memories until sunset.

Overall financial costs were minimal (wood and nails for the coffin were worth a few dollars, as were the cider and other refreshments) and we were able to earmark whatever was left of Mary Jane's bank account (after her bills were paid) for publication of a book of her final writings.

From 'Caring For Your Own Dead' by Lisa Carlson.

Rural parts of Montana in the United States can include an extreme form of 'recycling' of the body after burial, according to Stephen Levine, who writes:

Fruit tree planted over body

Often, in the back country of Montana, a hole will be dug and the body, in a plain pine coffin or perhaps just wrapped in a tie-dyed cloth, will be lowered into the ground. Instead of a tombstone, a fruit tree is planted over the body. The roots are nourished by the return of that body into the earth from which it was sustained.

And in the years to follow, eating the fruit from that tree will be like partaking in that loved one. It touches on the ritual of the Eucharist.

From 'Who Dies?' by Stephen Levine.

In the UK the early Quakers were often buried in their gardens. But nowadays, how do people in the UK go about arranging a funeral on their own land? One of The Natural Death Centre's contacts arranged this after the sudden death of her husband from a heart attack by asking her lawyer to set aside a part of the large back garden in perpetuity for the grave, so that this part would not sold with the rest of the house and grounds. Few council officials will know how limited the laws are surrounding private burial – see Ian Alcock's struggles, below – so if you approach them for their blessing, go armed with the information in this chapter. Myths abound – some books say, for instance, that there must be no neighbours within a hundred yards, but this relates to a part of the 1855 Burials Act (Ch. 128, S. 9) which has been repealed (and in Scotland applies only to council cemeteries).

Planning permission for private burial?

Ian Alcock in Aberdeenshire wants himself and his wife to be buried in their wildflower meadow on their own hill in a special conservation area (SSSI). He was told to approach the Nature Conservancy Council for Scotland for initial permission and then had to pay £77 for a planning application for 'change of use of hill land to private burial ground' and £60 for a small ad in the local newspaper under 'developments which may cause concern in the neighbourhood'. 'There is no obligation to seek the approval of neighbours,' he writes. And the environmental health officer confirmed that the burial was not likely to cause pollution.

Alcock has built his own coffin: 'It cost me £40 for the plywood and is big enough for two (in case my wife and I go at the same time) and on account of my lack of carpentry expertise, has a certain "rustic charm". The postman refused to believe that it was a coffin until I put rope handles or slings round it (to avoid the corpse falling out of the bottom) and sprayed "RIP" on it with a black sheep marker. It is now in store in a building awaiting me. The dogs peed on it when it was outside, but I had a strong friend help me to move it. Incidentally, a friend has told me that she has recently paid a £1,000 undertaker's bill (and it is cheaper up here) for the "simplest possible" funeral for her father.'

Ian Alcock, Shannel, Ballogie, Aboyne, Aberdeenshire AB34 5DR (tel & fax 03398 84207).

Ian Alcock subsequently successfully appealed against the need for planning permission. The Scottish Office, in the person of the Deputy Chief Reporter R. M. Hickman (Ref. P/PPA/GD/342, Nov. 25th 1992), ruled that 'a limited number of unmarked and unfenced graves would not constitute a material change of use and I conclude that the planning consent issued to you by the district council is superfluous'. This precedent could be quoted by any family planning a d-i-y burial. The Natural Death Centre has prepared the following summary of the requirements for England, gathered from a cemetery's superintendent and from material sent in by J. B. Bradfield and from other sources.

Requirements for burial on private land

• All disposals by burial are governed by the various Burial Acts and Regulations enacted by Parliament from 1847.

• There is nothing in the law of burial which prohibits burial in private or unconsecrated land or which requires a coffin or a service or permission from any government minister. A place of burial without fences or gravestones is not a cemetery in planning law and 'subject to any restrictive covenants, can be established by any person without statutory authority, provided that no nuisance is caused' (Halsbury's 'Laws of England', Butterworth, Fourth edition, 1975, p. 504). Incidentally, no one can legally 'own' a body.

• If a search of the property deeds reveals a covenant restricting burial which no longer seems to serve a useful purpose, a court application can be made to remove the covenant.

• By all means check with the local planning authority whether or not they consider that planning permission is required for the use of the ground. As mentioned, planning permission, whether in Scotland or elsewhere in the UK, should not normally be required for a limited number of unmarked and unfenced burials. Planning departments have a free 'Certificate of Lawfulness' procedure whereby a member of the public can write in to establish formally whether or not permission is required.

• It is also wise to contact the local environmental health department. However, they should only intervene (with abatement notices, etc) after the event, when public health has been put at risk or there has been a 'statutory nuisance'. D-i-y graves do not legally need their sanction in advance.

• No offensive matter from the grave shall flow or foul any stream, canal, reservoir, aquaduct, pond or watering place. It could be as well to consult with the National Rivers Authority (which may soon be merged with HM Inspectorate of Pollution; their present phone number is 071 820 0101). Animal carcases, for instance, normally have to be buried 250 metres from any human-consumption water supply, 30 metres from any other spring and 10 metres from any field drain.

• There is no knowing how future owners of the land might regard the presence of a grave in it.

• They could not exhume the body without a licence from the Home Secretary, but it would be possible for them to apply for such a licence in order that they might arrange for reburial elsewhere. It is difficult to comment on what view the Home Office would take on such an application.

• It is necessary to carry out the requirements of the Registration Acts and to make a proper record of such a burial, at the local Registry for Births and Deaths.

Burial grounds as nature reserves

Jonathon Porritt has written of the need for 'memorial groves' – which might suit those without land of their own:

Memorial groves

My recommendation to the DoE would be to think laterally. There has been a lot of talk about new community forests since the Government recently committed £70 million to support a new scheme from the Countryside Commission. The obvious answer is to set aside special 'memorial groves' where every new burial plot would be planted with three or four hardwood saplings, provided free by the Forestry Commission. The combination of built-in fertiliser, plus unlimited tender loving care from the relatives, would pretty well guarantee a thriving woodland in next to no time.

From Jonathon Porritt's column in the Daily Telegraph.

Green, no-frills burial ground

Nick Evans, a gardener and builder and ex-sales manager in Shropshire, is seeking to purchase a two or three acre field near Ludlow, subject to planning permission, that will allow him to turn it into a green, no-frills burial ground for 100 plots. Disgusted by all the trimmings and waste at a family funeral he attended, he is trying to encourage funerals without hearses, etc, where the body would be buried in the simplest coffin. To make the site as natural as possible, rather than using a gravestone a commemorative tree would be planted, hung with a discreet plaque. The aim is to cut the expenses involved in funerals, to have funerals 'without fuss but with dignity', and to make it an option suitable particularly for people who want a secular, environmentally-friendly burial. (Nick Evans, The Bell House, Wooferton, Ludlow, Shropshire SY8 4AL, tel 0584 711 342.)

Carlisle woodland burial

The City of Carlisle is planning to build a 'return to nature' cemetery, with graves in small groups and oak trees planted on top. The public locally seem keen on the idea, the council are in favour, and only ratecapping is delaying the scheme. Here are adapted extracts from an article by their cemeteries superintendent, Ken West:

> The creation of a memorial woodland resource would benefit the environment and could be returned to the community after the expiry of grave rights. It could then form part of a country park or a green lung, for walking, pony trekking or similar. However, part of the intangible benefits are a 'return to nature' and the need to encourage insects, birds and mammals. This cannot be achieved if everybody visits their grave, stamping out paths and disturbing the woodland. Nor can memorials be placed on graves, as rank natural growth could denote neglect. I have opted for a memorial wall at the entrance to the woodland which would allow a small plaque for every grave.
>
> For the layout of the graves, I prefer a double grave with burials side by side, at a depth of 4ft 3in. This allows, after a burial, the planting of a tree on the used portion of the grave. There would be space for 900 graves to the acre, about 9% less than our current setting out. This is more than compensated for by the reduced excavation costs, drainage problems, backfilling, reinstatement of sunken graves, etc. Additionally, the cost of a traditional new grave had to include new roads, deep drainage, etc, which will not apply in the same degree with this scheme.
>
> People choosing the woodland concept before death will have gained a real psychological benefit – a piece of woodland and a real, living memorial instead of a dull, dead stone. Perhaps the test of any product is 'would you use it yourself?' I can state clearly that I would and refer you to these lines from 'Drummer Hodge' by Thomas Hardy:
>
>> His homely Northern breast and brain
>> Grow to some Southern tree
>> And strange eyed constellations reign
>> His stars eternally.
>
> *Ken West, The Cemetery Office, Richardson Street, Carlisle CA2 6AL (tel 0228 25022). Woodland graves for a 50 year endowment period are being sold in advance from this address.*

Burial ground as nature reserve

J. B. Bradfield of Harrogate writes: 'After two and a half years of correspondence with the Charity Commsission, I've finally got agreement in principle to create a registered charity that combines nature reserves and human (and pet) burial grounds. I believe that by being able to select burial in land in which nature has a prior claim, there will be a qualitative shift in emotional experience, away from the "warehousing of the dead" in cemeteries and churchyards.' Plans are in hand for the first site to be adjacent to an ancient woodland designated as a Site of Special Scientific Interest, which has strong approval from English Nature and the County Wildlife Trust. Access to the graves will be encouraged, particularly to assist with wildlife management. Trees from local seed could be planted on graves.

I'm concerned that we should be able to take *full* control over dying and death. This means being able to avoid the use of undertakers (et al) or to buy only those services required from them. It could mean digging the grave oneself having chosen the location, or digging it with a group of friends and relatives. Health and safety factors need to be fully taken account of, but are not barriers in themselves. Risks can be reduced by making shallow graves, which are also more environmentally benign. 'The depths of graves are not legislated for unless the cemetery is situated in an area where the Towns Improvement Act 1847 is in force, which then specifies a minimum of 30 inches from ground level to the top of the coffin. It would not be illegal for a company to bury a coffin 12 inches ...' (Stride, M. [1990:58] 'Burial in "The Back Garden" – is it Lawful?' J. Inst. Burial & Cremation. Admin. Summer 1990 Vol.58, No.2, p. 58). [Eds: The burial needs to be deep enough to prevent foraging dogs from trying to dig up the body. The Local Authorities' Cemeteries Order 1977 specifies 24 inches for clay soil and 36 inches for sandy soil.]

I'm also keen that coffins not be used unless environmentally benign, such as second-hand timbers from doors, floors and pallets. A ban will be placed on tropical hardwoods even those from assumed sustainable sources. A coffin is said by some to be required for transporting the corpse, but a choice may be exercised to use nothing, or a shroud, the person's own clothes, or some other alternative, such as basket from willow or sustainable ossier beds, cardboard or carpet.

My only real concern is how to keep a precise plan of the site, noting the exact position of each grave. There will have to be some fixed points of some sort, from which to take measurements, without them being a visual intrusion.

J. B. Bradfield, 7 Knox Road, Harrogate, N. Yorks HG1 3EF. There is a similar scheme entitled 'Ecchoing Green' being promoted by Jeremy Ripton, 20 Bedford Court, Oakwood Lane, Roundhay, Leeds LS8 2PL (tel 0532 350056).

Making the coffin

The Oregon-based novelist Ken Kesey (author of 'One Flew Over the Cuckoo's Nest') wrote to his friends about the death in a traffic accident of his twenty year old son Jed: 'It was the toughest thing any of us has ever had to go through, yet is also had and always will have a decided glory. There was also the support we got from friends and family, from teachers and coaches and schoolmates. Without this support I don't think we would have attempted the kind of funeral we had. A homemade ceremony is legally possible. All you need is the land, the determination and the family.'

Jed Kesey's funeral

We built the box ourselves (George Walker, mainly) and Zane and Jed's friends and frat brothers dug the hole in a nice spot between the chicken house and the pond. Page found the stone and designed the etching. You would have been proud, Wendell, especially of the box – clear pine pegged together and trimmed with redwood. The handles of thick hemp rope. And you, Ed, would have appreciated the lining. It was a piece of Tibetan brocade given Mountain Girl by Owsley fifteen years ago, gilt and silver and russet phoenix bird patterns, unfurling in flames. And last month, Bob, Zane was goose hunting in the field across the road and killed a snow goose. I told him be sure to save the down. Susan Butkovitch covered this in white silk for the pillow while Faye and MG and Gretch and Candace stitched and stapled the brocade into the box.

It was a double-pretty day, like winter holding its breath, giving us a break. About 300 people stood around and sang from the little hymnbooks that Diane Kesey had Xeroxed – 'Everlasting Arms', 'Sweet Hour of Prayer', 'In the Garden', and so forth. With all my cousins leading the singing and Dale on his fiddle. While we were singing 'Blue Eyes Crying in the Rain', Zane and Kit and the neighbour boys that have grown up with all of us carried the box to the hole. The preacher is also the Pleasant Hill School superintendent and has known our kids since kindergarten. I learned a lot about Jed that I'd either forgotten or never known – like his being a member of the National Honour Society and finishing sixth in a class of more than a hundred.

We sang some more. People filed by and dropped stuff in on Jed. I put in that silver whistle I used to wear with the Hopi cross soldered on it. One of our frat brothers put in a quartz watch guaranteed to keep beeping every 15 minutes for five years. Faye put in a snapshot of her and I standing with a pitchfork all Grantwoodesque in front of the old bus. Paul Foster put in the little leatherbound New Testament given him by his father who had carried it during his 65 years as a minister. Paul Sawyer read from 'Leaves of Grass' while the boys each hammered in the one nail they had remembered to put in their pockets. The Betas formed a circle and passed the loving cup around (a ritual our fraternity generally uses when a member is leaving the circle to become engaged) (Jed and Zane and I are all members, y'unnerstand, not to mention Hagen) and the boys lowered the box with these ropes George had cut and braided. Zane and I tossed in the first shovelfuls. It sounded like the first thunderclaps of 'Revelations'.

The following is adapted from a postscript by George Walker about the making of Jed's coffin:

We selected some clear white boards for the sides and top. Nice looking and easy to work with, pine is also traditional.

It was a very good coffin, as coffins go, very beautiful everybody said, and certainly a labour of love. But I don't really believe that is the point. The real value of that coffin was in the doing, in the building of it ourselves. Not in the coffin, as a thing, but in the act of creating it, as an event. It made us all feel better to do this ourselves, to take charge of things as much as we could, not just the coffin but the burial as well. Perhaps it's because, when we lose someone close, particularly someone young and in the prime of life, we feel more than a little burned that things have been jerked so irrevocably beyond our control. Anything we can do to regain our handle on events is gratifying.

Whatever the reason, all who kept themselves actively involved in getting Jed buried agreed: we all gained something through our efforts. We felt better about it than if we had just turned it all over to the professionals, and gone about our business of feeling bad. So, I would say to anybody who feels that they might want to give it a try when someone close dies, absolutely yes; build it yourself. Even if you can't do basic carpentry, you can nail together a kit. If you do have skills, you can make something that will make you feel good long after it's buried out of sight. It doesn't have to be fancy; simple and neat is just fine, but do make it strong. You'll be surprised by the weight.

> *From an article in CoEvolution Quarterly (Summer '84; now called Whole Earth Review, 27 Gate Five Road, Sausalito, CA 94965, USA; subs. $32).*

The Huelin d-i-y coffins

If expense is the main consideration, it is worth noting that making a coffin yourself will probably work out almost as expensive just for materials as the cheapest coffin available from a funeral director (see the next chapter – the cheapest is probably that supplied by James Gibson in Bolton – about £45, including handles and lining, delivery negotiable).

Nevertheless the Huelins, a couple in Oxford, gained a great deal of satisfaction from making their own coffins recently and found themselves quite a centre of media attention as a result. Barbara Huelin outlines the story:

> My husband, aged 77, has recently finished building our coffins. We have spent a most enlightening few months organising and preparing for our deaths; the idea has caught on amongst our friends in Oxford.
>
> The coffins are made in blockboard at a cost of about £50 each (not including our time). They are painted green and have nautical-looking rope handles (from the boat chandlers). The coffins are stored in the workroom. We have bought a double-decker site in the local Council cemetery for £150 to which we intend that family and friends shall physically bear us. We are leaving the commemorative gravestone for our survivors to add if they wish, so that they have something they can do.

There were a number of interested enquiries from members of the public so her husband David sent the Natural Death Centre the following detailed description and drawings of the design that he used:

Materials: The most convenient, though possibly not the cheapest, material is three quarter inch (18mm) blockboard; it is lighter and stronger than chipboard, and is much easier to work. It is normally sold in sheets measuring 8ft x 4ft (2.44m x 1.22m); each sheet costs about £30 (March 1992). The half inch (12mm) version is cheaper but seems rather flimsy for a coffin, and the one inch (25mm) appears unnecessarily heavy, and costs more.

Three sheets of 8ft x 4ft blockboard are enough for two coffins, with a little fiddling. It is possible, though more difficult, to make one coffin with a sheet and a half, though it is not always possible to buy half-sheets. The following suggestions are for making two coffins with three sheets of board.

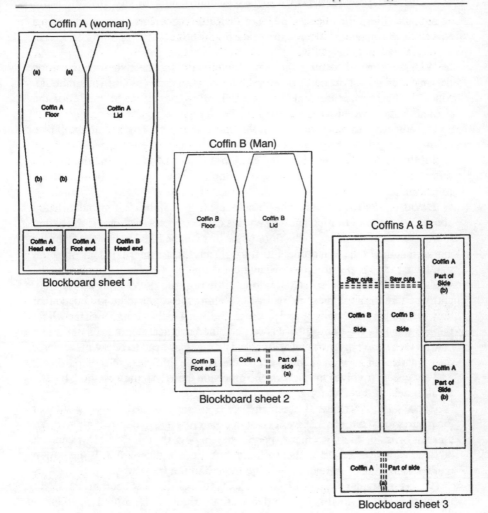

Coffin A (woman)

Coffin A Floor

Coffin A Lid

Coffin A Head end | Coffin A Foot end | Coffin B Head end

Blockboard sheet 1

Coffin B (Man)

Coffin B Floor

Coffin B Lid

Coffin B Foot end | Coffin A Part of side (a)

Blockboard sheet 2

Coffins A & B

Saw cuts | Saw cuts | Coffin A Part of Side (b)

Coffin B Side | Coffin B Side

Coffin A Part of Side (b)

Coffin A Part of side (a)

Blockboard sheet 3

Other Materials (for two coffins):

- 36ft (11m) wood strip 35mm x 10mm (rim round lid)
- (42ft (12.8m) batten 25mm x 25mm; this is not needed if the joining is by dovetailing – see below)
- 400 (2 boxes) steel wood-screws, gauge 8 x one and a quarter inch
- 100 panel pins three quarter inch
- 250ml (quarter litre) wood-working glue, e.g. Evo-Stik Wood Adhesive
- 1 litre paint (optional)
- Handles: special subject dealt with separately below.

Tools: A hand-held electric circular saw is invaluable for cutting the basic shapes in the blockboard, which by hand would be arduous work. If dovetailing is intended a coping saw is useful; beyond that, a tenon-saw, chisel, angle-gauge, and sanding equipment for finishing off.

Method: Take the measurements of the future occupant of each coffin, not forgetting the hip width; allow extra space for the possibility of putting on weight before the coffin is needed.

With these measurements the main components for the two coffins can be drawn out on the blockboard: floor and lid, sides and ends (see the illustrations). Since the basic measurements are internal, allowance must be made for the thickness of the wood when drawing the basic shapes.

It is advisable to defer cutting out the lids until the main boxes are built (see below).

Joining: Attaching the sides and ends to the floor of the coffin, and to each other, can be done in several ways; the simplest would seem to be one of the following:

1. With internal battens or corner-blocks, using the 25mm x 25mm batten listed above. With plenty of glue and screws this can be quite satisfactory; the batten joining the sides and ends to the floor of the box can be fixed below the floor for extra strength. As the four corners are not right angles, the internal block or batten will have to be shaped to the actual angle.

2. With dovetailing (so called, though it is not true dovetailing); that is by cutting alternating tongues and recesses all along the edges to be joined, so that they fit together. Each tongue and recess can be 3 or 4 inches long; once the whole thing fits snugly together, the joins can be glued and screwed with a one and a quarter inch screw through every tongue. The recesses need to be a whisker over three quarters of an inch (19mm) deep to match the thickness of the board.

This system involves more work and precision than the batten method, but the result is neat and very strong.

Shaped sides: To achieve the bends in the sides of the coffins, the inner surface of the board should have five or six saw-cuts made across it, to a depth of about three quarters of its thickness; it will then bend to the shape of the floor. The saw-cuts can be filled with glue to add to their solidity, but this is not essential. If the batten method is used, the batten itself can be treated in the same way.

(In this particular lay-out for three sheets of board it has been necessary to divide the sides of coffin 'A' into two sections; they can be joined together by dovetailing at the appropriate angle. With four boards this dividing would not be necessary.)

Lid: The precise shaping of the lid of each coffin can be left until the main body of the box is complete; this can be placed inverted over the piece of board reserved for the lid, and its outline drawn straight onto the wood. The lid should have a rim or lip all round its edge, made from the 35mm x 10mm strip listed above; this can be fixed with glue and panel pins.

Once it fits nicely, the lid can be drilled for screws, about 8 inches apart, using gauge 8, length one and a quarter inch screws, and pilot holes can be drilled in the main box. The thoughtful coffin builder will provide a bag of screws for the purpose, and possibly a screwdriver too.

Head-rest: A dead person's head falls back unbecomingly unless it is supported. The coffins should therefore have a small platform across the head end, slightly sloping, some two to three inches from the floor of the box.

Packing: Though not strictly part of the construction, there is the question of packing or lining. A very economical, attractive, and adequately absorbent packing is wood-shavings. If shavings of nice-smelling woods, such as cedar or pitch pine, can be obtained, so much the better. One dustbin-liner-full is probably enough.

Paint: Blockboard is not a very interesting colour; a litre of matt emulsion paint will make the two coffins look much more interesting; they can also be embellished with paintings of flowers, or boats, or castles, to taste.

Handles: The importance of handles depends on how the coffins are to be carried: if at shoulder height by skilled men, then no handles are required at all (professional bearers never use them). If the intention is that a coffin should be carried by family and friends, with their hands, then the handles are necessary and should be functional.

Metal or tough plastic handles, such as are used on swing and sliding doors, are inexpensive, but great care is needed in fixing them. It may be advisable to use one and a half inch screws going through the comparatively soft block-board into a hardwood block inside. Note that if cremation is chosen, then no large metal parts such as handles should be employed.

Another method is with nylon rope of half inch diameter. Half inch holes, some five inches apart, in three pairs, to be drilled in the sides of the coffin; the rope (must be nylon) is cut into lengths of 12 or 13 inches (30 to 33cm) and the ends are threaded into the holes from the outside, so that at least one inch projects on the inside of the box. Next a metal washer with exactly a half inch hole is fitted over the projecting end of rope, which is then melted with a hot-air gun so that it flattens down and spreads over the metal washer; when it cools and hardens it is very firm.

This method is easier than it may seem; it is extremely strong, and the rope loops on the outside of the coffin look attractive and appropriately modest.

Materials: 4 metres (2m each coffin) half-inch nylon rope obtainable at boat chandlers' shops. 24 half-inch washers.

Tool: Hot-air gun.

Barbara and David Huelin, 69 Kingston Road, Oxford OX2 6RJ.

A simple burial box

Ernest Morgan in his excellent book about funerals in the United States, 'Dealing Creatively with Death – A Manual of Death Education and Simple Burial', describes the making of a simple burial box, which has top and sides of quarter inch plywood, and the bottom and ends of three quarter inch plywood. Two reinforcing battens, three quarter inch thick, run the length of the box on the inside, attached to the side pieces (at the top edge, so the top of the box rests on them – as in this illustration). Ernest Morgan writes:

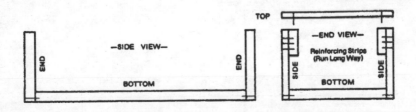

Using nails or screws [eds: the latter, say gauge 8, length one and quarter inch, would give extra strength, particularly for the ends. Wood glue, such as Evo-Stik Wood Adhesive, would also give additional strength]:

• Attach the reinforcing battens to the side pieces, flush with the edge and the end, making sure to have the good side of the plywood facing outwards;

• Attach the side pieces to the bottom.

• Attach the ends, again with the good sides out, to the bottom and to the side strips.

Four chest handles, two screwed to each end, could be useful for ease of carrying when going through doors [eds: or rope handles could be used, as in the Huelin coffins, above]. The handles could be stored in the box and screwed on when needed. Likewise, the cover could be tacked lightly in place until the box is needed, and then when the time comes fixed firmly down.

A birch coffin

For those who would like something finer, and who have the skills, a coffin made of birch planks dovetailed together could look good, with the name carved into the wood and patterns around the edges as desired, and a final polish with beeswax or linseed oil.

Re-usable coffin design

A carpenter has written to The Natural Death Centre with ideas for coffin-making workshops, mail boxes in the side of coffins and re-usable coffins:

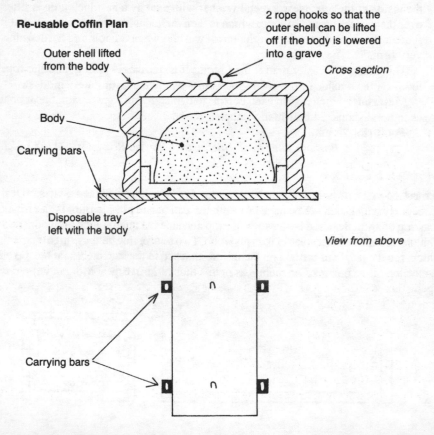

I run courses in creative woodwork and have long-term plans for running workshops where people could design and make their own coffin. With professional guidance people could design and build a coffin in exact accordance with their wishes. Family members and close friends could be invited to contribute, thus enhancing the quality of the process.

This could also be a family project. Each family member could participate in designing and building a family coffin that could be re-used as the need dictated. When it was not being used as a coffin, it could have a functional use, perhaps as a coffee table or even as a plant trough.

There could be a cheap, sealed inner box within the outer shell of the coffin that could be disposable. This would mean that the body does not have to be wrapped up or disturbed. And why the regular shape? Why not pyramid shape or even dolphin shape!

Another of my ideas is to provide some form of mail box either in the coffin or as a small container that could be buried or cremated with the body. The plan would be for there to be a period of silence during the funeral service when those attending the service could write out their final farewell message to the deceased which would then be posted in the box. This could add a valuable dimension to the grieving process.

A spokesman for the National Association of Funeral Directors has been concerned at the prospect of re-using coffins, of hauling bodies in and out of coffins. In answer to this I suggest a false and disposable bottom to the coffin that would allow the main shell to be removed with the body being left respectfully at peace. Maintaining dignity is very important and I feel that there are many ways in which this can be honoured.

From a letter to The Natural Death Centre.

Coffins for cremation – avoiding pollution

If the coffin is destined for cremation rather than burial, there are various requirements for avoiding air pollution. The best approach is to check with your intended crematorium as to whether first, they would accept a home-made coffin (see next chapter); second, what the maximum size of the coffin may be – one crematorium in the United States has said that home-made coffins tend to be made larger than they need be (Lisa Carlson in 'Caring for your own Dead' writes that 'two feet wide and 18 inches deep is sufficient for most bodies'); third, whether the particular construction you are planning needs modifying in any way; fourth, whether any lining or handles you are planning for the coffin or clothing for the body are unacceptable (for instance, PVC linings and rubber soled shoes are discouraged); and fifth, whether any medical implants in the body will be problematic. A pacemaker would probably need to be removed, for instance, in case it explodes during cremation. A doctor or funeral director can do this, although, writes Lisa Carlson, 'anyone can do it. A pacemaker is about the size of a small coin, embedded just under the skin, usually near the neck or lower on the rib cage. It is attached to wires which should be snipped.' Some crematoria may also not want to burn a body with silicone implants – in Southern California the silicone turned into a sticky goo on the floor of the cremator, although a UK crematorium had no difficulties in a test it ran.

Instructions for funeral directors have been issued by the cremation authorities, many of which would apply to those running a funeral themselves. P. J. Wilson, the secretary of the Federation of British Cremation Authorities, writes to the Natural Death Centre that 'Crematoria invariably require that bodies are conveyed to the building in a reasonable manner. A rigid coffin able to withstand any handling or transportation problems, adequately secured and identified and suitably lined to prevent leakage of fluids or other material will be required.'

Instructions from the Federation of British Cremation Authorities

• *Bearers:* Sufficient bearers should convey the coffin reverently from the hearse to the catafalque.

• *Coffin construction:* The coffin must be made of wood or a wood by-product which, when placed in a cremator and subjected to the accepted cremation processes, is easily combustible and which does not emit smoke, give off toxic gas or leave any retardant smears or drips after final combustion. No metal furniture or fittings whatever shall be used on a coffin for cremation. No metal of any kind shall be used in the manufacture of such a coffin except as necessary for its safe construction and then only metal of a high ferrous content [eds: eg use ferrous screws]. Cross pieces must not be attached to the bottom of the coffin. If it is desired to strengthen the bottom of the coffin, wooden strips may be placed lengthwise for this purpose. The coffin must not be painted or varnished but may be covered with a suitable cloth. Products manufactured in polyvinyl chloride (PVC) must not be used in the construction of the coffin or its furnishings. The use of polystyrene must be restricted to the coffin nameplate only, in which case it must not exceed 90 grams in weight.

No coffin shall be accepted unless it bears adequate particulars of the identity of the deceased person therein [eds: normally this would include the name, age and date of death of the person].

• *Lining of the coffin:* The use of sawdust or cotton-wool must be avoided. If circumstances require, suitable sealing material may be used, but no metal, rubber or polyvinyl chloride (PVC) will be permitted and on no account must pitch or a similar substance be used. [Eds: no lead-lined coffins would be permitted.]

• *Size of the coffin:* Where the external dimensions of a coffin are likely to exceed length 81 inches (206 cm); width 28 inches (71 cm); depth 22 inches (56 cm) the proper officer of the crematorium must be given advance notice.

• *Cremation of infants:* In cases when bereaved parents desire the cremation of the body of an infant, they should be warned that there are occasions when no tangible remains are left after the cremation process has been completed. This is due to the cartilaginous nature of the bone structure.

If the warning is not given the parents may have been denied the choice of earth burial and thereby been subjected to understandable distress.

• *Cremated remains:* An urn or casket for cremated remains should be of sufficient internal dimension to provide a minimum of 200 cubic inches (3,280 cubic cm) and securely labelled. The container should be strong enough to resist breakage in transit. The lid must fit tightly and the fastening should be strong enough to prevent the lid being forced open by distortion of the container through maltreatment in transit.

Adapted from a text sent by the Federation of British Cremation Authorities.

Deirdre Martin has sent the Natural Death Centre an encouraging description of the funeral of her mother, Dorothy, which they organised themselves and for which they made the coffin. The description, adapted extracts from which appear below, ties together many of the elements previously discussed in this chapter. Deirdre Martin is prepared to give advice to any others in the Brighton area trying to plan a similar funeral themselves (as is the similarly experienced Sheila Barratt in Woking – make contact through the Natural Death Centre).

In memory of Dorothy Miller – a simple funeral

My mother died in the Royal Sussex Hospital, Brighton, at 11.20am on Friday February 21st, 1992, at the age of 85. Early that morning my husband and I were called to the hospital and she died when we were both present. She was quiet and peaceful and looked very calm. A young nurse and I laid her out, and I placed some flowers by her before we said goodbye.

My mother had always said she wished to be buried 'simply', and we had already told the hospital matron that we would like to make the arrangements ourselves. She was extremely sympathetic and very helpful. She made an appointment for my husband and me to see the hospital registration officer that afternoon, and told us the hospital would be able to keep my mother's body until we had made adequate arrangements. She also advised us to speak to the crematorium, and to ask them for advice.

At 12.30 pm that day we visited Brighton's Woodvale Crematorium. The staff were marvellous. We asked if we could make the coffin, and deal with all the funeral arrangements ourselves. 'Certainly.' They provided us with a leaflet 'Information and specifications for an interment or cremation arranged without the guidance of a funeral director'. [Eds: this present chapter covers everything in the leaflet that is of more than local significance.] They told us how to make the arrangements, but my main worry was what to do with Grandma. They said she can be kept as long as convenient in the borough mortuary for up to three weeks at no charge – after that a small sum would be necessary. I feel this is always a problem with death – everyone seems to want to dispose of the person too soon! The fact that we had time to think, and time to make arrangements was the first step. The staff said they would help with carrying Grandma into the chapel. We went to look at the chapel to see how high the platform was for the body to be placed on. They told us to telephone and come at any time if we wanted more help or information. At 3 pm that afternoon we were with the hospital registrar. She was delighted someone wished to arrange their own funeral – the ward sister had arranged for my mother to be taken to the hospital mortuary, and the registrar spoke to the mortician on our behalf. He was happy to keep my mother until the day of the funeral – no problem – no charge. He gave us the dimensions of the coffin. Width and length: 5ft 9" by 18" wide. All we had to do was to let him know the time for collection and they would help us lift her in and to seal the lid. So my mother's last resting place was the hospital mortuary until March 3rd.

This gave us time to make the coffin and sort ourselves out. I telephoned the Natural Death Centre for some information, which came very promptly, and for which I am grateful. Also I wrote to the British Humanist Association who sent me a booklet 'Funerals without God'. It was very reassuring getting information from various sources, showing us that we could do this ourselves and that it would be very personal and that our mother's passing had not been taken away from us and dealt with by strangers. She had very rarely attended a church and we had been to a number of funerals – in 1989 twelve members of our family and friends had died – and none of the funerals seemed to have been satisfactory for the bereaved. Something appeared to be missing.

The coffin was made in our garage in a day. My husband enlisted the help of George Haines, a friend who is in his seventies, who said he always wanted to make his own coffin, so was delighted to have the chance to practise. Much tea and merriment went into the work, and chipboard and timber arrived from the local yard. Most of the neighbours and friends came to have a look and to try it out.

Really it was the fun bits that started to emerge, such as finding music that my mother liked. On a check-up trip to the crematorium to speak to them about the tapes and how to set them up, they told me they had loads of tapes available. They set all the taping up for us, again giving us every assistance. They also suggested that the funeral should be the last one of the day, to be able to give us assistance and extra time in case we had any hiccups.

The registrar was fascinated; she advised me to take several copies of the death certificate at £2 each as she pointed out that any further copies would cost £5-50 each. That was wise advice as my brothers and the solicitor and crematorium all wanted copies. We dealt with all the paper work which had come from the mortuary, hospital, etc, and that is usually handled by the Funeral Directors – it was simple. We needed burial certificates, doctors' certificates and one or two other certificates mentioned in the interment leaflet from Woodvale, and again we were assisted by everybody.

I tried to involve the family as much as possible. My eldest daughter made a lovely cake for the funeral tea, and also put together a wonderful photographic display, with photos of my mother's life, and the paintings she did in her later years. My brother's estate wagon was measured for the coffin – it would fit in OK. As a precautionary measure, we also hired an estate car for £42 in case of emergencies. Fortunately it was not required to carry the coffin, but it could have been used if necessary. The rest of the family prepared readings from my mother's favourite books and we prepared a programme containing readings, remembrances and music. We timed this for approximately 30 minutes. It was enough. We requested no flowers, but did in fact have a lovely display of everlasting flowers made by my sister-in-law, in a basket, which was placed on the coffin with an Indian rug from my brother, and this looked really great.

So at 4 pm on March 3rd we were ready to conduct the service. What went wrong? Not a lot – one late-arriving relative wanted to view her grandmother and we did not think to let the mortician know in advance of collecting the body. The body was not prepared and obviously did not look its best for the occasion and there was an upsetting reaction. My husband, the friend who made the coffin, George, my brother from Kent, and his two children (a son and daughter) and another grandson from Wales, all went to fetch the body. Lesson number one – double check who knows who is coming, when and where. At the crematorium it was difficult getting the coffin out of the car – nobody realised quite how heavy it would be. One granddaughter wished to help carry the coffin, which was great, but this needed a rehearsal. The crematorium staff helped and it was OK. We made a mess-up of getting everyone into the chapel, and in the end they went in after the coffin was placed on the rostrum. The staff worked the tape recorder and I compered the show. My husband videoed the event and Mother would have been very, very pleased, because basically it went off OK. And it did – it dealt with a lot of emotions, and people were able to work on their own grief; mainly, I felt, because they had helped to get the show on the road.

We collected the ashes the next day from the crematorium, free of charge. We later gave the mortician a bottle of wine and the crematorium staff a Christmas box, saw to the nurses and staff at the hospital for their Christmas fare and hoped we had not forgotten anyone.

A hundred days after her death we held a Celebration for her death and life at the Chithurst Monastery, where a Dhana was given to the monks, and family and friends came once again to join with us in the memorial.

All this activity has helped me to deal with my grief and my feelings of guilt and resentment at having to look after quite a difficult lady. I feel I was also able to deal with my father's death – he died in 1961 at the age of 54 and the funeral was too quickly dealt with, with little time to realise how we all felt at that time. So I was able to lay to rest some unresolved grief over his loss.

Many people have spoken to us regarding making their own coffins and are surprised at how little we spent. For the record the absolutely necessary expenses were:

Fee for the crematorium £105; fees for the doctors £57; death certificates £8; purchase of chipboard and timber £30. Total: £200.

In fact we spent a further £42 on the reserve car, for a grand total of £242. Several people asked, did we do this because we couldn't afford it? The answer to this is, No. I felt doing this ourselves was very rewarding, it helped to deal with our grief and the resentments that we had, and which had built up through the years as a result of some of the difficulties of looking after my mother during her lifetime. The main thought seemed to be that it was just as she would have wanted and this came over very strongly from all who helped and were present.

Deirdre's husband adds this note about the coffin:

Dorothy Miller's coffin

We made the coffin from half inch chipboard and 2" by 1" finished battens. First we cut the base and used this as a template for the lid. Although the hospital mortician gave us a width of 18" we erred on the generous side, at 20", to make sure the shoulders would go in all right. On reflection it would have been ample to make the sides and top with quarter inch chipboard or even hardboard if one really wanted to economise on expense and weight. Below the bottom (and flush with the edges) we fixed battens. We then cut the side pieces 12" high and fixed these on to the battens so that the battens were concealed. Then we fixed battens on the inside of the side pieces a half inch from the top to accommodate a flush-fitting lid. We found it necessary to strengthen the joining to the lid-battens at the junction of the angle at the widest part of the coffin. We pre-drilled the lid so that it was simple to screw down after putting the old lady in at the mortuary.

We used ferrous screws throughout because after the cremation they were removed from the ashes with a magnet. In the foot end we fixed a small rope handle to use in pulling the coffin out of the car. It was not necessary to fit any other handles.

The mortician said that the coffin was one of the best he had seen.

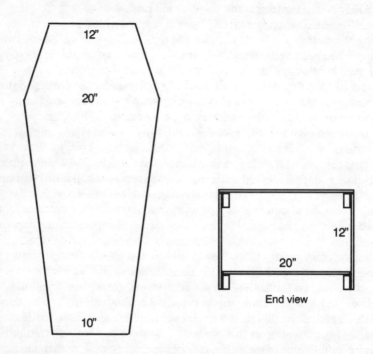

End view

Dorothy Miller's coffin

Burial at sea

In theory, burial at sea seems an attractive proposition: the body becomes food for the fish, and it is just a matter of getting a free licence from the Ministry of Agriculture, Fisheries and Food (MAFF) and then finding a person with a boat to take the coffin out. In practice, sea burial is mildly discouraged by the authorities and there are quite complex requirements. For a start, there are very few places around the coast where sea burials are allowed, as there are concerns about commercial fishing trawling the bodies back up. You need to contact your local fisheries District Inspector for the free licence. Either go via Marine Environmental Protection at MAFF, (tel 071 238 5872 or 5870 or 5873, A.P. Patel, or fisheries chief inspector M.G. Jennings); or make contact locally:

• *North Eastern:* W. Bridge, tel North Shields 091 2574520/2570159.
• *Humberside:* W. Lewis, tel Grimsby 0472 355112/355113.
• *Eastern:* N. Stone, tel Lowestoft 0502 573149/572769.
• *South Eastern:* T.H. Whyatt, tel Hastings 0424 424109/438125.
• *South Western:* C. George, tel Plymouth 0752 228001/2.
• *Western:* R.Thomasson, tel Penzance 0736 62805/65014.
• *Wales:* M. Hearn, tel Milford Haven 0646 693412/693466.

• *North Western:* Mr Parker, tel Fleetwood 0253 873515/873516.

These inspectors may also be able to advise on finding a suitable boat.

You should tell the registrar when registering the death that you plan a sea burial and you can then obtain from the registrar a 'Coroners Out of England Form' (Form 104), and the local coroner's address to which this should be sent.

The MAFF has new conditions under discussion at present which include:

• Obtaining a certificate of freedom from fever and infection from the GP or hospital doctor.

• The body must not be embalmed.

• There must be a narrow plastic band around the waist on which is put a telephone number (normally the undertaker's – but perhaps that of a local solicitor or other firm would be accepted) and case number, but no name of the firm or the deceased.

• The coffin must be solid softwood (such as pine) with butt-jointed corners (or normal strong joints) but with right-angled brackets screwed on the inside of the ends to strengthen all joints.

• The coffin must be weighted by iron, steel or weak concrete mix, with a minimum weighting of 100 kgs. Lightweight concrete building blocks must not be used. It is suggested that the weighting should be evenly distributed and attached to the coffin, with further weighting on the body, in case these become separated.

• To let out air pressure, at least twelve holes, minimum diameter 20mm, must be drilled in each side and the top of the coffin. Three similar holes must be drilled in each of the end boards.

• The body must not be dressed but may be covered loosely with a cotton or paper sheet.

• At least two steel bands must be placed around the coffin at right angles to ensure it survives the impact on entry to the sea and on arrival at the sea bed.

• The MAFF reserve the right to inspect the coffin prior to the burial. (Ask if they want the steel bands in place for then.)

• The local MAFF office must be informed on the day prior to the date of burial and immediately after. An at-least-verbal amendment to the licence is needed if adverse weather or other circumstances delay the burial beyond the week of the licence.

Pricey burials at sea are offered by the Britannia Shipping Company, Britannia House, High Street, Newton Poppleford, Sidmouth, Devon EX10 OEF (tel 0395 68652) from about £1,500, which includes collection from most places in the country; the trip out at sea takes about two hours; they tend to go out some four miles from Plymouth but can do the burials elsewhere.

Non-assembly line funerals

There are indeed many ways that people have found to prevent funerals from becoming assembly-line affairs, including funerals for which undertakers were used. Here are some more examples:

• **Reminders**: Having some reminder of the person on top of the coffin during the service – such as a favourite hat or scarf.

• **Fires, candles, lanterns**: John Fox of Welfare State International ('the celebratory arts company' – see the Resources chapter under Organisations) suggests a funeral or memorial service outdoors, the space framed with poles, bunting and music, tables decorated with cloth, flowers and papercuts, and the use of fires, candles and lanterns. His book 'Engineers of the Imagination' (Methuen, 1990) describes, inter alia, how to make the lanterns.

• **One flower each**: You could ask friends not to buy flowers but to bring one flower each, preferably from their garden, and to place it on the coffin. Here is Allegra Taylor's description of everyone bringing one daffodil each to the funeral of Claire, an eight year old girl who died of leukaemia:

A grave lined with moss and leaves like a bird's nest

The funeral, organised magnificently by Margot's husband, was a triumph of life over death. Many children from Claire's old school came, as well as some she'd known in hospital. Their drawings for Claire were stuck up all round the church: drawings of butterflies, flowers and big yellow suns. A few children stood up and read poems. Everyone was given a candle to hold – the place was ablaze with the illuminated faces of children – and a yellow daffodil to throw in the grave.

The minister – a friend of the family – held the little coffin in his arms as he spoke of Claire's courage and of the lightness and joy she'd brought into the world during her short life. The grave was lined with moss and leaves like a nest for a baby bird. We stood with our arms around each other as we threw in an avalanche of daffodils and sang 'The Lord of the Dance' together: 'Dance, dance, wherever you may be ...' It was the most beautiful funeral I had ever been to and an inspiring example of how it can be. We have begun to reclaim birth and death from the medical profession after generations of abdication – begun to reinstate choice and personal responsibility. Let's do the same with funerals.

From 'Acquainted with the Night' by Allegra Taylor.

• **Home funerals**: You could get the priest to conduct the funeral or memorial service in your home or out in the garden. Anglican priests are not officially allowed to conduct a funeral service at home but others, such as Unitarian ministers, are willing to do this. In fact most Unitarian ministers are willing to officiate at very personalised or even humanist (that is, atheist or agnostic) funerals. (See Organisations in the Resources chapter).

Christianne Heal described in a newspaper interview the funeral she arranged for her mother, outside a church setting:

Letting off helium balloons at the graveside

'We wanted a service which would reflect my mother and the person she was.' Heal asked her siblings and other family members to write down the things they remembered about their mother, good as well as bad, to be read out at the funeral. 'But we didn't think that the arrangement of benches in a church would be helpful. We wanted to sit around the coffin, so that my mother was clearly there at the centre and so we could all participate,' says Heal.

The funeral parlour at the chapel of rest seemed to be the best available option, and Heal and her family booked that for the service. 'It wasn't a place where funerals were held very often, but in the end it worked very well. We found a priest who was willing to come along and say mass but who understood it was for us and that we wanted to be in charge of what happened.'

The most imaginative aspect of the funeral though, took place at the graveside, when Heal and her family released helium-filled white balloons into the sky. 'I bought them the day before from a party shop. Letting them go represented her spirit moving off, and it was a very significant part of the ceremony for me.'

An unidentified newspaper cutting in The Natural Death Centre library records a very exuberant funeral:

Cortège in 250 mile pub crawl

A 20-car funeral cortege set off from Peterborough General Hospital at 8.30am and arrived in Haverfordwest in Wales, 12 hours later. After drinking the Bull Inn there dry, the 100 mourners, mostly Irish travellers, caught the overnight ferry to Rosslare.

The cortège was following the last instructions of Mrs Johanna Connors, who was buried at the end of the trip in New Ross, County Wexford.

• **Humanist funerals**: For a fee of between £50 and £60, you can get a trained officiant from the British Humanist Association (see Resources chapter) to act as master or mistress of ceremonies for a humanist funeral. Or you or a friend or relative can do it. The Association puts out a very helpful pamphlet, entitled 'Funerals Without God', by Jane Wynne Willson on how to run such services, with sample texts and poetry (see Resources chapter). The pamphlet explains how a humanist service tends to divide into distinct parts. First there is about eight minutes' worth of entry music, which is played until people have settled down in their seats – if an organist is not being used, this music should be recorded on side A only of a tape marked clearly 'Entry Music' and should be presented to the crematorium preferably the day before. The service proper opens with thoughts on life and death; then a tribute to the dead person (perhaps by a relative); followed by the committal (where everyone stands, the officiant turns towards the coffin, 'commits the body to its natural end' and a button is pressed to close the curtains). Up to about 40 seconds of slow and solemn music is sometimes used for the committal, with the person operating the machine cued to switch it on the moment specific words are said (a second tape should be clearly marked 'Committal Music' with the tape in position to deliver music the moment the Play button is pressed); and the service ends with closing words, after which the officiant walks over to the main mourners and leads them out of the exit door; a tape (marked 'Exit Music') can be played for about five minutes from the moment the officiant steps down from the lectern. Be sure to ask the crematorium to play the music loudly, if this is what you want, or you may find it all very restrained.

Michael Rennie in Dundee used the 'Funerals Without God' book to help him design a secular funeral for his father:

During my father's funeral, after welcoming all present, I dealt with the need to come to terms with death and read some words from Pasternak about the essence of our existence on earth. After a poem by Swinburn about the peace to be found in death, we stood in silence for some moments moments in which those who had religious faith were asked to pray. I then paid tribute to my father's memory, incorporating anecdotes giving an insight into his character and contribution to life. My daughter played on the violin tunes emphasising my father's links with the sea, with Scotland and with the Tyne, as his coffin was taken from the hall. Later I committed him to earth, and read a poem by C. Day Lewis, which was sufficiently broad in its humanity to resonate with any secular or religious beliefs.

From a letter to The Independent (Oct. 28th '91).

• **Longer services**: It may be possible to book two or even three sessions at the crematorium, if the standard time is not enough, and if there are many people who wish to speak. See the next chapter for what this may, or may not, cost, depending on the crematorium.

• **Other cultures, other times**: In the UK, two world wars made funerary pomp on the home front seem out of place and accentuated our Puritan heritage of simple funerals. Indeed in 1644 the Puritans directed that the dead were to be interred 'without any ceremony'. In 1648, when the body of King Charles I was brought to the Royal Chapel at Windsor, the governor of the castle refused to let Bishop Juxon read the funeral service from the Book of Common Prayer:

The funeral of King Charles I

The Bishop of London stood weeping by, to tender that his service might not be accepted. Then was Charles I deposited in silence and sorrow in the vacant place in the vault about three of the afternoon; and the Lords that night, though late, returned to London.

From 'The History of the Worthies of England' edited by J. Fuller, Publishers IGWL and WG, 1662, quoted in 'The English Way of Death' by Julian Litten.

There is a beauty of its own in the simplicity expected at a Quaker funeral today, where the disposal of the body is supposed to be done with no unnecessary expense and with no flowers. But the diversity of funeral practices in other cultures and religions around the world and the beauty or at least depth of some of their rituals can widen our vision of the potential of funerals to 'enchant' the participants, raising their consciousness above the mundane. The Ecuadorians, for instance, are buried with their eyes open so that they can see their way to heaven; the Yanonami Indians of the Amazon believe that it is barbaric that Westerners do not drink the ashes of their relatives; the Merina hold periodic 'dances with the dead' where the women dance with the dried-out remains of their next of kin; rural Greeks tend the graves daily for five years before the corpse is disinterred and placed in a communal ossuary, with clean bones being seen as a reflection of a good life; and for traditional Hindus even the grandchildren are closely involved:

The Hindu rites of death

Hindus should arrange for the dying person to be brought home to die. The dying person should concentrate upon the mantram given at initiation, or if the person is no longer conscious, a family member should chant the mantram softly in his or her right ear.

After death, the relatives place a simple cloth on the person. Each of the relatives comes and applies sesame oil to the deceased's head. The body is bathed with the water from nine kumbhas, and is placed in the coffin. Each of the granchildren takes a small lighted stick and stands around the body and sings.

From 'Death and Dying – A Hindu Point of View', £1-50 from Himalayan Academy Publishers, Rakesh Mathur, 6 Carolyn House, 95 Larkhall Rise, London SW4 6HR.

A pagan death

There is a Pagan Hospice and Funeral Trust in the UK (see the Resources chapter). In the future it hopes to have a network of counsellors to aid dying pagans, to provide pagan funeral services and to purchase a hospice and burial grounds. At present it has a newsletter and leaflets and provides information on pagan approaches to death and dying, reincarnation and other subjects.

Pagans aim to design rituals that bring them very close to nature and the seasons. An eloquent description of a pagan death and memorial ceremony is that by Tony Kelly and his friends, concerning his wife Betty who died from cancer.

> Betty was now lying in a green-covered bed in the sunshine at the window, the window open and the air full of warmth and birdsong, willow and birch branches in front of her and a great leafy birch bough at the foot of the bed and the littler branches by the open window. It looked like a woodland glade and she was pleased. Among all the greenery were two bunches of daffodils in big jars, and jars of dandelions and celandines and yellow polyanthus on the windowsill. And I put a few little branches of silver birch on the bed where she could take hold of them and handle them and feel them in the way she always liked to do ...
>
> I was sitting at Betty's side, speaking to her softly as she dreamed, saying, 'The Goddess loves you,' and other things that I knew would make her happy, and I was holding her hands. Betty stopped breathing ...
>
> We stripped all the alien words and the glitter off the coffin; the wood was beautiful. We laid Betty naked inside it and dressed her with daffodils, tastefully, beautifully, in her hair and about her body, some of them fresh and a few to speak her fading ...
>
> The cremation was without ceremony and we brought her ashes home and kept them with us in the box I made, its lid scalloped like the waves of the sea, till the Hag Moon of Samhain called us to a distant shore ...

The ceremony for the scattering of the ashes took place seven months later, at a remote spot by the sea:

> The Sea-lady came over the grass to where I was standing and she raised the lid of the box, and the ashes, speckled black and grey, lay open to the wide open sky. As I held the box to my breast and she took the lid into her own two hands I spoke the message that for seven moons my heart had borne:
>
> > I am come, beloved Mabh
> > To do a thing for Betty
> > And to do the thing for thee
> > For love of Betty
> > And for love of thee

Each spoke their own devotion and to each the priestess responded with the same words that had been Betty's own spontaneous response when their phone calls had been conveyed to her, and they sang a six-verse song they had composed for the occasion:

> > ... Green Lady Earth,
> > Deep Lady Sea ...
> > Carry the ash ...
> > Her life has flown;
> > Thou dost abide ...

We joined our hands in a ring, all nine of us, and a kiss from the Green Lady passed from lip to hand all around the ring. 'With thee for always, Mabh,' I spoke

as the love of the Goddess moved me. At last we loosed our hands.
> *For a copy of the full 16 page text send £1 incl. postage to Tony Kelly, Can y Lloer, Ffarmers, Llanwrda, Dyfed.*

Public memorial

Remembering the dead begins immediately after death, and continues after the funeral. One suggestion for improving grieving is to set up 'open houses' for bereaved people who can't face going home. Nowadays, many people hold impromptu wakes after the funeral. The wake or after-funeral gathering is common in most cultures, like the wedding feast. However, it is the tone or style of the wake that is all-important. A feast that is too formal might accentuate the loneliness of the bereaved person once the guests have gone home. On the other hand, an informal gathering of mourners who want to share their feelings may begin a sharing process that will come to be of benefit to the bereaved. Laughter and jokes as well as tears are likely to erupt because remembering the dead person is also recalling the richness of life and relationships through stories and anecdotes.

Holding a memorial service at some time, perhaps months after the death and immediate obsequies, may be a way of bringing out the essential cheerfulness and spirit of life with which most of us would like to be remembered. We want to be celebrated as well as mourned. Here is such a celebration, designed by Margaret Chisman for her husband Stan. There is some human instinct that makes us want to be present at such a celebration of people who were our friends. It is rather like giving wedding gifts. We want to give the gifts, be part of the celebration. Why should we deprive ourselves of being part of such a ceremony, the feasting of a life?

A table of objects to commemorate the person

The celebration and commemoration of Stan was held at our home in the double rooms on the ground floor. About 40 friends and relations were present. It was a beautiful day, the garden was full of flowers and their scent drifted in through the open french doors. After welcoming everyone I took the cloth cover off the table and explained that on it were articles that Stan loved or that exemplified his life.

The first thing that everyone noticed about him was his outstanding physical vigour. By contrast many people seemed only half alive. He was fully and gloriously alive in every fibre of his being. He loved rambling – I held up his walking boots – and whenever he decided to go on a walk he began to get excited and I would know to get his boots out. He loved skiing – I showed his goggles – and sadly had a holiday fixed for January by which time he was too ill. There were several photos amongst those displayed of him enjoying this sport. When living in Ipswich he played in the Post Office Table Tennis Team, and they won the cup one year and each player received a small trophy, here displayed. He also played five-a-side football and his old football boots were still in the cupboard upstairs. He took up sailboarding within the last two years and there were several photos of him displayed. These were taken on our holiday in the South of France. I regret I have no photos of him hang-gliding (whoever heard of a man of 62 taking up hang-gliding?), but George, who also introduced him to this sport describes the last occasion; Stan had become airborne to a height of 50 ft and was looking decidedly unhappy but absolutely determined to go through with it.

John White, who could not be present today said that for him he would always remember Stan for playing the glorious voice of Paul Robeson singing 'I thought I saw Joe Hill last night.' We played this record, and as I heard that vibrant voice singing the words of optimism in the face of death I felt once more overcome with grief and loss and wondered whether, despite all my supportive and loving relations and friends, all my active outside interests, my comfortable and satisfying home, I would manage to achieve serenity and full acceptance of his death.

The next part was pure joy. Nearly everyone had an anecdote or memory to share. Some of them were new to me, and I felt as if Stan came alive again for a few minutes.

Alan Mayne commented in the Visitors Book: 'I knew that Stan was a man of many parts but I didn't know how many.'

I asked everyone to end as Stan would have wished – to hug and kiss their neighbours.

From Interim', a private newsletter circulated by Margaret Chisman.

Incidentally, Ernest Morgan warns that those who speak up at memorial services should not allow themselves to be cut short by whoever is conducting the service. 'I have known family members who carried regrets for years that they were cut off from speaking because the service was running too long.'

Memorials by Artists

Memorials by Artists puts bereaved families in touch with artists, for the designing of headstones and other memorials in a style requested by the individual. Themes have included homely domestic items, animals and birds, a typewriter and other symbols suggested by the commissioning person or devised by the artist, as well as epitaphs. The movement was founded by Harriet Frazer.

The demands for real memorials have proved so great that she has had to employ an assistant. 'The work can sometimes be very sad. Actually, really sad,' she said. 'But what is wonderful is that it is so much to do with life. The artists are so creative, making beautiful things, and celebrating a person is a very hopeful thing to do.'

From an article by Mary Greene in The Sunday Telegraph (April 28th 1991).

Prices of headstones average from £1,000, including the Memorials by Artists fee. An illustrated booklet is available from Memorials by Artists (see the Resources chapter) for £5, including postage and packing.

Elizabeth Lawlor, who used Memorials by Artists for her husband's headstone, commends them to The Natural Death Centre:

The headstone is up. I wanted a wave on top for symbolic reasons – waves of consciousness, waves being reabsorbed into the ocean, etc – and for my husband's naval and sea-loving connection. The help I received from Memorials by Artists was wonderful.

A memorial of course need not be a gravestone: you may want to plant a tree in memory of the person; or to pay for a glass window in church; or to pay for a park bench; or to have a sponsored walk or children sponsored to learn poetry for a recital in aid of the person's favourite charity. A lively memorial recently consisted of mixing the deceased's ashes with gunpowder, and launching them into the night sky as a series of giant firework rockets,

It may have been mainly a publicity gimmick, but a pub in Hereford (The Packhorse, tel 0299 403 762) announced the genial offer for regular customers of placing their ashes behind tiles in the pub, with a wake in their honour when they die and free drinks all round once a year thereafter – for a price ranging from £50 for a tile in the toilets, to £5,000 for a tile close to the fire. The money was to have been lodged with a local solicitor.

Alternative urns

John Fox of Welfare State International suggests redecorating the normal small wooden caskets used for ashes: remove the paint with varnish stripper, undercoat with filler and two coats of white wood primer; then paint imagery or words – he uses fluorescent enamel varnish (Brodie and Middleton); re-varnish, allowing 24 hours for the drying. He adds this story:

> I commissioned a pottery urn from a friend who specialised in throwing decorative slipware. It was for the ceremony to scatter my father's ashes in the Humber Estuary, where he had earned his living as a sea captain.
>
> We ended up with a dome-shaped circular lidded pot about a foot high and a foot diameter at the base. A little like a tiny bee hive.
>
> The lid had to be surprisingly wide too – about six inches, for the ashes to scatter easily downwind.
>
> In white slip on the dark brown of the pot's surface, we inscribed:
>
> 'The last voyage of Captain Fox, MBE. May his spirit be at peace with the sea.'
>
> At the ceremony myself, my wife and our two children then ten and eight played 'Eternal Father' on brass instruments. (My father was a Christian.)
>
> It was memorable and healing for us all.

Welfare State International (artistic director John Fox – see the Resources chapter) offers a consultancy service for those wanting a very special memorial service.

Incidentally, Yvonne Malik (see the Resources chapter), an artist and a consultant to the Natural Death Centre, would like further commissions to decorate coffins for anyone who wishes it. She also makes beautiful glass-engraved death meditations with collage backings which could make a memorial or be for contemplation during life. And see also (at the end of the Practical Help for the Dying chapter) her work on Memory Boxes for the dying.

Probate

In chapter four on Training for Dying, under the heading 'Simplifying Your Affairs Before Death', it was outlined how someone could leave their estate so that neither probate, inheritance tax nor Inland Revenue account was required. Probate otherwise involves the executors of the will applying to the probate registry for a grant of probate which confirms their power to process the will (if the person died without a will, the relatives apply for similar powers, known as letters of administration). Solicitors can do the whole thing for you, but in one typical recent instance they charged a rate of £80 per hour, plus half a per cent of all the cash, stocks and shares in the estate and one per cent of the property. To this total they then added 25%. Shop around for the cheapest solicitor you can find – for instance, avoid central London; ones advertising their cheapness in the London Yellow Pages include Stevens and Co (Welling, Kent, tel 0800 289504) and Walford and Co (London NW2, tel 081 452 3000). Yet assuming the estate is relatively straightforward (with no business partnership, self-owned business, agricultural land, insurance syndicate or family trusts) it can be done by anyone businesslike, with patience enough to wade through all the fiddly details and to write the many formal letters. Again, as when preparing one's will, the most useful book is the Consumer Association's 'Wills and Probate'. The following is a sketch of what is involved:

You will need forms for a personal application for a grant of probate from your local Probate Personal Application Department – if you were not given this address in a booklet at the time you registered the death, you can find it out from the Probate Registry (see the Resources chapter). You can get Form PA2 from the local office which tells you how to do things without a solicitor and the Citizens Advice Bureau may be able to help further. Once you have filled in and returned these forms, you will be given an appointment to go to your local office in person to swear that the information is true. At this point you will need to pay the probate fee (if the estate was worth £250,000 net, for example, the fee would be about £600); and a couple of weeks later you will need to pay any inheritance tax owing (although inheritance tax on land or buildings can be paid over a ten year period at – currently – eight per cent interest).

If the deceased's funds were in a bank these will be frozen until after probate is granted (you could try asking the bank to put any current account amount on deposit, so that at least it earns interest; the bank also has discretion to let the executors continue operating the account, if idemnified by the executors against loss). Because the account is frozen, the executors may have to get an expensive overdraft from the same bank to pay the inheritance tax (although a helpful bank may be willing to set any assets in the deceased's accounts against the required overdraft – and a prudent person might enquire of their bank before death whether they are helpful in this regard). It would have saved money if the dying person were to have transferred sufficient money to National Savings (see chapter five for the other advantages) as these, plus some of the bigger building societies, are the only ones who will pay inheritance tax directly out of the deceased's assets and in advance of probate.

The executors will also need to deal with the Land Registry to transfer any property (form 56 from an Oyez shop) and with the Income Tax people – their forms Cap 30 (to show that any inheritance tax has been paid), form 59 (an income tax return for the year in which the person died) and form R185E (income tax deduction certificates).

Valuing stocks and shares with the exactitude required for probate purposes, filling in the probate schedule of them and handling their transfer or sale are small bureaucratic nightmares. To repeat chapter four: any dying person who has accumulated the odd lot of shares in privatised Telecom, etc, would save their executors a great deal of trouble by selling them before death.

Executors will also need to deal with the deceased's mortgage company, house insurance company, district valuer, bank, building society, life insurance company, pension company, state benefits office and local post office (for forwarding of mail) – plus in some cases advertising in the newspapers for any unknown creditors.

Anyone appointed as an executor who, understandably, cannot face the work involved, can fill in a renunciation form or a form appointing an attorney to do it (both forms are available from an Oyez shop); or you can hand over to a professional half way through.

Chapter 7

THE GOOD FUNERAL GUIDE

The previous chapter told how people could organise a funeral themselves. This one is for those who want help from the trade, and is a guide to the best cemeteries, crematoria, funeral suppliers and undertakers – for those who may want just one service from an undertaker, such as a coffin or cold storage facilities, or a complete service, whether an inexpensive basic funeral or a magnificent coffin with glass sided carriage and Friesian horses.

Natural Death Handbook Awards

At the same time as the publication of this book, framed certificates will be presented in the following categories:

• The Natural Death Handbook Award for the **Most Helpful Funeral Director**. This award is jointly shared by James Gibson in Bolton (see pages 155, 156 and 168) and by David Coster of Sunbury-on-Thames, Middlesex (see pages 158 and 177).

• The Natural Death Handbook Award for the **Most Helpful Funeral Supplier**. This award goes to Green Undertakings in Leeds (see pages 155 and 170).

• The Natural Death Handbook Award for the **Most Helpful Crematorium**. This award goes to the Mid-Warwickshire Crematorium (see pages 165 and 172).

• The Natural Death Handbook Award for the **Most Helpful Cemetery**. This award goes to the Carlisle Cemetery (see page 129, 166 and 168).

For this first edition of the Handbook, the editors have had to rely on their own surveys and investigations in determining these awards. For future editions, nominations from readers are invited.

Good undertakers

In our view, the ideal undertaker is a *facilitator,* one who helps the family to do as much of the funeral arranging themselves as they can bear, as exemplified in the following excerpts from an account by an American undertaker, about what he learnt from the funeral of his father:

A funeral director helping with his father's funeral

I was sitting on the hospital bed holding my father's hand when he died. I hated the scene but I wouldn't have been anywhere else. Such helplessness and desperation I have never felt at any other time. When he died, we wept.

Two men came with a cot – men I had never seen before. They didn't know me or my profession. My emotion didn't leave room for explanations, so I simply asked them to stand aside. It was my dad and I would do it. Hesitatingly they obliged, while I took the cover from the cot, positioned the cot and gathered Dad's limp body into my arms. It was my job. I was his son. It was our love.

I felt a sense of desertion as I watched those two strangers disappear down the hall with dad. Dad didn't know them.

One of my best friends, a funeral director from the next town, came to get Dad and did all the embalming work. I did the rest – the death certificate, the notification of newspapers, cemetery, minister, church, family, friends, neighbours, all the scores of details which accompany the task of being a funeral director.

My family did lots of other things: we tucked Dad in (it's rough but it's real) and closed the casket; we took him to church ourselves. My brother, sister and I carried Dad to his grave, we lowered him into his grave with straps and our own muscle power. We closed the vault and shovelled the dirt ourselves. We closed out his life ourselves.

Later, weeks later, I asked myself: how many sons, daughters, parents and spouses had I delayed the grief work for because I had performed all of the tasks for them, because I, as a functionary, had usurped their role as care-giving family members. How many times had I made decisions for a family without their opinion, because I had assumed 'they couldn't take it?' They have a right to be heard. The focus must be on their needs, reactions and prior experience. Immediately, my role in funeral service shifted to being that of a facilitator and it has remained there.

By Roy and Jane Nichols from 'Death – The Final Stage of Growth' edited by
Elisabeth Kübler-Ross.

Good coffins

The last chapter dealt with making a coffin. This one, inter alia, tells you how to buy one ready-made – not always an easy purchase (as Jane Spottiswoode discovered). Many funeral directors refuse to sell just a coffin, or do so at grossly inflated prices. No ideal Green coffin is as yet marketed in this country – the nearest is the designer coffin from recycled scrap pallets sold by Vic Fearn Ltd (see East Midlands region listings below) and a plan by Andy Moore of Friends of the Earth and the Community Recycling Network (10-12 Picton Street, Montpelier, Bristol BS6 5QA, tel 0272 420142 w; 0272 556095 h), who is interested in developing papier mâché coffins. The Natural Death Centre would like to help make Green coffins the norm. Burning 390,000 wooden coffins each year is not as ecological as it might be. Other countries are further advanced:

A cardboard self-assembly coffin

Alexandre Haas, a packaging manufacturer in Lausanne, Switzerland, has produced the Peace Box, a smart self-assembly cardboard coffin, costing about £45. It weighs 12 kilos, can carry 200 kilos, has a liquid-proof insert and resists temperatures from 250 degrees C to minus 180 degrees C. But it is above all kind to the environment, says Haas, 'and it is light, foldable, easily transported and can be slotted together in five minutes'. He is seeking UK distribution, preferably through a funeral director, and only wants to take orders for 1,000 or more – but could refer people wanting just one coffin to sales outlets elsewhere in Europe. (Alexandre Haas, Sondeur Diffusion, CH-1029 Villars-Ste-Croix, Switzerland, tel and fax 010 41 21 634 70 26.)

In the United States and in Canada it is possible to rent a decorous outer coffin for the funeral service, with only the cardboard inner coffin cremated (normally a thin piece of pine or plywood is placed under the deceased to keep the cardboard rigid). For instance, Joanna Moorhead in an interview in the Observer (April 14th '92), spoke with funeral director Kem Timlick who offers Western Rent-A-Casket Ltd, a 'cheap, no frills' service in Vancouver. His funerals cost about a tenth of the average. 'If you want to spend a lot of money remembering someone who's died, donate money to crippled children or heart-disease research.'

Alexandre Haas (above) has a 'patented ground mechanical opening system for a luxury over-coffin' (perhaps a variant of the idea on page 136) and M. G. von Bratt has written to the Natural Death Centre from New Zealand saying that he has patents for the UK, USA and other countries on a disposable cardboard coffin with a re-usable outer core:

Cardboard coffin with disposable outer core

The re-usable outer represents a standard coffin and is easily removed from the disposable inner at the crematorium or graveside with no dignity lost. The outer need not be used as the inner is very presentable. If the funeral director had a re-usable outer at say an initial cost of $1,000 and he charged $100 per burial or cremation, his outlay would be recovered after ten funerals. He could charge between a further $100 and $150 for the disposable inner coffin.

The cardboard coffin costs $30 to produce in New Zealand in numbers of 25, plus $20 for the 16mm lightweight wooden base board. If these items were produced in quantity the prices would be considerably reduced – almost halved.

Cardboard coffins would be ideal for sea burials as there would be instant water absorption and no buoyancy.

M. G. von Bratt, 24 Claremont Terrace, Otumoetai, Tauranga, New Zealand.

Coffins from recycled newspapers

Mr T. Fowler of Sullivan Engineering in Ebenezer, near Sydney in Australia, has told the Natural Death Centre of plans for a $3.5m plant to produce coffins made from recycled newspapers. They are hoping for a worldwide franchise operation and he has had 'overtures from England'. The coffins look very similar to wooden ones, and are very strong. As he told the Funeral Services Journal, 'I've put one on trestles and jumped up and down on it and it showed no signs of breaking.' (Mr T. Fowler, tel 010 61 45 751 252.)

Cheapest coffins in the UK

But in the meantime, how does somebody in the UK go about buying a coffin, whether Green or otherwise? One way, if all else fails, is simply to ask a local carpenter. The Natural Death Centre tried a small-looking one at random out of our local Yellow Pages, **Lignum Vitae** of London NW10 (tel 081 965 8839), and they estimated that they could make a cheap one for about £100, but could only add handles, lining, etc, if they were supplied with them (or they could do rope handles).

The Natural Death Centre circulated a questionnaire to 2,800 funeral directors in September 1992, and, of the mere 45 (excluding branches of the same firm) who deigned to reply – presumably representing the *crème de la crème* – a total of 29 were prepared to sell just a coffin, without other services, at prices ranging from £45 to £325 for the cheapest fully fitted coffin – with a resultant average price of £115. The 24 who were prepared to sell a coffin without other services and for less than £150 – 0.86% out of the 2,800 funeral directors or 53% of those who replied, depending on how you look at it – are listed regionally later in this chapter (one or two are also listed who are exceptional for other reasons). Probably the best value coffin is that supplied by the funeral director **James Gibson of Bolton** (see North West region below), whose cheapest comes fully fitted with lining and handles for £45, plus a negotiable charge for delivery anywhere in the UK. One person living in the wilds of Scotland (whose need was not urgent) has complained to the Natural Death Centre about very slow processing of her order from James Gibson, so plan well ahead!

Mr Foreman of **H. J. Bent & Co** (see London region below) was cagey about giving any prices on our questionnaire form, but when tackled by phone said that he would supply an unfitted chipboard container, which he felt was barely suitable for a funeral, from £30, with delivery charges negotiable.

Coffin makers

We assumed that the funeral suppliers, the people who make the coffins and supply the funeral directors, would be the cheapest, but there was an almost universal refusal to supply the public. A typical comment on the telephone was that their trade depended on the 'big four' companies of funeral directors who do 90% of the funerals in this country and they weren't going to risk that trade by supplying one-offs. You may wish to try the Yellow Pages (under funeral suppliers) and to see if you have better luck with your local firms, perhaps even popping in to see them. You have a better chance of being served if you know in advance the exact width and length you want, are prepared to accept any form of lining or handles, can collect, and generally make it clear you will be offering minimum trouble, whilst keeping their name and the fact that they have supplied you confidential. When Jane Spottiswoode wanted a coffin for her husband, she got one by subterfuge, as related in the previous chapter, by pretending it was for a play. And there are two funeral suppliers who are prepared to take orders from individual members of the public if they come via the Natural Death Centre – although they charge more than James Gibson (see above) and Green Undertakings (see below). **Henry Smith Ltd** (below under London region) is willing to supply a standard coffin only, fully fitted, at a rather pricey £94 incl. VAT to the general public; **Vic Fearn Ltd** (see under East Midlands) offers fancy painted coffins from £500, a standard coffin, and one, as mentioned earlier, from recycled scrap pallets.

If you are trying to buy a coffin locally and none of the above leads are helping, it may be worth approaching your local pet funeral service (see under 'Pet services' in the Yellow Pages). They do not have the funeral directors to worry about and may be more amenable to the idea of supplying a human-sized coffin. For instance **Pets Meadow** (see under Radlett, East Anglian region) can arrange to have an adult-size coffin delivered anywhere for £80 (they also do reasonably priced caskets for ashes).

However, winner of The Natural Death Handbook Award for the Most Helpful Funeral Suppliers is **Green Undertakings of Leeds** (see North East region below) who are not a mainstream funeral supplier but who are willing to offer a flatpack coffin from £35 upwards in MDF, ply or veneer, with delivery extra. Their cheapest standard coffin costs £87, fitted with handles and delivered. Urgent orders can normally be processed and delivered within three to four days (weekends permitting). They also sell body bags (£15 delivered), handles from £6 for a set of three pairs, name plates from £5, lining material from 85p per metre, and lowering webbing for burials at £12 per 9yds (by 3") length.

Transport

If you are arranging a funeral yourselves but just need help with transport, your local undertaker may well be as cheap as a local hire firm. Those who replied to our questionnaire were no doubt the more enlightened members of the profession; but 82% of these would supply just transport for the body or coffin, without other services, at prices ranging from £25 to £150 locally; and one offered just a mileage charge of £1-20 per mile. These prices are given in the regional listings below.

Those readers who are so Green that they cannot accept the idea of motor vehicles being used to transport the body could try asking a local church or cemetery if they can lend or rent, with a suitable deposit, a wheel bier. For instance, Manchester Cemetery (see North West region below) do have such wheel biers – they hire them out for use within the grounds for £2-50. More feasible, more expensive and more dashing is to arrange for a horse-drawn hearse. Three firms which offer such vehicles, complete with Friesian horses, are T. Cribb & Sons (from £575 – see London region below), James Gibson (from £450 to £900 – see North West region below, although they can go nationwide) and Peter Taylor (from £500 – see East Anglian region below).

Cold storage

80% of our progressive respondents were prepared to supply cold storage facilities to families who were not using the undertaker for the funeral – which could be reassuring for those, for instance, who have to wait for relatives arriving from abroad for the funeral. The price asked for this service ranged from nothing at all (in five instances) to £26 per day, with an average price of just over £10 per day.

Embalming

Embalming involves draining blood from the body, and replacing it with formaldehyde (plus a pinkish dye such a safranine) pumped in under pressure, which has a hardening and disinfecting effect. 'The cheeks become fuller and firmer, and the eyeballs and surrounding skin become harder,' writes Robert Wilkins in 'The Fireside Book of Death'. He describes how the mouth is prevented from hanging open, sometimes by a needle passed from the lower lip up through the nostril, and how the abdomen is suctioned clean. Unlike Egyptian embalmers, modern embalming aims only for a short-term preserving effect. The funeral trade argues that embalming helps prevent the body smelling and removes some of the trauma from the face. As one of our contacts put it: 'I would certainly look better after death pumped full of pink dye, with the lines on my face smoothed away.' Embalming probably appeals to the kind of person who appreciates heavy make-up for the living, and less so to those who want the body to be handled only by close family or to allow the body to look very evidently dead. But it is, of course, a certain way of ensuring that the deceased is not buried or burnt alive, for those who have this particular fear.

'Do you embalm the deceased as a matter of course or on request?' we asked the funeral directors in our questionnaire. Several firms replied 'Yes, we do embalm as a matter of course,' some adding the proviso 'unless asked not to' – so it is important to make your wishes clear in this regard. The majority claimed only to embalm on request, but often again with provisos such as: 'unless the body is to be exported or conveyed long distance' or 'unless the family wishes to view the body'. One firm wrote: 'We embalm when we consider it necessary for hygienic reasons and for viewing purposes. If there is a risk of infection we will insist on it for our own staff's sake.'

Complete services

What can people hope for in a good undertaker? Libby Purves in Country Living magazine described Tony Brown of Saxmundham, Suffolk 'whose cheerful sensitivity makes bereavement more bearable' (see East Anglia region below for his address):

A very independent funeral director

If you arrange a funeral in a town or an urbanised country area, you may of course find a humane and sensitive undertaker, but it is more likely that you will end up on a slick, calculatedly inoffensive and utterly bland production line. You will be edged subtly towards the more expensive coffins and trimmings and given assurances about 'hygienic treatment' – ie surface embalming – and the 'tastefully appointed chapel of rest' – all plastic flowers and melamine.

So in celebration of the few independent, cussed, beloved and legendary undertakers left, it seemed worth listening to the story of Tony Brown of Saxmundham. Burial of the Dead, after all, is listed as the last of the Seven Acts of Mercy in Christian belief, on a par with feeding the hungry and comforting distress. What men like him do, because of the way they do it, is as useful as any social work, but largely unacknowledged.

He was an ambulance driver who started 'moonlighting for a funeral director, digging graves at six in the morning before a shift'. He took over an undertaker's business in 1979. 'I did farmwork to keep going. I'd be ploughing and my wife would come and wave from the hedge and leave me her bike and I'd jump on it and go quick.'

But some refinements of the trade he rejected from the start. 'I don't embalm, not unless a body's going abroad. I don't touch the body any more than I need to. I don't do all that arranging of their hair and face-painting and that, and I don't sell people fancy shrouds because I do not class myself as a salesman.

'I do like singing. I sing good and loud. I've done "The Old Rugged Cross" three times this week.'

A funeral director who accepts, even revels in, the individuality of each corpse goes a long way to easing the misery. 'There was an old Romany horseman, the other week. We dressed him up in his black suit and neckerchief, like he always wore, and put his cap on him. And it was just him, old Tinker. You know, I felt like putting a fag in his mouth!

'Everyone ought to go the way they want. That's why I hate these pre-paid funerals and I hate taking money in advance. I'd rather people had insurance in the old way, then it can all be done as a family want. People are always having ideas and saying to me, "Tony, is that silly?" and I always say No. One woman wanted to go in her own Volvo Estate. We got her in. Why not? When I go, I'm going on a horse and cart.'

He is a Methodist, and is shocked by the fact that when people die without any relatives or friends to bury them, the social services merely stipulate that the body be disposed of correctly. 'There's nothing in law saying that anyone's got to say one single word. So I say the prayers. I've taken a whole cremation service. I'm not a preacher, and of course I don't charge anything for it. But you can't just put someone in a hole and walk away.'

Adapted extracts from an article by Libby Purves in Country Living, reprinted
in Funeral Service Journal.

It is hard to find an independent undertaker – many of the big firms hide behind the name of the small firm they have taken over, and often it takes some persistence to find this out. But a bigger problem in choosing an undertaker is that in the first shock of a relative dying 97% of people, according to an Office of Fair Trading investigation, sign up with the first undertaker they contact. Arranging a funeral is not like buying any other consumer service, and people need to be aware that this could lay them open to exploitation, even if most undertakers in fact are well-meaning and dedicated people. Our advice is that you get a friend who is not so emotionally involved to phone around for you and to report back to you when an undertaker has been located who meets your criteria.

It is perhaps worth emphasising at this point that although The Natural Death Centre is campaigning for improvements in the funeral trade, and advocates that families organise funerals themselves wherever possible, it acknowledge that funerals in the UK are as cheap or cheaper than most countries in Europe; are cheap compared with what the average family is prepared to spend on a wedding; and are carried out in the main by sensitive professionals doing a difficult and stressful job which most people would not have the courage to do.

For those whose main consideration is price and who want a complete funeral organised for them, the cheapest seem to be offered by those for whom the funeral business is a sideline. For instance, **T. Finn in Plymouth** (see South West region below) is about as unorthodox as you can get. He is a retired insurance agent and ex-Royal Marine. He gets his coffins from James Gibson (see above) and will sell these to local people, or will arrange a very basic funeral for those who don't want d-i-y. He will merely add 10% to the final total for his services. So with £76 for a coffin, £127 for the cremation fee, £57 for the medical fees, £50 for the estate car, the total with his percentage would come to about £340, plus about £77 for catering, coffin carrying, flowers etc, if desired. And at a simple £10 per hour rate he can also help with wills, probate, etc. Please let the Natural Death Centre know how you find his services if you use them, as the Centre relies on such information to monitor those it publicises. W. Parsons, a spokesman for the National Association of Funeral Directors, comments: 'Suffice it to say that Mr Finn and I have met and his knowledge of funerals and funeral procedures or paperwork was decidely limited. I would strongly recommend that any family interested in his scheme obtain a detailed estimate in writing before giving him the go-ahead.'

David Coster of Sunbury, Middlesex (see London region below), a fully qualified member of the British Institute of Funeral Directors, offers probably the best value funeral for anyone in the London area or to the West of London, even allowing for an additional mileage charge of £1 per mile, outside his 20 mile zone. As he writes 'We do not seek to make our living solely from the sale of funeral services, so we can offer all the provisions normally available to the public, through high street funeral directors, for considerably less cost.' They use a quality estate car rather than a hearse (which would cost an extra £65) and expect the family to provide bearers (or they can supply them at £17 per man). This way the basic funeral (including coffin, transport, embalming and documentation) costs a mere £250. Take as an example a funeral 60 miles to the West of his office: to this basic fee of £250 have to be added crematorium fees of £120, two doctors' fees of £28-50 each, a 40 miles extra mileage charge of £80 for removing the body for embalming and returning it for the service – a total of £507. This is still just less than half what the average family pay for a funeral in the South of England (£1025; £867 in other areas – according to a recent Chosen Heritage survey). David Coster, as mentioned above, is joint winner of The Natural Death Handbook Award for the Most Helpful Funeral Director.

All members of the National Association of Funeral Directors are supposed to offer a basic funeral, but this needs asking for by name. In response to our questionnaire, several neglected or refused to fill in the questions asking prices, but for those who were willing to state them publicly, a basic funeral costs from £463 to £887, with an average of £668. (This includes our notional allowance of £213 for the extras, the so-called 'disbursements' paid out for the client by the undertaker: the cremation fee, doctors' fee and minister's fee.) Rule 15 of the National Association of Funeral Directors' Code of Practice states that even this basic funeral price should be reduced still further if certain services such as bearers are not required. In fact eight funeral directors told us that they would make no such reductions, and six of these eight claimed to be members of the Association.

Some of the cheapest funerals go by names that seem designed to put the customer off from asking for them. For instance, **Rowland Brothers of Croydon** (see South region) offer what they term a 'disposal service' for £295 (crematorium and doctors' fees extra), which turns out to be a perfectly respectable funeral complete with hearse and coffin.

If you are genuinely hard-up, many undertakers are kind hearted enough to make allowances and will not turn you away. One of our contacts offered an undertaker £400 cash on the spot (the most he could afford) for a £795 funeral and was accepted. The highly commendable and distinctive Islamic funeral service offered by **Haji Taslim** (see London region below), based at the East London Mosque and aimed primarily at the Muslim community, offers free burial to the indigent, besides being prepared to give cheap or free help of various kinds to those planning their own funeral.

Cheap funerals for council residents

It is also worth phoning your local council's cemeteries department, who might be well informed (eg for Brent, this would mean looking under 'B' for Brent and then under 'Cemeteries' within the list of Brent's services) and asking if the council has made a special agreement to provide cheaper basic funerals for residents (note that the requirement is normally that the deceased should have lived in the borough, not the person organising the funeral, but check this). In London the **Co-op Funeral Service** has for several years provided a not-so-cheap basic funeral for certain boroughs: the CWS Co-op does one for residents of Southwark, Lewisham, Lambeth and Camden (tel 081 317 7317 for details; or the local council); the CRS Co-op for residents of Islington (tel 071 607 2828), Hounslow (tel 081 570 4741) and Haringey (tel 081 808 3837) – or try the local councils for details of these too. The cost excluding disbursements for the CRS funerals is about £400, for the CWS ones from £460 (Lambeth) to £570 (Lewisham). In **Wigan** (see North West region below) the borough council uses the services of two local funeral directors to offer cremation for £465 and burial for £469 (both all-inclusive prices), which is as cheap as any we found offered privately nationwide. A similar slightly more expensive service is offered by the St Helens and Bolton council (see North West region, under Bolton).

Memorial Societies

There is scope for religious and neighbourhood groups of one sort or another in the UK to help each other with the funeral arrangements, just as within some Jewish communities it is considered an honour to be of service to the deceased in this way. Neighbours could help each other with advice, with transport, by providing bearers, by helping with the making of coffins or even by buying a plot of land for a wildlife cemetery (besides of course helping before death with caring for the dying at home, and after the funeral with reintegrating the bereaved into the life of the neighbourhood). In the United States, communities in many local areas over the last fifty years have formed their own Memorial Societies (some 150 to date) which use the power of their membership numbers to make agreements with particular undertakers for cheaper than normal services (society members tend to pay less than a fifth the average cost of an American funeral). A lifetime fee of some $25 is charged, many of the staff are volunteers, and some of the societies offer workshops and meetings and informative leaflets and advice. People who join fill in a pre-arrangement form indicating their detailed funeral preferences. Anyone contemplating forming a similar society in the UK – a project which The Natural Death Centre would be happy to help publicise – will find useful their $10 handbook for Funeral and Memorial Societies; this is available from the Continental Association, 6900 Lost Lake Road, Egg Harbor, WI 54209-9231, USA (tel 0101 414 868 3136).

Free funerals

Free funerals are available (on claims made before or within three months of the funeral, on Social Security office form SF200), if the relative organising the funeral is on Income Support or Family Credit or Housing Benefit, although that person's money over £500 (£1,000 if sixty or over) will be used towards the costs, and any money in the estate of the deceased will go towards the costs. So in a family of relative poverty it is worth ensuring that the relative who requests the funeral is the poorest one who falls into one of the three above categories. Social Security (see leaflet FB29, a guide to benefits when someone dies) also gives out a Widow's Payment of £1,000 if the husband paid enough National Insurance contributions and was not getting retirement pension, and if the widow is under sixty.

The local authority is obliged (under the Public Health – Control of Disease – Act 1984 Part III Disposal of Dead Bodies Section 46) to organise disposal of a body when no relative is willing to do so. A. C. T. Connolly (of 26 Broadfields Avenue, Winchmore Hill, London N21 1AD) decided to test this Act by refusing to arrange for the disposal of a relative's body (which was in the coroner's mortuary at the local hospital). He resisted ('wrongful') pressure from the registrar of deaths to take various forms before he would register the death. Finally a helpful official in the council's Social Services department agreed to arrange the funeral and to register the death in the name of the council, with the Connolly family reimbursing the council for the £315 cost. The family was notified in advance of the time for the service and the commital at the crematorium. Mr Connolly concludes: 'It is a legally imposed duty on local authorities to carry out this public health function *no matter what the financial position of the bereaved might be.* Yet very few people indeed know of this local authority option.'

Donating the body

Ernest Morgan quotes a poetic statement by Robert Test in favour of organ donation:

Give my sight to the man who has never seen a sunrise

The day will come when my body will lie upon a white sheet tucked neatly under the four corners of a mattress located in a hospital busily occupied with the living and the dying. At a certain moment a doctor will determine that my brain has ceased to function and that, to all intents and purposes, my life has stopped.

When that happens, do not attempt to install artificial life into my body by the use of a machine and don't call this my deathbed. Let it be called the Bed of Life, and let my body be taken from it to help others lead fuller lives.

Give my sight to the man who has never seen a sunrise, a baby's face or love in the eyes of a woman. Give my heart to the person whose own heart has caused nothing but endless days of pain. Give my blood to the teenager who was pulled from the wreckage of his car, so that he may live to see his grandchildren play. Give my kidneys to a person who depends upon a machine to exist from week to week. Take my bones, every muscle, every fibre and nerve in my body and find a way to make a crippled child walk. Explore every corner of my brain. Take my cells, if necessary, and let them grow so that, someday, a speechless boy will shout at the crack of a bat or a deaf girl will hear the sound of rain against her window.

Burn what is left of me and scatter the ashes to the winds to help the flowers grow.

If you must bury something, let it be my faults, my weaknesses and all my prejudice against my fellow man. Give my sins to the devil. Give my soul to God.

If, by chance, you wish to remember me, do it with a kind deed or word to someone who needs you. If you do all I have asked, I will live forever.

'Dealing Creatively with Death' by Ernest Morgan.

If you feel the same way as Ernest Morgan and Robert Test, you need to persuade your next of kin (who will have charge of your body after death), to tell your doctor and your hospital ward and to get a donor card from your local health centre, doctor or chemist. Animal Aid (7 Castle St, Tonbridge, Kent TN9 1BH, tel 0732 364 546) issues a Humane Research Donor Card which requests that the body be used for medical and scientific research. A card for donating eyes and other organs is also available from the Royal National Institute for the Blind, 224 Great Portland Street, London W1N 6AA (tel 071 388 1266); and a DHSS-printed all-organ donor card can be got from the British Heart Foundation, Distribution Dept, 14 Fitzhardinge St, London W1H 4DH (tel 071 935 0185). The cornea of the eyes is the only part that can wait up to 12 hours for removal; the rest have to be removed within half an hour of death.

It is not possible to guarantee a free disposal of your body by leaving it for dissection by medical students. Only a percentage is accepted. Medical schools generally accept only bodies that are unautopsied after death, non-cancerous, relatively whole and within easy range of the school. Dr David Delvin wrongly claimed in the Independent recently that the bodies of paupers are still sometimes used for dissection purposes – although this is a fear that has haunted the poor ever since the 1832 Anatomy Act (as described by Ruth Richardson in her book 'Death, Dissection and the Destitute' published by Pelican, 1989). To offer to donate your body, contact the professor of anatomy at your local medical hospital or HM Inspector of Anatomy, Department of Health, Wellington House, 133-155 Waterloo Road, London SE1 8UG (tel 071 972 4342); or for those in the London area, contact the London Anatomy Office, all hours, on 071 387 7850 or 071 741 2198.

Pre-paid funerals

It has been estimated that the pre-paid funeral market could become as big a business in the UK as in the United States, where about three quarters of all funerals are paid for before death. The advantages claimed include that: people planning in advance tend to choose simple funerals; it allows for leisurely comparison shopping; in some of the plans you are protected against inflationary price rises; relatives do not suddenly face a big bill at a time of stress; it provides peace of mind for those elderly with no relatives; and it would reduce your capital and thus perhaps entitle you to social security benefits you might not otherwise have received.

In our view, the advantages of some of the schemes could be outweighed by the potential disadvantages: pre-paid funerals militate against family participation – what if your family decide that they want to make your coffin or to look after your funeral arrangements? Many of the schemes tend to favour the big chains with their assembly-line funerals and to drive the smaller firms to the wall. They encourage TV advertising and other heavy marketing ploys. And there is at least one horror story in the United States where the money was simply pocketed, and the pre-paid cremation bodies were stacked in the basement of the mortuary, with others buried in mass graves.

A first step is to consider questions such as: what happens if you do not need a funeral in the UK after all, for instance if you die abroad or if your ship sinks at sea? What happens if you die before completing payments? What happens if you need that capital sum in an emergency? Would you not have done better to put the money into a form of investment that you could recover? What happens if the trust or foundation backing your pre-paid scheme goes bust? What if whoever attends your dying is not aware of your pre-paid arrangement? If you want such an arrangement, would it not be more interesting to discuss your funeral wishes with your most trusted next-of-kin and to pay money into an account or investment controlled jointly by them? Or, probably a less financially attractive option, to put regular premiums into a funeral insurance scheme (or to top up your life insurance) which would pay a lump sum to your relatives on your death, leaving your relatives with more freedom of action? **Sun Alliance** (tel 0800 27 21 27), for instance, offers a funeral insurance scheme whereby a 70 year old male, whatever his state of health, pays £17 a month for life, and during the first two years this money is paid back on death plus half as much again; thereafter it pays out £1635 on death. The Independent Order of **Odd Fellows** (tel 061 832 9361) offers a whole life insurance, without medical examination, for people aged 50 to 85, whereby a 70 year old can pay £100 per annum with a guaranteed £884 paid out at death. Other such firms with their own schemes include Ambassador Life (tel 0800 262422), CIS (tel 041 332 6531), the Ideal Benefit Society (tel 021 449 4101) and the Tunbridge Wells Friendly Society (tel 0892 515353). An interesting variant is **Rest Assured** of Funeral Payment Cover Ltd (tel 0785 40000 to find out participating funeral directors in your area) where a 70 year old, after three medical questions, could pay £114 per annum for ten years for a guaranteed funeral costing £750 at today's prices and booked in advance with a particular undertaker, with the deceased's estate getting any surplus bonus if there is one. Also offered is the Omega plan, designed in part for those who are terminally ill.

Nevertheless, if your circumstances are such that one of the more high profile pre-paid plans seems desirable, try to find a scheme which, as well as satisfactorily answering the above questions, is mainly for small independent firms; places at least 90% of the pre-paid funds in trust; will not add extras when the time comes; allows a wide range of choice if you move to another part of the country; allows for no-questions-asked cancellation with refund of money *and* interest (less any small administration fees); and returns any unspent money and interest after the funeral. You will not be able to find such a scheme as yet in the UK (although the last two points are required by law in some American states).

Possibly least objectionable at present is the Golden Charter, since it is specifically designed for the small, independent funeral directors and their association SAIF, the Society of Allied and Independent Funeral Directors (a splinter group within the NAFD). Indeed the 'Which?' recommended Best Buy in February 1992 for those wanting a simple funeral was the **Golden Charter** Standard (tel 0800 833800) at £775 including all cremation funeral costs (to which additional paid-for elements can be added).

The next best is probably the **Perfect Assurance Funeral Trust** run by the National Association of Funeral Directors (NAFD – for details of your local participants, tel 021 709 0019), which offers no standard plans but allows you to choose any firm, small or large, that offers the scheme and to tailor-make a plan to your requirements. The firm then pays the money into the presumed safety of the Perfect Assurance trust fund.

The market leader and the first to advertise on TV has been **Chosen Heritage** (tel 0800 525555), whose cheapest Simplicity Plan funeral costs £750 (disbursements included). If the person dies abroad or ends up not needing their funeral, relatives are refunded. 100% of the funds is claimed to go into the trust fund. Chosen Heritage allows cancellations at any time, minus interest and a £55 fee. There are no extras. It does have a 'personal choice' option for those wanting a non-standard package. The snag is that 146 of its (claimed) 500 funeral directors are part of the Great Southern Group, and such huge chains are in our view to be discouraged.

There is an enormous gulf between Chosen Heritage's price and the cheapest plan offered by the Co-op's CRS division (Lyn Buckley, tel 0244 341135), whose **Caring Covenant** Funeral Plan costs £815 with no disbursements paid (so probably leading to a final bill of well over £1,000); in addition cancellations are allowed only at their discretion, subject to loss of interest and a fee of about 5%.

The Co-op's CWS division (tel 0800 289120) offers the **Co-operative Funeral Bond** where the Earl cremation plan (including disbursements) costs £839. One unusual feature of this plan is that it allows two people to be named on the form and the plan can eventually pay for either of them.

The scheme **Dignity in Destiny** (tel 0800 269318) is almost completely tied to the big chain Plantsbrook, using independent funeral directors only in those places where it has no coverage itself. Its equivalent cheapest funeral costs £850. It only allows cancellations at its discretion and charges a £50 fee. Less than 100% of the funds goes to the trust fund – a variable amount is paid in, whatever Price Waterhouse advises, but 'Yes, less than 90%.'

Crematoria

In our view, most crematoria are to be shunned. Who wants a rushed funeral service in buildings which have been described as looking like newspaper reading rooms in public libraries or waiting rooms in airports? Several people of late have suggested a different approach. Rather than say a service in church followed by just some of the family going on to a commital at the crematorium, with consequent confusion and disruption for any party or gathering afterwards, both the service and something similar to a committal can be held in the church (or other preferred location), with the coffin borne out towards the end of the service. Then just one member of the family goes with the coffin to the crematorium (or just the vicar goes if a committal service at the crematorium is wanted). Crematoria will prefer this too, suggests funeral director Philip Tomlins in the Funeral Director journal (Nov. 1991), as they then do not have the difficulty of finding a time that fits with the church service.

Perhaps the ideal crematorium would be a building designed to allow the mourners to gather round a high tech version of a funeral pyre. Tony Walter in 'Funerals and How to Improve Them' has suggested a number of slightly less radical design improvements: a coffin visible and central and near floor level throughout the service, which can be touched, kissed, circled round or filed past; a building in which the coffin can be moved by the mourners, possibly by being lowered down under the floor; and a building as beautiful and significant as a church, so that the local community will want it for births and marriages too, which is close to the elements – surrounded by forest and wildlife, rather than manicured lawns and regimented rows of rosebushes.

A wonderful sounding new crematorium is being planned with the above design suggestions in mind by Deborah Hinton, for woodland that she owns near Basingstoke (see Southern region below). A £1.5m investment is planned and it should open in 1994. Hinton is also determined that the crematorium should be welcoming to all, whether using undertakers or not, and irrespective of the body container used.

Of the 52 respondents to our survey of crematoria nationwide, only 21% claimed anything more unusual in the way of grounds than 'formal gardens'. 92% would allow a few mourners to witness the coffin entering the cremator, often with the proviso that this should be 'by prior arrangement' (in Newcastle-under-Lyme Crematorium up to 60 people can watch). 60% would allow the mourners to move the coffin to the cremator. And one – Stockport Crematorium – see North West region below – would even permit one mourner to 'charge' the coffin into the cremator. 12% had the more participatory 'half-moon' seating, rather than 'audience facing the front' style – or were prepared to allow seating to be moved to achieve this effect.

Another off-putting aspect of crematoria is the factory conveyor belt sense of: In – 30 minutes – Out – Next. Some crematoria, again highlighted in our regional listings below, are good at providing either extra long services (Brighton crematorium, for instance, allows 45 minutes, see South region) or cheaper additional sessions (Brighton can give extra time free if available).

Contrary to myth, crematoria do burn all the coffins (which is a pity, we feel that they should be re-used), and the ashes you get back will be the right ones.

Most crematoria are run by local authorities and have very reasonable fees (although these fees are having to be increased in many places so as to finance the cost of new facilities that will meet stringent EC anti-pollution requirements. This will cost the average crematorium at least half a million pounds and as a result some of the local authority ones are begining to sell out to the larger private firms). At present the cheapest one that met our other criteria for inclusion was Putney Vale Crematorium (£83 for 20 minutes – see London region below). The most expensive was Weymouth Crematorium (at £178 for 30 minutes – see South West region below).

Our questionnaire was circulated to all 226 or so crematoria in the country. Our main interest lay in finding out how helpful they were to people organising a funeral without using an undertaker. Of the 52 who replied, a very stuffy four (ie 8% of those who bothered to reply) said that they would deal only with undertakers, not with the family direct. An equally terrible ten (ie 19%) said they would not accept a home-made coffin even if it met all the anti-pollution requirements and if everything were done 'in a dignified manner without disturbance to other mourners or to staff'. These have been excluded from our selective listings below. Only eight crematoria (ie 15%) were prepared to go much further and to accept not only a home-made coffin but also our suggestion of a 'rigid container as long as it is draped with a cloth'. or 'an alternative container, ie a heavy carboard box supported on a piece of pine or plywood and covered with a drape.' These are detailed in the listings. But only three (ie 6%) – Mid-Warwickshire Crematorium (see Leamington Spa, East Midlands region), Carlisle Crematorium (see North West region) and Worthing Crematorium (see

South region) – were willing to take simply a 'body bag suitable for cremation, again supported on a piece of pine or plywood and covered with a drape'.

The following is the full set of questions and answers given by Mr D. H. Thompson, the manager of the **Mid-Warwickshire Crematorium** (address under East Midlands region, below) winner of the Natural Death Handbook award for the Most Helpful Crematorium. You can use these questions to select the ones which are relevant to your own situation when approaching your local crematoria, and so that you can evaluate the extent to which your local findings match the high standards set by our winner:

What is your parent organisation if any? Warwick District Council.

How much time is allotted for each funeral service? 30 minutes.

Can extra time be paid for? Yes.

If so, at what cost per minute? £16 per 30 minutes.

What are your minimum charges for a simple service and cremation? £95 (resident), £118-75 (non-resident).

How much does a casket for cremated remains cost? £7 (wooden), polytainer free.

What is your estimated delivery charge for cremated remains in the UK:
  – by next day courier delivery? £19.
  – by post? £9.

What is your storage charge for cremated remains? None.

Can payments be on account? Yes, in 30 days.

Provided the paperwork is correctly done, and any pacemaker has been removed, will you accept a body directly from the family (no funeral director)? Yes

Is a home made coffin acceptable? Yes.

Is a rigid container acceptable, as long as it is draped with a cloth? Yes.

Is a heavy cardboard box supported on a piece of pine or plywood and covered with a drape acceptable? Yes.

Is a body bag suitable for cremation acceptable, supported on a piece of wood and covered with a drape? Yes.

Can the seating be in the round or horse-shoe shaped? Our seating is half-moon in shape.

Can the seating be rearranged? No.

Can the coffin be easily seen by all the mourners throughout the service? Yes.

Does the set-up allow for some mourners to gather around the coffin in a circle at a point in the service? Yes.

Is the coffin close to floor level during the service (ie can mourners easily see into the coffin or touch the coffin if they so wish)? No.

Can mourners easily file closely past the coffin as they enter or exit, if they so wish? As they exit they can file past.

Does the coffin go directly to the cremator after the service? Yes, but if all three cremators are in use it would have to wait, but normally we have one available if notified in advance that immediate cremation is required.

Can mourners view the coffin entering the cremator? Yes.

How many at one time? Six.

If they so wish, can a few mourners help move the coffin to the cremator at the end of the service? Yes – but not into it. They damaged the cremator last time!

How would you describe the immediate surroundings of the crematorium? Informal woodland.

How would you describe the architecture and feel of the crematorium building and interior? Modern.

In what ways do you feel that your crematorium excels, either in terms of its services, prices, attitudes, practices, architecture or surroundings? Our crematorium must be one of the most flexible and helpful crematoria in the UK. The atmosphere is extremely peaceful and the woodland is home to many forms of wildlife. We do not have memorials and there is no 'commercialism'.

Cemeteries

We wrote to over 500 cemeteries, and of the 65 respondents (some administering several cemeteries) we have included in the regional listings below only the 31 (ie 48%) who will accept a home-made wooden coffin and burial by the family without involving undertakers. Southern Cemetery in Manchester (see North West region) and Brookwood Cemetery in Woking (see South region) allow coffinless burials for Muslims – 'the majority of Muslims are buried in coffins or caskets, but there are a couple of Muslim communities who bury their dead in kaftans and then the casket or boards are placed over the top'. Hastings Cemetery (see South region) would allow not only a home-made coffin but a heavy cardboard box supported on pine or ply. And Highgate Cemetery cautiously 'sees no reason why not to accept most kinds of body containers'. But The Natural Death Handbook Award for the Most Helpful Cemetery goes to **Carlisle Cemetery** in Cumbria (see North West region below). It (and its two nearby associated cemeteries of Upperby and Stanwix) will definitely accept virtually any kind of body container made of biodegrable material. So will the runner-up for this award, the York Cemetery (see North East region). Carlisle Cemetery, however, is also exceptional in its plans for a new wildlife reserve cemetery (see the description of this in the previous chapter). Here are its full answers to our questionnaire, which, as with the crematorium award-winner, provide a high standard by which you can judge your own local equivalents:

Does your cemetery have chapel facilities? Yes.
How long is allotted for each funeral service? There is no time limit.
How much does a plot cost? £159.
How long do grave rights last? 50 years.
What are your charges for a:
    Simple service and burial? £130 (£142-50 for non-residents)
    Maintenance of plot? There is no charge for this.
How is payment made (in advance, on account in X days, by credit card, etc)? In advance.
Provided the paperwork is correctly done, will you accept a body directly from the family? Yes.
Which of the following types of body container are acceptable?
    Home-made coffin? Yes, if made of natural materials.
    Body bag or shroud? Yes, if made of natural materials.
    Body bag with rigid support? Yes.
    Heavy cardboard box supported on pine or ply? Yes.
    Other (please specify)? Basket (wicker), etc.
Can chapel seating be rearranged, eg into a circle or horseshoe? No.
Can the coffin be seen by mourners during the service? Yes.
If they so wish, can mourners help move the coffin towards its final resting place? Yes.

Is a memorial allowed, optional or mandatory? Allowed and optional.

What requirements do you have for a memorial? Any choice of vase or headstone, etc, up to 3' high and 3' 6" wide.

What are the surroundings like? It is a very large formal cemetery, Victorian in appearance and very attractive with parkland trees and fine memorials. Wildlife includes occasional deer, red squirrels, etc. Herons nest annually.

What is the architecture of the chapel? Churchlike, Victorian Gothic.

What does your cemetery offer to help make each service as individual as possible? Open communication channels, few restrictions and ample time.

How do you feel that your cemetery excels, either in terms of its service, prices, attitudes, practices, architecture or surroundings? All Carlisle cemeteries are considered well maintained and spiritually uplifting. Our management attitude is flexible and orientated to satisfying people using our services, not placing restrictions in their way.

Contrast this approach with the Southern Cemetery in Manchester which has a rule booklet of 56 pages. Articles it prohibits on graves include wooden crosses ('except those supplied by the city council'), sea shells, rockery and other stones. Those bringing the coffin to the cemetery in other than a funeral director's hearse must transfer it at the entrance gate to a wheeled bier. Not unreasonably, it also wants to be notified if the coffin size will exceed 6' 4" by 22" width, 15" depth (the width measurement must allow for any protruding handles. 'It is difficult and may be dangerous to alter the width of the grave once it has been excavated'). There are occasional stories in the various funeral journals of the embarrassment felt by funeral directors and priests when the coffin will not fit the grave.

Another strong runner-up to Carlisle Cemetery for our award is the Mold Cemetery in Clywd (see Wales region). Not only is it the cheapest (£90 includes the plot, the digging, the burial and the minister) but it also sounds one of the friendliest. Tony Davies writes: 'We live within the cemetery confines and people are able to discuss their grief at any time of the day and night. We have lived here for 16 years. We listen to people and have real feeling and empathy for them. It can be easier for people to talk to a stranger and express their feelings more fully than they would to their own families. We find once the inital grief is overcome we become firm friends. Death is a natural thing which causes grief to everyone concerned. It is terrible to see people suffering grief but it is such a wonderful thing to see life once again taking over and smiles and laughter returning.'

Just as house prices vary by region, so too do the rights to a burial plot – from £85 at Mold Cemetery to £2,200 at Highgate Cemetery (see London region). The average plot price nationwide (for those who met our home-made coffin criteria) was £291 (for an average of 72 years). However the price within a cemetery could vary widely too: Southern Cemetery in Manchester's cheapest plot was £190, its most expensive £2,315. Some also charge non-residents either extra or double the price; or, in the case of East Sheen and its associated cemeteries, three times the price.

Remember to insist, if buying burial rights, that ownership is put in the name of the surviving partner, to ensure their eventual right to be buried together.

As well as the plot, there is also the cost of digging the grave and the burial. The range here was from £5, again at Mold Cemetery, to £510 at Highgate Cemetery, with an average of £183. Maintenance was normally either not charged or optional, with prices ranging from £15 per annum to £82 per annum at Woking Cemetery. Woking (see South region) is, incidentally, another example of a cemetery with a pleasantly liberal and enlightened approach to memorials, with virtually any design accepted.

Good Funeral Guide Regional Listings

Unless otherwise stated, you can assume that all the funeral directors in the listings that follow will sell you a fully-fitted coffin for under £150 without your having to use any other of their other services, and that all the cemeteries and crematoria accept home-made coffins (if they also accept just body bags, etc, this will be stated). Listings are by region, and then by town within the region. If you wish to nominate others not included here for the next edition of (or updating sheets for) this book or for one of our awards, please write to The Natural Death Handbook (20 Heber Road, London NW2 6AA, tel 081 208 2853, fax 081 452 6434) with your experience of using their services, and including as many of the kind of details here that you can find out.

The North West

Comprising Cumbria, Lancashire, Greater Manchester, Merseyside and Cheshire.

• **Bolton**: Gibsons Funeral Service, 342 St Helens Road, Bolton, Lancs (tel 0204 655869). Cheapest fully-fitted coffin only: £45 (delivery locally £10, nationally negotiable). Cold storage only: yes, £10 per day. Body transport only: yes, no charge stated. Advice for d-i-y: yes, £10 per hour. Basic funeral: £360. Pre-paid plan: none. Full horse-drawn funerals on request, from £450 to £850. Joint winner of The Natural Death Handbook Award for the Most Helpful Funeral Director.

• **Bolton**: The St Helens and Bolton council (tel 0744 24061 and ask for reception) have an agreement with the Co-op for a basic funeral service for residents costing £492 (incl. of burial) or £486 (incl. of cremation). It can be booked through the Co-op in St Helens (tel 0744 23675) or through the Co-op in Newton-le-Willows (tel 0925 226257).

• **Carlisle** Cemetery, Richardson Street, Carlisle CA2 6AL (tel 0228 25022). Plot (50 years): £159. Digging, burying and use of chapel: £130. Maintenance not charged. Victorian Gothic church-like chapel. Time for service: no limit. Also would accept: shroud, body bag, body bag with rigid support, heavy cardboard box and baskets (wicker). Grounds: parkland trees, wildlife – deer, red squirrels, heron's nest. Winner of The Natural Death Handbook Most Helpful Cemetery Award (see further details above). Also administers Stanwix Cemetery, 110 Kingstown Road, Stanwix, Carlisle CA3 OAT and Upperby Cemetery, 15 Manor Road, Upperby, Carlisle CA2 4LH.

• **Carlisle** Crematorium, Richardson St, Carlisle CA2 6AL (tel 0228 25022). Price: £146. Time allotted: 40 mins, extra time free. Also would accept rigid containers as long as draped with a cloth; and 'alternative' containers, eg a cardboard box, if supported on pine or plywood and draped in a cloth; and body bag suitable for cremation, again supported as above. Grounds: 12 monthly gardens, themed to seasons, outer native wood screen.

• **Crewe** Crematorium, Market Street, Crewe CW1 2NA (tel 0270 212643). Price: £92. Time allotted: 20 mins, extra time £1 per minute. Situated in cemetery grounds.

• **Lytham St. Annes**, Park Cemetery, Regent Avenue, Lytham St. Annes FY8 4AB (tel 0253 735429). Plot (100 years): £167. Digging, burial and use of chapel: £100. Maintenance £31-50 per annum, with plants. 1960s chapel. Time for service: 30 mins. Grounds: formal. Memorials: natural stone up to 3ft tall.

• **Lytham St. Annes**: Park Crematorium, Regent Avenue, Lytham St. Annes FY8 4AB (tel 0253 735429). Price: £115, Time allotted: 30 mins, extra time free if booked in advance. Situated within cemetery grounds.

• **Manchester**: Southern Cemetery, Barlow Moor Road, Chorlton, Manchester M21 2GL (tel 061 881 2208). Plot (50 years): from £190 to £2,315 (from £365 non-residents). Digging, burial and use of chapel: £300 (£425 non-residents). Lawn cemetery with no charge for maintenance. Church-like chapel. Time for service: 20 mins. Also accept (for Muslims): shroud, body bag, body bag with rigid support. Grounds: wooded.

• **Manchester**: S. Wellens and Sons Ltd, 121 Long St, Middleton, Manchester M24 3DW (tel 061 643 2677). Cheapest fully-fitted coffin only: £100 (delivery locally 'probably free'). Cold storage only: yes, £3 per day. Body transport only: yes, £75. Advice for d-i-y: yes, £30-£50 per hour. Basic funeral: £490. 'We will reduce our fees to help needy families.' Pre-paid plan: our own.

• **Penrith** Cemetery, Beacon Edge, Penrith, CA11 7RZ (tel 0768 62152). Plot (100 years): £125 residents (£250 non-residents). Burial and use of chapel: from £28. Maintenance not charged. Chapel is church-like, late Victorian and sandstone. Time for service: 30 mins. Grounds: formal lawns etc. Also administers Appleby, Alston, Nenthead & Garrigill Cemeteries.

• **Preston** Cemetery, New Hall Lane, Preston (tel 0772 794585). Lawn cemetery plot (75 years): £290. Digging and burial: £168. Both fees doubled for non-residents. Time for service: unlimited. Grounds: wooded and Victorian in the old cemetery, bleakly formal grid in the new. Memorials of almost any kind allowed, except wooden crosses.

• **Preston** Crematorium, Newhall Lane, Preston PR1 4SY (tel 0772 792391). Price: £105. Time allotted: 30 mins, extra time free of charge if available and booked. Also would accept 'alternative' containers, eg a cardboard box, if supported on pine or plywood and draped in a cloth. Grounds: open parkland at front, woodlands at rear.

• **Preston**: United Co-op Ltd funeral department, 550 Blackpool Road, Preston PR2 1HY (tel 0772 729057). Cheapest fully-fitted coffin only: £120 (delivery locally free). Cold storage only: yes, £10 per day. Body transport only: yes, £40 (£80 hearse). Advice for d-i-y: yes, £20 per hour. Basic funeral: £560. Pre-paid plan: Co-op Funeral Bonds. Parent company: United Norwest Co-operatives. Branches in Southport (tel 0704 213530) and Chorley (tel 0257 266316).

• **Stockport** Crematorium, 31a Buxton Road, Heaviley, Stockport SK2 6LS (tel 061 480 5221). Price: £111-30, £130 after 4 pm. Time allotted: 30 mins, extra time £47 per 30 mins. Grounds: walled gardens, formal lawns, rockeries, within cemetery.

• **Wigan** Cemetery, Cemetery Road, Lower Ince, Wigan (tel 0942 866455). No plots left, but they also manage eight other cemeteries, some with 99.9 year plots from £106 to £160. Digging and burial: £132-50. No maintenance charge. Grounds: lawns.

• **Wigan** Crematorium, Cemetery Road, Lower Ince, Wigan (tel 0942 866455 or 828507). Price: £120. Time allotted: 30 mins, extra time free. Grounds: surrounded by burial plots.

• **Wigan** Municipal Funeral Service, organised by Registrar of Cemeteries and Crematorium, Trencherfield Mill, Wallgate, Wigan WN3 4EF (tel 0942 828507). Basic funeral if deceased a resident, including cremation, doctors' fees and minister's fee: £465 (burial £469). The service is booked through either of two undertakers: Banks & Son (Pemberton, Wigan, tel 0942 222156) or Abbey Funeral Service (Tyldesley, Manchester, tel 0942 891331).

The North East

Comprising Northumbria, Tyne and Wear, Durham, Cleveland, North, West and South Yorkshire, Humberside and Lincolnshire.

• **Dewsbury**: George Brooke Ltd funeral directors, 27 Bradford Road, Dewsbury (tel 0924

454476). Cheapest fully-fitted coffin only: £195 (delivery locally £25, nationally 65p per mile). This £195 price would normally exclude the firm from this Handbook, but it is redeemed by its estimable fully-itemised price list. Cold storage only: yes, £7-50 per day. Body transport only: yes, £25. Advice for d-i-y: yes. Basic funeral: £350. Pre-paid plan: 'our own, with a building society.'

• **Durham** Crematorium, South Road, Durham DH1 3TQ (tel 091 384 8677). Price: £88.80 (non-residents £121). Time allotted: 30 mins, extra time £20 for half hour max. Grounds: open parkland.

• **Grimsby**: Kettle Ltd funeral directors, 135 Granville St, Grimsby (tel 0472 355395 and 0507 600710). Cheapest fully-fitted coffin only: £90 (delivery locally £27-50, nationally 42p per mile over 15 miles). Cold storage only: yes, price undecided. Body transport only: yes, from £33. Advice for d-i-y: yes, fee undecided. Basic funeral: £338. Pre-paid plan: Chosen Heritage. 'Independent family business. We have supplied coffins to families for their own use.' Branch in Louth.

• **Harrogate**: W. Bowers funeral director, Birstwith Road, Hampsthwaite, Harrogate HG3 2EU (tel 0423 770258). Cheapest fully-fitted coffin only: £135 (delivery £45 locally, nationally by mileage). Cold storage only: yes, £10 per day. Body transport only: yes, £25. Advice for d-i-y: yes, £10 per hour. Basic funeral: £670 (incl. fees to crematorium, doctors and clergy). Pre-paid plans: Chosen Heritage and Golden Charter. Member of SAIF. Excellent bereavement booklet and unusually comprehensive help and advice to the bereaved.

• **Leeds**: coffins and funeral supplies from Green Undertakings, orders through 79a Gloucester Road, Bristol BS7 8AS (tel c/o Bristol 0272 246248; fax 0272 248065; can be slow; if problems and urgent try also via Natural Death Centre 081 208 2853). Flatpack coffins from £35; fitted coffin £95; body bag £15; handles £6 for 6, name plate £5 also coffin lining material and lowering webbing for burials. Winner of The Natural Death Handbook Award for the Most Helpful Funeral Suppliers (see above under Coffin Makers).

• **Leeds**: Lawns Wood Crematorium. Otley Road, Adel, Leeds LS16 6AH (tel 0904 673188). Price: £130. Time allotted: 30 mins, extra time £130. Grounds: formal gardens.

• **Middlesborough**: Teesside Crematorium, Middlesborough Borough Council, Public Protection Dept, Vancouver House, PO Box 68, Central Mews, Gurney St, Middlesborough TS1 1QS (tel 0642 245432 ext. 4227). Price: £145. Time allotted: 30 mins, extra time free in special cases. Grounds: landscaped grounds, trees, shrubs, formal gardens.

• **Stamford**: R. J. Scholes funeral directors, 18 Empingham Road, Stamford, Lincolnshire PE9 2RH (tel 0780 63092). Cheapest fully-fitted coffin only: £145 (delivery prices by negotiation). Cold storage only: yes, price negotiable. Body transport only: yes, price negotiable. Advice for d-i-y: yes, price negotiable. Basic funeral: £481. '5th generation family owner/operator.'

• **York** Cemetery, The Gatehouse, Cemetery Road, York YO1 5AJ (tel 0904 610578 day, 0904 640949 evening). 'We will take any body container from body bag to home-made coffin, as long as it is all done with dignity.' Plot (99 years): £160 lawn, Victorian section £200. Interment fee £45, plus they can supply the details of three self-employed grave diggers who charge between £70 and £110 for their services. Maintenance: £10 to £25 per annum. Grade IIA listed classical chapel, prize-winning decoration, warm feel. Time for service: up to one and a half hours if needed. Grounds: formal, wild, wooded. Ecological management plan to encourage wildlife. Memorials should be large and Victorian in style.

• **York**: City of York Crematorium, Bishopthorpe Road, Middlethorpe, York YO2 1QD (tel 0904 706096). Price: £123. Time allotted: 30 mins, extra time free by prior arrangement. Grounds: 'plenty of trees, nothing too formal.'

Wales
Comprising Clwyd, Gwynedd, Powys, Dyfed, Gwent, and West, Mid and South Glamorgan.

• **Aberdare**: Llwydcoed Crematorium, Aberdare, Mid-Glamorgan CF44, ODJ (tel 0685 874115). Price: £94. Time allotted: 25 mins, extra time free in exceptional circumstances. Grounds: formal gardens, ornamental pools, trees.

• **Mold** Public Cemetery, Alexandra Road, Mold, Clwyd CH7 1HJ (tel 0352 753820). Plot incl. burial and minister's fee: £90. Plots cannot be purchased in advance. No chapel. Grounds: town cemetery with flower borders and trees, surrounded by football field and playing ground. Memorials: to be made of stone with reverent wording. Friendly management (see earlier in this chapter). 'Family mourners often lower the coffin.'

West Midlands
Comprising Shropshire, Staffordshire, West Midlands, Hereford and Worcester and Gloucestershire.

• **Dudley**: Gornal Wood Crematorium, Chase Road, Gornal Wood, Dudley DY3 2RL (tel 0384 252665). Price: £134. Time allotted: 20 mins, extra time £25 per 30 mins. Grounds: formal gardens.

• **Dudley**: J. Freeman & Son funeral director, 95 St Peter's Road, Netherton, Dudley DY2 9HN (tel 0384 252943). Cheapest fully-fitted coffin only: £80 (no delivery except as part of basic funeral). Cold storage only: no. Body transport only: no. Advice for d-i-y: yes, £10 per hour. Basic funeral: £300. Pre-paid plan: clients' account at bank. 'As a reader in the Church of England, I could and frequently do conduct the funeral service myself.'

• **Newcastle-under-Lyme** Crematorium, Chatterly Close, Bradwell, Newcastle ST5 8LE (tel 0782 635498). Price: £110. Any container that meets Federation of British Cremation Authority regulations. Can accommodate up to 60 people to watch coffin entering the cremator. A family member may push the burner ignite button. Time allotted: 30 mins, extra time free if booked in advance. Grounds: formal gardens, seasonal monthly gardens.

• **Redditch** Crematorium, Bordesley Lane, Redditch B97 6RR (tel 0527 62174). Price: £115 up to 9.30 am and £150 after 10.00 am. Time allotted: as requested, extra time charged at discretionary rate. Would also accept a rigid container; or 'alternative' containers, eg a cardboard box, if supported on pine or plywood and draped in a cloth. Grounds: informal gardens set in rolling countryside.

• **Shrewsbury** Crematorium, Emstrey, Shrewsbury (tel 0743 356974/359833). Price: £97.50. Time allotted: 40 mins, no extra time allowed. Prepared to discuss other body containers with family. Grounds: formal gardens, wooded backdrop.

• **Stourbridge** Crematorium, South Road, Stourbridge DY8 3RQ (tel 0384 372403). Price: £134. Time allotted: 20 mins, extra time £25 per 30 mins. Grounds: formal, within cemetery grounds.

• **Worcester** Crematorium, Astwood Cemetery, Astwood Road, Worcester WR3 8HA (tel 0905 22632). Price: £130. Time allotted: 30 mins, no extra time allowed. Grounds: semi-formal, within large cemetery, many large trees.

East Midlands

Comprising Derbyshire, Nottinghamshire, Leicestershire, Warwickshire, Northampton-shire, Bedfordshire, Oxfordshire and Buckingshamshire.

• **Amersham**: Chilterns Crematorium, Whielden Lane, Amersham HP7 OND (tel 0494 724263). Price £120. Time allotted: 30 mins, no extra time possible. Grounds: woodlands, lawns, roses. 'We like to think we are fairly flexible.'

• **Chesterfield** & District Joint Crematorium, Chesterfield Road, Brimington, Chesterfield (tel 0246 234346). Price £103. Time allotted: 30 mins, extra time £14-40. Grounds: formal gardens.

• **High Wycombe**: G. Smith Ltd, 7 The Green, Woburn Green, High Wycombe HP10 OEE (tel 06285 23566). Cheapest fully-fitted coffin only: £120 (delivery locally free, nationally 70p a mile). Cold storage only: yes, £10 per day. Body transport only: yes, mileage rate. Advice for d-i-y: yes, £50 to £60 per hour. Basic funeral: £540. Pre-paid plan: £540.

• **Leicester**: Gilroes Crematorium, Groby Road, Leicester LE3 9QG (tel 0533 527382). Price: £100 resident, £110 non-resident. Time allotted: 30 mins, extra time £26 per 30 mins. Situated within cemetery grounds.

• **Leamington Spa**: Mid-Warwickshire Crematorium, Oakley Wood, Bishops Tachbrook, Leamington Spa CV33 9QP (tel 0926 651418. Price: £95 (£118-75 for non-residents). Time allotted: 30 mins, extra time £16 per 30 mins. Also would accept rigid containers as long as draped with a cloth, or 'alternative' containers, eg a cardboard box, or body bags, if supported with a piece of pine or plywood and covered in a drape. Grounds: informal woodland. Winner of The Natural Death Handbook Most Helpful Crematorium Award.

• **Leighton Buzzard**: Andrew Capp funeral directors, 12 Orchard Lane, Stewkley, Leighton Buzzard, Beds. LU7 OHS (tel 0525 240205). Cheapest fully-fitted coffin only: £120 (delivery locally free, nationally 20p per mile). Cold storage only: no. Body transport only: yes, £50. Advice for d-i-y: yes, £10 per hour. Basic funeral: £300. 'Personal service and keen prices.'

• **Luton** Church Cemetery, 26 Crowley Great Road, Luton (tel 0582 22874). Plot (99 years): £124 (incl. opening grave and burial fee: £236-50). Maintenance: £45 per annum. Non-denominational chapel. Time for service: no limit. Grounds: garden and wooded.

• **Nottingham**: coffin maker Vic Fearn Ltd, Crabtree Mill, Hempshill, Bulwell, near Nottingham (tel 0602 271907). The firm does artist-painted coffins using water-based paints (which can be cremated) from about £500. Mr J. D. Gill has arranged that for orders coming via the Natural Death Centre the public could also be supplied with a conventional veneered chipboard coffin, fitted with handles and lined, or a rather fine solid wood coffin made from recycled scrap pallets made to their own design.

• **Oxford Cemetery**, The Lodge, Wolvercote Cemetery, Banbury Road, Oxford OX2 8EE (tel 0865 513962). Administers four cemeteries. Plot (75 years) £185. Digging & burial: £90. Both fees doubled to non-residents. Maintenance if wanted: £30 p.a. Victorian chapel. Grounds: formal. Memorials: more or less any design, any height (lawn graves up to 3' 6").

• **Rushden**: A. Abbott & Sons funeral directors, Bedford Road, Rushden NN10 OLZ (tel 0933 312142). Cheapest fully-fitted coffin only: £75 (delivery locally free, nationally by mileage). Cold storage only: yes, no charge. Body transport only: yes, £100. Advice for d-i-y: yes, charge to be arranged. Basic funeral: £749 cremation, burial £584, both prices including disbursements. Pre-paid plan: Golden Charter. Member of SAIF. Counselling and services of a solicitor free.

East Anglia
Comprising Norfolk, Suffolk, Essex, Cambridgeshire and Hertfordshire.

• **Cambridge** City Cemetery, Newmarket Road, Cambridge, Cambs (tel 02205 2210). Plot (50 years) plus burial: £207 residents, £415 non-residents. Time for service: 30 mins. Grounds: formal.

• **Clacton** Cemetery, Burrs Road, Clacton-on-Sea (tel 0255 423416 or 831108). Plot (99 years): £244 (includes digging and burial; chapel with organ, fee £29 extra). Maintenance: £18 to £22 per annum. Church-like chapel. Time for service: 45 mins. Grounds: formal.

• **Colchester** Cemetery, Mersea Road, Colchester CO2 8RU (tel 0206 573252). Plot (25 years, renewable up to 75 years): from £84 to £151. Digging, burial and use of chapel: £132 (£155 non-residents). Maintenance £13-50 per annum, lawn area free. Time for service: 30 mins. Grounds: wooded and lawns. Memorials: hard natural stone or granite.

• **Colchester** Crematorium, Mersea Road, Colchester CO2 8RU (tel 0206 573252). Price: £126.50. Time allotted: 30 mins, no extra time allowed. Grounds: 9 acres of trees, shrubs, rose gardens.

• **Harwich**: Dovercourt Cemetery, Main Road, Dovercourt, Harwich (tel 0255 503652 or 831108). Plot (99 years): £244 (includes digging and burial; chapel with organ, fee £35 extra). Maintenance £18 to £22 per annum. Church-like chapel. Time for service: 45 mins. Grounds: formal.

• **Kirby Cross** Cemetery, Holland Road, Kirby Cross (tel 0255 831108). Plot (99 years): £244 (includes digging and burial). Maintenance: £18 to £22 per annum. No chapel. Grounds: formal.

• **Norwich**: Peter Taylor funeral services, 85 Unthank Road, Norwich NR2 2PE (tel 0603 760787). Cheapest fully-fitted coffin only: £65 (delivery locally £10, nationally 65p per mile). Cold storage only: yes, £10. Body transport only: yes, £50. Advice for d-i-y: yes, £25 per hour. Basic funeral: £440. Pre-paid plans Chosen Heritage and Windsor Life (regular contributions, free choice of funeral). Parent company: Anglia Funeral Services Ltd. Eight branches in Norfolk and Suffolk with same prices and policies. Phone for details. A horse-drawn hearse can also be supplied from £500.

• **Radlett**: Pets Meadow (possible source of coffins), Harper Lodge Farm, Harper Lane, Radlett, Herts WD7 7HU (tel 0923 852470). Pet cemetery that may supply adult coffins fully fitted and delivered anywhere for £80 (also do caskets for ashes).

• **St Albans**: Phillips Funeral Services, 68 Alma Road, St Albans, Herts AL1 3BL (tel 0727 851006). Cheapest fully-fitted coffin only: £97-50 (delivery locally £85, nationally £1-50 per mile). Cold storage only: yes, £ 25 per day. Body transport only: yes, £85. Advice for d-i-y: yes, £30 per hour. Basic funeral: £550. Pre-paid plan: Golden Charter. Member of SAIF.

• **Saxmundham**: Tony Brown's funeral service, The Funeral Parlour, Chantry Road, Saxmundham, Suffolk IP17 1DJ (tel 0728 603108). See the description by Libby Purves earlier in this chapter. Would not supply coffin only. Cold storage only: yes, no charge. Body transport only: yes (mileage rate). Advice for d-i-y: no. Basic funeral: price not stated. Pre-paid plan: no, 'Privately if required, but I do not believe in it.' Would not give price breakdowns over the phone 'because I have had other firms phone in for this', but would in writing. 'I conduct a personal family business I like doing and I object to all

unnecessary red tape. I give a very good Christian service and treat everybody the same unless they want something elaborate. People are important in my work and I have built up a busy business by treating them as such.'
• **Weeley** (Essex): Weeley Crematorium, Colchester Road, Weeley CO16 9JP (tel 0255 831108). Price: £128. Time allotted: 45 mins, 'extra time unnecessary'. Grounds: formal gardens.

The South West
Comprising Avon, Somerset, Dorset, Devon and Cornwall.

• **Bath**: Haycombe Cemetery, Whiteway Road, Bath BA2 2RQ (tel 0225 423682). Plot (75 years): £165 (for advance reservation, an extra 50%). Non-residents double fee. Digging and burial: £95. Maintenance and planting, if wanted: £60 p.a. Time for service: one hour. Grounds: formal. Memorials must be of natural quarried stone.
• **Bournemouth**: North Cemetery, Strouden Avenue, Bournemouth BH8 9HX (tel 0202 526238). Plot (50 years): from £153 to £234. Digging and burial: £173. All fees doubled to non-residents. Maintenance from £27 per annum. Church-like chapel. Time for service: 20 mins. Grounds: formal. Also administers: Kinson Cemetery, South Kinson Drive, Bournemouth; East Cemetery, Gloucester Road, Bournemouth; and one at Wimborne Road, Charminster Road, Bournemouth.
• **Bournemouth** Crematorium, Strouden Avenue, Bournemouth BH8 9HX (tel 0202 526238). Price: £142.50. Time allotted: 30 mins, extra time £142-50. Also would accept rigid containers as long as draped with a cloth, or 'alternative' containers, eg a cardboard box, if supported with a piece of pine or plywood and covered with a drape. Grounds: formal gardens.
• **Bristol** General Cemetery Company, The East Lodge, Arnos Vale, Bath Road, Bristol BS4 3EW (tel 0272 713294). Plot (60 years): £450. Digging, burial and use of chapel: £250. Maintenance: £25 per annum. Grade II listed church-like chapel. Time for service: 20 mins. Grounds: Victorian Arcadian garden, unique woodland setting and a lot of character from 20 listed buildings.
• **Dorchester** Cemetery, 31a Weymouth Avenue, Dorchester DT1 2EN (tel 0305 263900; mobile 0836 280840). Plot (100 years) £220. Digging, burial and interment fee: £135. Maintenance not charged. Victorian chapel with pews and stained glass window. Time allowed for service: flexible, if informed in advance. Built in 1856, the cemetery has traditional Victorian buildings set amongst winding paths, mostly grassed areas with yew trees. Memorials up to 6ft high.
• **Paignton** Cemetery, Colley End Road, Paignton (tel 0803 327768). Details same as Torquay, see below.
• **Plymouth**: Efford Cemetery, Efford Road, Efford, Plymouth (tel 0752 264857). Also administers Weston Mill Cemetery, Ferndale Road, Weston Mill, Plymouth (tel 0752 264837). Plot (25 or 100 years) from £78 to £375. Digging & burial: from £174. Maintenance if wanted: £17-63 p.a. Church-like chapel. Grounds: formal, plus some wooded area. Memorials: quarry stone only, area and height restrictions.
• **Poole** Crematorium, Gravel Hill, Poole BH17 9BQ (tel 0202 602582). Price: £132-20. Time allotted: 30 mins, extra time £132-20. Grounds: formal gardens and woodland, interior floral court.
• **Torquay** Cemetery, Hele Road, Torquay TQ2 7QG (tel 0803 327768). Plot (100 years)

£176 (doubled to non-residents). Digging and burial: £142. Use of chapel: £33. No maintenance charges. Non-denominational church-like chapel. Time for service: only limited by availability. Grounds: formal. Memorials: natural stone, inscriptions rarely disagreed with.

• **Torquay** Crematorium, Hele Road, Torquay TQ2 7QG (tel 0803 327768/329977. Price: £116. Time allotted: 20 mins, double time allowed at no extra charge if available. Grounds: formal gardens.

• **Weymouth** Crematorium, Quibo Lane, Weymouth DT4 0RR (tel 0305 786984. Price: £178. Time allotted: 30 mins, extra time £15 per half hour. Also would accept rigid containers as long as draped with a cloth, and perhaps others, if seen first. Grounds: formal garden.

• **Weymouth**: Stocking Funeral Service, 22 Crescent St, Weymouth DT4 7BX (tel 0305 785915). Cheapest fully-fitted coffin only: £100 (delivery locally £25, nationally £25 plus £1 per mile over 20 miles). Cold storage only: yes, approx. £10 per day. Body transport only: yes, £70. Advice for d-i-y: yes, £15 per hour. Basic funeral: £425. Pre-paid plan: Perfect Assurance Funeral Trust. Parent company: Grassby & Sons Ltd.

• **Winscombe**: C. V. Gower & Son funeral director, The Square, Winscombe, Avon BS25 1BS (tel 093484 2945 or 2187). Cheapest fully-fitted coffin only: £125 (delivery locally £10). Cold storage only: yes, £5. Body transport only: yes, price by distance. Advice for d-i-y: yes, no charge. Basic funeral: £650. Member of SAIF.

• **Yeovil** Cemetery, Preston Road, Yeovil (tel 0935 23742). Plot (75 years): £169. Digging, burial and use of chapel: £164. Maintenance: £15-32 per annum. Church-like chapel. Time for service: 30 mins. Grounds: formal garden.

• **Yeovil** Crematorium, Bunford Lane, Yeovil (tel 0935 76718). Price £145. Time allotted: 25 mins, no extra time allowed. Grounds: parkland.

The South

Comprising Wiltshire, Berkshire, Surrey, Kent, Hampshire, West Sussex and East Sussex.

• **Basingstoke** Crematorium (Carpenters Wood), c/o Deborah Hinton, 22 Westmoreland Place, London SW1V 4AE (tel 071 828 3965) opening '94, with unusually good design (see earlier discussion) and woodland setting, and very helpful to d-i-y families. Price: £225. Time allotted: 40 mins, extra time £1 per min. Also would accept any kind of body container including body bag as long as it meets pollution requirements and protects public decency. Flexible seating, coffin close to floor and visible throughout service, mourners able to file past coffin.

• **Brighton** Crematorium, Woodvale, Lewes Road, Brighton BN2 3QB (tel 0273 604020). Price: £130. Time allotted: 45 mins, extra 45 mins allowed free of charge. Also would accept rigid containers as long as draped with a cloth. Grounds: wooded valley, stream, waterfall, rockeries, gardens.

• **Eastbourne** Crematorium, Hide Hollow Langney, Eastbourne BN23 8AE (tel 0323 761093). Price: £145. Time allotted: 30 mins, extra time £145. Grounds: formal gardens.

• **Hastings** Borough Cemetery, The Ridge, Hastings TN34 2AE (tel 0424 721204). Plot (50 years): £140. Digging, burial and use of chapel: £190. Maintenance: £30 per annum. Modern church-like chapel. Time for service: 20 mins. Also would accept: heavy cardboard box supported on pine or ply. Grounds: formal, lawned, 80 acres, unrivalled views over Sussex countryside. Headstone optional, not more than 3ft high.

• **Hastings** Crematorium, The Ridge, Hastings TN34 2AE (tel 0424 721204). Price: £118. Time allotted: 20 mins, extra time limited to 20 mins (£118). Also would accept rigid containers as long as draped with a cloth, or 'alternative' containers, eg a cardboard box, if supported with a piece of pine or plywood and covered with a drape. Grounds: lawned or semi-wooded.

• **Haywards Heath**: P. & S. Gallagher funeral directors, Fraser House, Triangle Road, Haywards Heath, West Sussex RH16 4HW (tel 0444 451166). Cheapest fully-fitted coffin only: £93 (delivery locally £15, nationally at cost). No cold storage facilities, only embalming. Body transport only: Yes, £40 (£70 hearse). Advice for d-i-y people: Yes, negotiable fee. Basic funeral: £525. Pre-paid plan: Private plan, client retaining fees.

• **Maidstone**: Vinters Park Crematorium, Bearsted Road, Maidstone ME14 5LG (tel 0622 38172). Price: £130. Time allotted: 30 mins, no extra time allowed. Grounds: formal and wooded.

• **Morden**: North East Surrey Crematorium, Lower Morden Lane, Morden SM4 4NU (tel 081 337 4835). Price £104. Time allotted: 30 mins, extra time £60 for 30 mins. Coffin must meet Environmental Protection Act requirements. Grounds: formal gardens.

• **Portchester** Crematorium, Upper Cornaway Lane, Portchester (tel 0329 822533). Price: £121. Time allotted: 30 mins, extra time negotiable. Grounds: gardens.

• **Portsmouth**: Mayfields funeral directors, 90 Elm Grove, Southsea, Portsmouth (tel 0705 875575). Cheapest fully-fitted coffin only: £75 (delivery locally £5, within 20 miles £10). Cold storage only: yes, £5-75. Body transport only: yes, £25. Advice for d-i-y: yes, £25. Basic funeral: £399. Pre-paid plan: Rest Assured life assurance policy. Aims to be unostentatious. New in 1992. Has a bereavement centre with trained counsellors.

• **Salisbury**: H. A. Harold & Son, funeral directors, 77 Estcourt Road, Salisbury, Wilts SP1 3AX (tel 0722 321177). Cheapest fully-fitted coffin only: £50 (free delivery locally, nationally by mileage). Cold storage only: yes, minimal, negotiable charge. Body transport only: yes, £65. Advice for d-i-y: yes, £40 management fee. Basic funeral: £450. Pre-paid plan: Dignity in Destiny. Parent company: Plantsbrook Group. Manager is an experienced bereavement counsellor.

• **Swanley**: Doves funeral directors, 35 Station Road, Swanley, Kent BR8 8ES (tel 0322 669000. Cheapest fully-fitted coffin only: £85 (delivery locally £25, nationally from 80p per mile). Cold storage only: yes, £15 per day. Body transport only: yes, for a Daimler Hearse £150. Advice for d-i-y: yes, no charge. Basic funeral: £440. Pre-paid plan: Golden Charter. Branches in Maidstone (tel 0622 688662), Bromley (tel 081 460 1888), Orpington (tel 0689 870030), Sevenoaks (tel 0732 740444), Staplehurst (tel 0580 892125), Larkfield (tel 0732 871188) and Sittingbourne (tel 0795 431300). 'We have grown as a family-run business to eight branches within four years.'

• **Uckfield**: Fuller Scott funeral director, The Wakelyns, Uckfield, Sussex TN22 1AJ (tel 0865 763241). Cheapest fully-fitted coffin only: £86-50 (delivery locally £12, nationally £80). Cold storage only: yes, £5 per day. Body transport only: yes, £1-20 per mile normally. Advice for d-i-y: yes, free in my office. Basic funeral: £580. Pre-paid plan: Perfect Assurance and Chosen Heritage.

• **Woking**: The Brookwood Cemetery, Woking, Surrey GU24 OBL (tel 0483 472222). 'Some of the Muslim communities bury their dead here in kaftans. We would accept most kinds of container if funeral dignified.' Plots (50 years): from £750 to £1050. Digging and burial: £200. Maintenance £82 per annum. No chapel. Vast 420 acre cemetery with beautiful trees, many areas overgrown, Victorian monuments. Virtually any design of memorial accepted up to 3ft.

• **Wokingham**: Easthampstead Park Crematorium, Nine Mile Ride, Wokingham, Berkshire RG11 3DW (tel 0344 420314). Price: £150. Time allotted: 30 mins, extra half hour £70. Also would accept rigid containers as long as draped with a cloth. Grounds: 22 acres of landscaped gardens.

• **Worthing** Crematorium, Horsham Road, Findon BN14 ORQ (tel 0903 872678). Price: £145. Time allotted: 40 mins, extra time free, if possible, otherwise £20 for 40 mins. Also would accept rigid containers as long as draped with a cloth, or 'alternative' containers, eg a cardboard box, or body bags, if supported with a piece of pine or plywood and covered with a drape. Grounds: wildlife sanctuary.

London region
Including Middlesex and immediate surrounds, though see also South region.

• **H. J. Bent & Co**, 343 Ladbroke Grove, London W10 6HA (tel 081 969 1170).Cheapest very basic coffin only: £30 (delivery negotiable). Gave incomplete information as follows: Cold storage only: yes, no charge stated. Body transport only: yes, no charge stated. Advice for d-i-y: yes, 'probably', no charge stated. Basic funeral: £600. Pre-paid plan: own scheme. Branches in NW8 (tel 071 723 1186) and W12 (081 743 3338).

• **Camberwell New Cemetery**, Brenchley Gardens, London SE23 3RD (tel 071 639 3121). Lawn grave plot (50 years) £264. Digging and burial: £316. Prices trebled for non-residents. Maintenance not charged. Church-like chapel. Time for service: 30 mins. Grounds: formal gardens. Natural stone memorials up to 6' 6".

• **Chingford Mount Cemetery**, 121 Old Church Road, Chingford, London E4 6ST (tel 081 524 5030). Plot (75 years) £270, residents only. Digging, burial and headstone foundation: £175. Grass-cutting not charged. No chapel. Grounds: semi-wooded, traditional lawn.

• **City of London Cemetery**, Aldersbrook Road, London E12 5DQ (tel 081 580 2151). Plot (75 years): £234 (lawn graves only). Digging and burial: £402. £115 reduction for residents. Optional maintenance £35 p.a. Victorian chapel. Time for service: 20 minutes. Grounds: formal. Memorials: marble or granite, 3ft high, 2ft wide.

• **T. Cribb & Sons** funeral directors, 112 Rathbone St, Canning Town, London E16 1JQ (tel 071 476 1855). Cheapest fully-fitted coffin only: £120 approx. (delivery locally free, nationally by mileage). Cold storage only: yes, no charge for reasonable time span. Body transport only: yes, price depending on time of removal, distance, etc. Advice for d-i-y: yes, no charge. Basic funeral: £495. Pre-paid plan: Golden Charter. Member of SAIF which has free medical and legal telephone helpline. Also offers 19th Century hearse drawn by black Friesian horses from £575.

• **David Coster** funeral director, 13 Martingale Close, Sunbury-on-Thames, Middlesex TW16 6NL (tel 0932 784168). Joint winner of The Natural Death Handbook Award for the Most Helpful Funeral Director. Cheapest fully-fitted coffin only: £150 (delivery locally free, nationally by quotation). Cold storage only: no refrigeration facilities, but would store embalmed remains for £20 per day. Body transport only: yes, £85 locally. Advice for d-i-y: yes, £15 to completion of arrangements. Basic funeral: £250 within a 20 mile radius, then £1 per mile extra (quality estate car, family bearers). Pre-paid plan: none. Member of British Institute of Funeral Directors and the British Institute of Embalmers.(See further details earlier in this chapter.)

• **J. E. Gillman and Sons Ltd** funeral director, 971 Garratt Lane, Tooting, London SW17 OLW (tel 081 672 1557). Cheapest fully-fitted coffin: £140 (free delivery locally, not possible nationally). Cold storage only: yes, £5 per day. Body transport only: yes, from £50. Advice for d-i-y: yes, no charge. Basic funeral: £460. Pre-paid plan: Golden Charter. Member of SAIF. Branches in SE27 (tel 081 670 4126), SW11 (071 228 0360), SW12 (081 673 8719), Mitcham (081 685 0349) and Carshalton (081 669 0483). Subject of a sympathetic documentary on BBC TV. 'Aim to treat the deceased as if it were a relative's funeral.'

• **East Sheen Cemetery**, Sheen Road, Richmond TW10 5BJ (tel 081 876 4511). Plot (50 years) from £167 to £267 (trebled to non-residents). Digging, burial and use of chapel: £131. Maintenance not charged. Edwardian chapel with non-religious stained glass windows. Time for service: 20 mins. Grounds: lawned sections, traditional plots. Memorials up to 6' 6", natural stone. Also administers Hampton Cemetery, Holly Bush Lane, Hampton; Richmond Cemetery, Lower Grove Road, Richmond; Twickenham Cemetery, Hospital Bridge Road, Twickenham; and Teddington Cemetery, Shacklegate Lane, Teddington. Teddington and Twickenham have Victorian chapels.

• **Enfield Crematorium**, Great Cambridge Road, Enfield EN1 4DS (tel 081 363 8324). Price: £120. Time allotted: 20 mins, extra time £120 for 20 mins. Possibly other body containers if inspected in advance. Grounds: formal gardens, landscaped areas.

• **Haji Taslim Muslim Funerals**, East London Mosque, 45 Fieldgate St, London E1 1JU (tel 071 247 2625 or 9583). Cheapest fully-fitted coffin only: £60 (delivery locally free, nationally 40p per mile). Cold storage only: yes, free. Body transport only: yes, £30. Advice for d-i-y: yes, free. Basic funeral: if indigent, free with private grave. Pre-paid plan: none. 'We are distinctive as you can judge from these answers. We are geared for Islamic funerals and shipping abroad.'

• **Highgate Cemetery**, Swains Lane, London N6 (tel 081 340 1834). Plot (70 years) from £2,200 to £6,850. Digging and burial from £510. See no reason not to accept home-made coffins, body bags, etc, once people have paid for burial rights. No chapel (St Michael's is adjacent). Grounds: 'Magical, one of the most famous in the world. Opened 1839, a kaleidoscope of Victorian personalities buried here.' Entrance fees for visitors and tours. Some restrictions on 'inconsistent' memorial materials.

• **E. M. Kendall**, Undertaker, 46 Dalston Lane, Hackney, London E8 3AH (tel 071 254 6519). Cheapest fully-fitted coffin only: £80 (delivery locally £15, nationally: would depend on location). Cold storage only: no. Body transport only: no. Advice for d-i-y: 'if so required', no charge stated. Basic funeral: £385. Pre-paid plan: 'our own'.

• **Kensal Green Cemetery**, Harrow Road, London W10 (tel 081 969 0152). Plot (perpetuity) from £850 to £2,500. Digging, burial and service £125. Maintenance if required £35-25 p.a. Would accept a securely made home-made coffin. Chapel: Victorian listed building, with Roman-style pillars. Grounds: Gothic plus a honeycomb of catacombs underground. Memorials: headstones not to exceed 5ft.

• **Lear of London**, Bryson House, Horace Road, Kingston Upon Thames, Surrey KT1 2SL (tel 081 546 2633) supplies various types of body bags – biodegradable (£5-15), heavy duty transport bag (£18-75), ones with windows and ones suitable for cremation (£4), postage extra. The firm has a minimum order of £30 however. (You can also go through Green Undertakings – see the listings for the North East region.) It sells a very absorbent lining for coffins which costs £1-80 for 2 meters (width 50cms); and cremation urns from £3-60 to £290.

• **Manor Park Cemetery Co. Ltd.**, Sebert Road, Forest Gate, London E7 ONP (tel 081 534 1486 or 4921). Plot (50 years) from £369 for lawn grave. Digging and burial £236.

Traditional grave from £835 to £3,000, including digging and burial. Maintenance £25-85 per annum. 'Free Church, friendly and warm.' Time for service: 20 mins. Grounds: formal.

• **Putney Vale Crematorium**, Stag Lane, Putney, London SW15 3DZ (tel 081 788 2113 or 081 789 8734. Price: £83. Time allotted: 20 mins and 5 mins entrance and 5 mins exit; extra time can be paid for. Grounds: formal garden, fountain, lily ponds, extending into wooded glade.

• **Henry Smith Ltd**, coffin makers, 192 Garratt Lane, London SW18 4ED (tel 081 874 7622). Mr Carter has arranged that the firm will supply to individuals one standard coffin only, and only if ordered via the Natural Death Centre and picked up by the individual concerned paying by cash or cheque. The price is £94, in one of two standard sizes only (5' 8" or 6' 2", both 20" wide and 14" high; three pairs of plastic handles; a simple inside lining; and a nameplate engraved with name, age and date of death).

• **South London Crematorium**, The Garden of Remembrance, Rowan Road, London SW16 5JG (tel 081 764 2255). Price: £137. Time allotted: 30 mins, extra time £75 per half hour. Grounds: formal gardens.

• **Southwark Crematorium**, Bockley Way, London SE23 (tel 071 639 3121). Price: £132. Time allotted: 20 minutes, extra time only if available. Also would accept 'alternative' containers, eg a cardboard box, if supported on pine or plywood and draped in a cloth. Grounds: formal gardens, shrubbery, wooded area, garden of remembrance.

• **South West Middlesex Crematorium**, Hounslow Road, Hanworth, Feltham, Middlesex TW13 5JH (tel 081 894 9001). Price: £100. Time allotted: 30 mins, extra time £55 for half hour. Grounds: formal gardens and woodland.

• **Walthamstow Cemetery**, Queens Road, Walthamstow, London E17 (tel 081 524 5030). Plot (75 years): £270. Digging, burial and headstone foundation: £175. Maintenance not charged. Time for service: 30 mins. Grounds: traditional plain setting.

Scotland

• **Perth Crematorium**, Crieff Road, Perth PH1 2PE (tel 0738 25068). Price: £166.20. Time allotted: 45 mins between each service; extra time has never been asked for. Also would accept rigid containers as long as draped with a cloth. Grounds: formal and wooded.

Chapter 8

'IMPROVING' GRIEVING

Anything written about grieving is unlikely to suit everybody because grief is an intensely personal emotion. It can be bewildering and surprising and make us do unexpected things. Grief can knock us sideways. The absence of grief, too, can be stunning. It is not always there when we expect it and need it. Grief is a volatile emotion: one moment we are engulfed in it, the next we are coping with everyday life, driving the car, calling on a friend, laughing at jokes over lunch. Like being in love, grief is something that is just there, it happens, it makes us feel we are somehow different from people who are not in that condition. For that reason, anyone who is suffering bereavement might read this chapter differently from someone who isn't. The title, for example: of course we cannot 'improve' your grieving. But society can improve the way it reacts to those who are grieving, and there are certain attitudes and practices, some of them reported below, which obstruct the natural expression of feeling and which could be improved upon, and certain evolving customs in modern life that may be worth sharing.

This chapter is built around the experience of grieving. Academic references and sources are given a secondary position. But see also the Organisations listed in the Resources chapter. For in many particularly hard bereavements, such as when grieving over the loss of a child, a support group can be a great help in gradually learning to cope.

The different levels of grief we experience can be very surprising. A dear friend dies and after the funeral we resume normal existence with an appetite that makes us almost guilty. Where has that person gone? Why don't we feel it more? We probably will experience the sorrow when reminders of past times crop up, but meanwhile the fact that life just goes on as before can seem almost unreal. And then someone dies who has shared our most intimate life and it is as if a part of the self has been removed without warning. Hence the wisdom of saying that when we mourn the other, we mourn the self. Such grief reaches into the part of us where the roles played in our identity by the self and the other – the partner, the mother, the child – seem indistinguishable. One mourner, just when he thought he was recovering from his wife's death, broke out in a violent rash. It took him a further eighteen months to realise what had happened:

Debilitating grief

I was much debilitated; the body had to excrete the accumulated stress of several years. Some mourners, I was to discover, are prey to nervous breakdowns, ulcers and much much worse: chronic arthritic conditions, heart attacks, even cancer. This is probably what accounts for so many instances, in centuries gone by, of persons dying of grief or 'a broken heart'.

From an article by Libby Purves in The Times (April 3rd 1992).

The potential phases of grieving are recorded in many textbooks, the results of professional and academic study of individual experiences. But here is Margaret Chisman's own personal and courageous account. In the first extract she expresses her immediate reaction to the death of her husband Stan.

Picking up the threads

When the hospital phoned at 3am on March 24th to say he had died I was alone in the house as my daughter, by chance, was away that night. After a short bout of numbed weeping I phoned near relatives and then made a cup of tea – remembering to add extra sugar for shock. I asked myself what I should do with the rest of my life now that the bottom had dropped out of it, and told myself that the most important thing was how to get through the rest of the night, and the next few weeks.

Later she wrote about the emotions of the first week:

During the first week after his death I made myself, in the privacy of my home, keep on saying out aloud 'My husband is dead and I'm a widow' until I could say it without weeping.

I am still weeping daily but it is mercifully lessening as I begin to pick up the threads again just a little.

After a few months she was able to write about the experience in a structured way and to begin to share with others and include a view of the future:

It is probable that most survivors experience similar phases of grief. First comes a numb inability to believe it. The reality of the loved one's presence is still so strong inside you that you know they are still alive and that they will return.

This is gradually replaced by an agonising acceptance of irretrievable loss bringing with it almost overwhelming grief. Never again to see, to hear or to touch your loved one. Oh, the unbearable pain of it all! You cry a lot, your face crumples uncontrollably, your whole torso shakes with hollowness, your throat aches with constriction and grief holds you in its iron grip.

Gradually the incidence of these attacks lessen; your horizon begins to open up a little and you begin to enter phase three. This is shot through with conflicting emotions. It is similar to the early stages of convalescence after a major accident or operation (such as the loss of a limb or of a sense resulting in blindness or deafness). You may feel resentment, 'Why should this happen to me?' You may try to reject the whole thing and suppress your feelings; you may be filled with self pity. There is one thing certain, however, about phase three, you have to fight! You have to confront your anger, resentment, rejection, self-pity – to realise that you won't get through to phase four unless you take these negative reactions and, with determination, turn them into something positive. This could include doing some things in a different way, doing new things, taking up a new hobby – you may have to fight a sense of disloyalty. Towards the end of this phase you feel you want to hurry things along, like a child picking away at its scab, only to be dismayed at the still unhealed flesh below. In many life processes there seems to be a natural flow that cannot be hastened, but neither should it be thwarted. You have to steer between nurturing grief beyond its proper bounds, and yet encouraging the first new shoots of post-bereavement independence, not feeling disloyalty to your loved one when you do something different or new.

Phase four shows a calm and serene acceptance of your bereavement and a need to build for the future, but even here there will be occasions when a trigger flashes fiercely your grief into life again – 'They're playing our tune,' a verse of poetry, a flower, a turn of phrase will bring your memories flooding back – even when your love is but a dream on the horizon of the past.

I see the process of bereavement, grief and recovery in pictorial terms. The black centre is the death of your loved one, phase one is shown in purple, two in red, three in orange and four in green. The grey smudge round the edge is your own death which, with the spiral revolution of time, will coalesce into a dense black dot at the centre of someone else's grief. The lesson we would do well to learn is that no previous phase is ever completely finished. You will get flashes of phase 1 even after years of being in phase four, but it is the balance that changes one phase to the next.

Time does heal if we let it. The scar will always be there, but we must not become like medieval beggars who hawked their festering cicatrices. We must do all we can in phases three and four to help the natural healing processes in ourselves and others.

From 'Interim', a private newsletter circulated by Margaret Chisman.

How long does it take to 'overcome' grief? Margaret Chisman quotes one widower in her newsletter:

How long till grief is 'overcome'?

You say that I am further along the path to recovery as my wife died over three years ago. I was told that it would be six months before I would get over the grief. It was much longer than that, about eighteen months before I stopped bursting spontaneously into tears, when driving, preparing lectures, etc. Now after three and a half years the emotions are still there, but more controlled. No doubt other people respond differently.

From 'Interim' by Margaret Chisman.

There is an element of grief we should perhaps not even try to overcome but instead build into our lives. If there is a meaning to life it is amply demonstrated in the emotions we feel for that which we have lost. Yes, there was a meaning after all, if only I could have seen it at the time! What is missing in our lives is not meaning but the ability to perceive it while it is there.

The academic structuring of grief does, after all, have a purpose. It may help us to deal with the overpowering aspects of the emotions we experience in that strange country. Other people have been there before us. We have not been singled out. There are maps. There is a geography of grief and loss:

A tentative 'map' of grieving

Grieving takes place after any sort of loss, but most powerfully after the death of someone we love. It is not just one feeling, but a whole succession of feelings, which take a while to get through and which cannot be hurried.

Although we are all individuals, the order in which we experience these feelings is very similar for most of us. Grief is most commonly experienced after the death of someone we have known for some time. However, it is clear that people who have had stillbirths or miscarriages, or who have lost very young babies suffer a similar experience of grieving and need the same sort of care and consideration.

In the few hours following the death of a close relative or friend, most people feel simply stunned, as though they cannot believe it has actually happened. They may feel like this even if the death has been expected. This sense of emotional numbness can be a help in getting through all the important practical arrangements that have to be made, such as getting in touch with relatives and organising the funeral. However, this feeling of unreality may become a problem if it goes on too long. Seeing the body of the dead person may, for some, be an important way of beginning to overcome this. Similarly, for many people, the funeral or memorial service is an occasion when the reality of what has happened really starts to sink in. It may be distressing to see the body or attend the funeral, but these are ways of saying goodbye to those we love. At the time, these things may seem too painful to go through and so are not done. However, this often leads to a sense of deep regret in future years.

Soon though, this numbness disappears and may be replaced by a dreadful sense of agitation, of pining or yearning for the dead person. There is a feeling of wanting somehow to find them, even though this is clearly impossible. This makes it difficult to relax or concentrate and it may be difficult to sleep properly. Dreams may be extremely disturbing. Some people feel that they 'see' their loved one everywhere they go – in the street, the park, around the house, anywhere they had spent time together. People often feel very angry at this time – towards doctors and nurses who did not prevent the death, towards friends and relatives who did not do enough, or even towards the person who has left them.

Another common feeling is guilt. People find themselves going over in their minds all the things they would like to have said or done. They may even consider what they could have done differently that might have prevented the death. Of course, death is usually beyond anyone's control and a bereaved person may need to be reminded of this. Guilt may also arise if a sense of relief is felt when someone has died after a particularly painful or distressing illness. This feeling of relief is natural, extremely understandable and very common.

This state of agitation is usually strongest about two weeks after the death, but is soon followed by times of quiet sadness or depression, withdrawal and silence. These sudden changes of emotion can be confusing to friends or relatives but are just part of the normal way of passing through the different stages of grief.

Although the agitation lessens, the periods of depression become more frequent and reach their peak between four and six weeks later. Spasms of grief can occur at any time, sparked off by people, places or things that bring back memories of the dead person. Other people may find it difficult to understand or embarrassing when the bereaved person suddenly bursts into tears for no obvious reason. At this stage it may be tempting to keep away from other people who do not fully understand or share the grief. However, avoiding others can store up trouble for the future and it is usually best to try to start to return to one's normal activities after a couple of weeks or so. During this time, it may appear to others as though the bereaved person is spending a lot of time just sitting, doing nothing.

In fact, they are usually thinking about the person they have lost, going over again and again both the good times and the bad times they had together. This is a quiet but essential part of coming to terms with death.

As time passes, the fierce pain of early bereavement begins to fade. The depression lessens and it is possible to think about other things and even to look again to the future. However, the sense of having lost a part of oneself never goes away entirely. For bereaved partners there are constant reminders of their new singleness, in seeing other couples together and from the deluge of media images of happy families. After some time it is possible to feel whole again, even though a part is missing. Even so, years later you may sometimes find yourself talking as though he or she were still here with you.

These various stages of mourning often overlap and show themselves in different ways in different people. Most recover from a major bereavement within one or two years. The final phase of grieving is a letting-go of the person who has died and the start of a new sort of life. The depression clears completely, sleep improves and energy returns to normal. Sexual feelings may have vanished for some time, but now return – this is quite normal and nothing to be ashamed of.

Having said all this, there is no 'standard' way of grieving. We are all individuals and have our own particular ways of grieving.

From the Royal College of Psychiatrists' free leaflet on 'Bereavement'.
(available for SAE from 17 Belgrave Square, London SW1X 8PG).

This basic structure is fleshed out in many books. Some of it has, however, now been questioned by five different studies of widows and widowers, studies which have found that between a quarter and two thirds of the bereaved are not greatly distressed, and that severe depression need not necessarily follow a loss. Dr Camille Wortman, a psychologist at the University of Michigan who has reviewed recent research in an article in the (American) Journal of Clinical and Consulting Psychology, comments that the absence of extreme distress 'can be a sign of resilience. Many have world views – often a spiritual outlook – that lets them see the loss in a way they can accept.' Those who are most upset after a loss tend also to be among the most upset a year or two later – findings which question the widespread assumption that a period of severe distress leads to a more balanced adjustment.

There is no such thing as 'The Good Grieving Guide'. There is no reason on earth why the bereaved person (ie each and every one of us at some time or another) should become the passive consumer of someone else's advice. We all have our own experience. And grief, as it happens, is a very active emotion – among other things it contains anger and even aggression, it can be sharply critical, and has its own sense of humour! Many of the books about bereavement in the Resources chapter are a mixture of impersonal wisdom and highly personal attitudes. Some come from the heart and offer comfort, however idiosyncratic. Others profess vigorous solutions and guidance. Some are biased towards research, others might touch a personal chord in one's own experience. They are all useful. Browse among them, and choose what is to your own taste. Reject what you don't like.

Suicide

Particularly difficult can be facing grief after a murder or a suicide, and this may require specialist help.

Feeling responsible for a suicide

The toughest question to ask Jill Winters is: 'How many children do you have?' Her son James killed himself when he was 34. If she says she has two children, she feels she is denying his existence. If she says she had three but one died, more searching, and unwelcome, questions may follow.

Eight years after her son jumped from a third-floor window, Mrs Winters has finally stopped blaming herself for his death. The sense of liberation has been, she says, remarkable. But it has taken her a long time to accept what happened and to feel at peace with herself again.

The families of those who have commited suicide have to cope with feelings of distress which go far beyond normal grief. Unlike other deaths, suicide carries with it a heavy social stigma. Those left behind may see it as a violent statement that the love they provided was not enough. Families can become ensnared in a hopeless search to find out why a child, or a parent, felt so desperate; there are profound feelings of guilt to cope with.

'When it happened it was completely unexpected, although looking back I could see it was on the cards,' Mrs Winters recalls. 'We were devastated by it. We were numb to start with. We found it very difficult to talk about; there was a feeling of isolation.'

Her husband came to terms with their son's death better than she did. 'I felt that I hadn't done the right things, that I had been a terrible mother,' she says. 'I wished I had done everything differently. I kept looking for ways that I could have prevented it. I took full responsibility.'

Mrs Winters went to a group for bereaved parents but felt out of place. 'These were people who had lost their children in the normal way. I didn't feel I was one of them,' she says. 'Suicide didn't seem acceptable.'

James was unmarried and had been a solicitor. A psychiatrist had been treating him for schizophrenia. Mrs Winters now realises she was not responsible for his actions. 'I think he was finding life so difficult and stressful that he could not stand it any longer. He was afraid of having another breakdown.'

Support agencies are waking up to the fact that families bereaved in this way often need specialist help. CRUSE, the national bereavement care group, has set up a number of support groups specifically for families of suicide cases and plans to establish more. Forbes Craig, a former nurse and now a counsellor with CRUSE, says that while all families feel loss on the death of someone close, with a suicide there is 'the intensity of the feelings, the inherent violence, the statement being made that whoever is left can't help any more. If it's a natural death we can take it because we all die. But when it's suicide there's a whole history of culture against it.' Suicide was only decriminalised in 1961, she points out. She says that there is no time limit to when someone who has experienced a suicide might need help. One woman sought help nineteen years after her mother killed herself.

Rose Hampton, the director of CRUSE, had a close friend who committed suicide many years ago. 'The experience lives with you for years and years ,' she says. 'I can still see her now as clear as day. In the end you have to realise that you can't be responsible for other people.'

From an article by Bernadette Friend in The Independent (Aug. 11th 1992).
See also the 'Shadow of Suicide' organisation in the Resources chapter.

The bereaved parent

To lose part of yourself ... Perhaps the loss of a child brings this aspect of grieving into real focus more than any other experience. Here is an account, quoted in full, of the loss of a stillborn child and the fierce reactions it provoked towards our modern attitude to death.

The loss of a stillborn child

Four years ago this summer, I was happy, healthy, seven and a half months pregnant and full of expectations. Within the space of 12 hours, struggling to shake off the effects of a general anaesthetic and an emergency Caesarean section, I was left holding my seemingly perfect stillborn daughter, Laura.

The four days that followed were spent being studiously avoided in a corner of the ante-natal ward, desperately trying to shut out the sight of pregnant women and the sound of newborn babies crying. Still quite poorly and in a state of shock, I leapt at the opportunity for the hospital to make all Laura's funeral arrangements for me – anything to have the whole nightmare taken away.

The result was a totally meaningless cremation service taken by a stranger exactly one week to the minute after her birth; there was no gravestone, no special place of hers that I could visit and care for. Most importantly, there was the guilt and regret: I felt I had failed my daughter in the one and only thing I was ever going to be able to do for her.

Four years on, I know that my experience and felings are not uncommon. I run a local branch of Sands, the Stillbirth and Neo-natal Death Society. The aim is to support people whose babies die at or around birth by offering a listening ear and a shared experience. I want to make some good come out of the tragedy of Laura's death by trying to ensure that others don't end up with the same regrets as me.

For example, I had absolutely no idea that I could have asked to hold Laura again a few hours or even a day or more later – at a time when I could have taken her in better and stored my memories of her. As it was, the only time I spent with her I was so dopey that I could barely lift my hand to stroke her face. I had no idea that I could have asked for a lock of her plentiful hair. Things are much better now, professionals much more thoughtful and aware that information may need to be given several times before it sinks in, but there is still room for improvement.

A national Sands survey showed that while some hospitals handle the situation well, others do not. Many foetuses, or 'foetal material', are incinerated with other hospital waste. Parents are not consulted and are totally unaware that they have any choices to make, totally unaware of the fate of their baby's body. Obviously it would be wrong, and in some cases quite inappropriate, to suggest that all babies lost through miscarriage should be held by their mothers. However, babies can be perfectly formed little beings long before they reach 28 weeks; I would suggest that they are most definitely not 'hospital waste fit for incineration only' and it is not the right of hospital staff to decide whether or not a mother should hold her child or decide upon the fate of its body; she should at least be told that she has a choice.

Just as holding your dead child plays an important part in the grieving process, so does saying a formal goodbye in the shape of a funeral or some other social ritual, be it religious or not. It is a way of sharing, of acknowledging the existence of, the child you have lost. This is especially true in the case of babies because society is keen to pretend they never existed ('Oh well dear, you can just have another one' ... 'At least you've got your other children' ... 'As soon as the next one's born healthy everything will be all right'). The more people around me negated Laura's existence, the more they implied that other things would make up for her loss, the more I fought to keep her memory alive.

For women who have had miscarriages or terminations for abnormality, society offers even less opportunity to say goodbye – after all, the baby didn't really ever exist, did it? But a loss is a loss and needs to be grieved for, needs to be acknowledged. Women who lost babies several years ago or more have to live with the fact that they were simply wrapped up and incinerated; there was no choice.

Our society is still singularly bad at dealing with death or allowing for the fact that the grieving process is a necessary part of carrying on with life. In China, they have an annual day set aside for national mourning: people tend graves or simply focus their thoughts on loved ones who have died. God forbid that the stiff British upper lip be subjected to such a public display of emotion!

Feelings of grief (often quite frightening in their ferocity and variety) must be hidden away behind closed doors; until, that is, they burst out, unleashing all sorts of problems and you end up, as I did, crawling desperately to a psychotherapist.

Whenever and however the death of a child occurs, it means shock and disbelief. It may mean regrets about decisions taken at the time; it may mean missed opportunities; it may mean guilt; it may mean anger. One thing is certain; it always means being scarred for the rest of your life.

From 'In Living Memory' by Caroline Jay in The Guardian.

'The Bereaved Parent' by Harriet Sarnoff Schiff and 'Beyond Endurance, When a Child Dies' by Ronald J. Knapp are sensitive explorations of the complex of emotions and realistic living circumstances surrounding the bereaved parent, offering both insight and comfort in great measure. Another book which deals explicitly with this area of loss is 'On Children and Death' by Elisabeth Kübler-Ross. The intensity of grief for the loss of a child is likely to be prolonged and may take half a year to reach its zenith and longer still if it was a violent death. There is an entire sub-culture of shared feelings created by men and women who have suffered the loss of a child from a wide range of causes. Nowhere is this more fully expressed than in the extraordinary and moving series of pamphlets and newsletters issued by The Compassionate Friends (address under Organisations in the Resources chapter – they even do a special newsletter called Sibbs for bereaved brothers and sisters). Here is an explanation of their policy of 'Befriending, rather than counselling':

Befriending

What do we mean by befriending? The Pocket Oxford Dictionary defines it as 'act as a friend; help at need'. Within The Compassionate Friends it takes on a greater meaning. Befriending is also sharing. We are all befrienders. We all share when we write a letter, make a phone call or talk with another bereaved parent at a meeting. We share when we read the Newsletter. Prayer, meditation and positive loving thoughts are a form of sharing.

The necessity to 'share' and 'talk' about our loved ones and emotions is a 'need' within all bereaved that requires to be met. As the pain of grief recedes, so the need to talk endlessly diminishes. We are then in a position to 'share discriminately'. To let the newly-bereaved talk – to be willing to share with a few sentences – to encourage expressions of feelings: 'Yes, I felt that and I also felt...' This is why those who have first contact with the newly-bereaved have been bereaved themselves for at least two years.

Grief is a natural reaction to the death of a loved one/ones. Talking about our dead child/children and the emotion let loose within us is the way forward along the path of grief. Being able to 'befriend' from the time of a death, giving the newly-bereaved permission to grieve, should mean that 'counselling' will be needed by a small minority only: those who become stuck in their grief; people who have other problems within their family; or difficulties within themselves due to past experiences. For these, bereavement counselling is very beneficial and could be viewed as complementary to 'befriending'.

> From 'Thoughts on Befriending' by Margaret Hayworth, in The
> Compassionate Friends Newsletter (Spring '89).

A child's understanding of death

Young children are curious about death. They have to negotiate the reality of death and fit it into their scheme of things. In a child's world, the loss of a pet can assume enormous emotional significance. When Grandma or Grandad dies, or a parent or a sibling, the loss has to be explained in ways the child can come to terms with. Otherwise there may be a hidden morbid element that will affect development and grown-up life. In the following extract, a hospice counsellor helps a father and son to speak about their joint loss. The little boy displays a mixture of childish expression (drawing a picture, as he would at school) and very realistic concerns. These show his awareness of how his dependency has shifted with the loss of his mother.

Coming to terms with a mother's death

A seven year old had been bereaved of his mother a week before. Father sought help for his son. There seemed to be a great deal of apprehension, not just for the boy. However, he happily accepted a large glass of squash – it was a hot day. Father sat slightly apart. In order to understand the outcome of this brief intervention, something of the father's manner and bearing needs to be known. He was a large man who worked with animals. A man who was used to being obeyed by animals and humans alike; this was the tension, I felt. He gave his son instructions to answer my questions honestly. After introductions about who I was and what I did, and the purpose of his visit to the Hospice, I asked about his mother's funeral, including Father in the conversation. Father refused to be drawn, prompting his son instead. The small boy looked at his father as he spoke with a mixture of fear and defiance in his eyes. He spoke of the funeral but quickly went on to say he had visited the grave earlier on his way here. He and his father had discussed the sort of stone they would put on the grave during the drive to the Hospice. I wondered if he would like to draw it for me; he wasn't particularly good at drawing, he said, but he agreed he would have a try when I said I wasn't either.

As he drew, he spoke of his dog which had recently died and the circumstances of its death; 'being put down'. He asked, 'Where was he?' looking all the while at his father. It seemed very hard for the father to be honest about where the body of the pet dog was, though his son did know where his mother's was. This was the theme of the picture. Two tombstones, one a slab and one a cross, drawn very small in the corner of the paper, with a bird in flight above. He spoke very naturally about what was going on the stone and referred to his father for help with the precise detail. I wondered about the cross in the picture.

'Well, that had been part of the talk in the car, about the shape.' The slab seemed to be preferred by the father so that the wording could be better managed.

I wondered what the cross meant.

'That Mummy had gone to be with Jesus.'

'What does that mean for you?' I responded.

'That Mummy no longer suffered great pain and she had left her poor body and was now in Heaven,' he replied.

'Do you know where that is?'

'No – not really.'

I wondered, 'Could you tell me about the bird you have drawn so cleverly?'

He said 'I thought it would make a nice picture. It reminds me of the churchyard in the country with trees around.'

I allowed a pause and then, 'So you are not sure where Heaven is – nor is anybody if they are really honest – none of us is sure – even grown-ups – but the bird is important to you. Could the bird be Mummy's spirit flying free, out of pain, able to go where she liked to the place we are not quite sure where which is called Heaven?' He liked this idea very much and repeated it.

His father softened and tears ran down his cheeks. His son watched.

I asked, 'Do you and your Dad cry together?'

'Yes,' he said, 'we do when we go to the churchyard, to the grave.'

'That's good,' I said, giving lots more permission in my voice.

There was something in the way he watched his father that prompted me to ask him if there was anything he found very hard to say to his dad which he might like to say if he found courage here. It seemed as though he had been longing for this opportunity. There was so much, he was worried about his dad working with bulls – he might get hurt; he was worried when his dad drove too fast – he might crash. He didn't want the goats or the calves to be slaughtered, they were his friends and he missed them. He wanted his bedroom to be the same room when he came home, not to be changed around. It was easy to see how insecure, worried and angry this small boy was towards his father, and how he was asking him to take care of himself in order to care for him. A brief interruption allowed him to say more about a visit to the grandparents which was planned and how dad would be in his absence. All his concerns came tumbling out and his anger was acknowledged.

From 'Brief Interventions in Anticipatory Grief and Bereavement'
by Lizette Pugh, in Counselling (Feb. '92).

What do children need? They need society to open up about death in much the same way as we all do. Children are no problem so long as we try to understand them. Adults are the problem, as one man discovered when he openly shared his bereavement with his children:

'Remembering Mum' book

After Adrian Crimmin's partner, Mandy, died of pneumonia, he made no attempt to conceal his pain from their two boys, Sam, five, and Eddy, three. The children went to Mandy's funeral, sang her favourite Jackson Browne songs at the service, drew pictures on her headstone and shared their father's tears.

But when the family sought to share their grief outside, it was a different story. They met with 'a wall of silence'. Even best friends wouldn't talk about Mandy, close relatives suggested they should have recovered from the death after only three months.

'My kids were confused by other people's strange reactions; a child can't understand that society is conditioned to be embarrassed by death.'

At school children who knew of the death displayed signs of anxiety.

'One child was so upset that he couldn't bear to let his mother out of his sight. If she was a minute late at home time, he broke down in tears. Some of the kids suffered nightmares, others just didn't want to come to school. There was obviously a need to talk about death and to help them to understand.'

It was one of the teachers at school who suggested the idea of collaborating on a children's book about bereavement.

'It was an idea I'd had in my mind for some years,' explains Sam's teacher Ginny Perkins. 'I'd taught classes before when parents had died and I'd felt totally helpless. Although I felt I had no problems now in talking to the children about Mandy's death, I could have done with a prop when I was younger, and I'm sure there are other teachers who wouldn't feel comfortable about tackling the subject by themselves.'

The initial stages of finding a publisher were simple, but again 'grown-up' obstruction was encountered before the book was accepted.

'I could get the idea past the editors, who were mostly young and female,' Perkins explains, 'but as soon as the word "bereavement" was mentioned at a board meeting, that would be the end of it.'

After months of persistence, the book was accepted. The result is a sensitive, true story called 'Remembering Mum'. Using large, colour photographs, it follows the family through a typical day, showing how Mandy's memory still touches every aspect of their lives. There are poignant reminders of her, like the daffodils she loved blooming for the first time since she died. At school, Sam and Eddy are seen making a model to take to her grave. At the cemetery, they are pictured hugging by her headstone. Before bed, the boys pore over snapshots of Mandy, immortalised one sunny afternoon at Hampstead Heath.

> *From an article by Fiona Cumberpatch in The Guardian (Dec. 17th 1991).*
> *'Remembering Mum', A & C Black, 35 Bedford Row, London WC1R 4JH.*

Hopefully this is one of many cases of 'improving' grieving by listening to children, supplying their needs and perhaps learning from them as well! The adult need to 'get rid of' death, to deal with bereavement by 'getting over it' quickly, is countered in that story by a clear demonstration of the fact that the bereaved child has to grow up with his loss. The pain may be lessened, but the reality is still there as part of his life, as a tailpiece to that story shows:

'Three years after Mandy died, they still have some anger and they still ask questions. A month ago Sam said, "I didn't even think she was going to die,

Daddy. Why didn't you tell me?" I'd much rather they expressed their feelings now, than carried them on through their lives. But they need other things, too. Sam and Eddy told me that photos of Mandy were very important to them and so was listening to the music she liked, which they used for dancing to.'

Private grief

'We mustn't intrude on private grief,' is a common, jokey saying we use when we want to be a little unkind about the misfortunes of others. Behind the saying, unfortunately, is the assumption that grief is something that should be draped and shrouded from view, and that the rituals of grief are designed to conceal rather than to express feeling. Nothing could be further from the truth.

Listen and be compassionate

My close friends and family were absolutely wonderful when Ernest died. But other people I knew well would cross the road if they saw me coming, and if they did have to speak and ask me how I was, I learned to my cost that I mustn't really tell. They wanted me to say just, 'I'm fine'.

Some people seem to delight in telling me of another bereavement. They asked how my husband died and when I said from a sudden heart attack, immediately told me about a heart attack that killed someone else. I had enough nightmares about my husband's death and I didn't need the harrowing details of anyone else's.

The most helpful thing people can do is listen, just let you talk and be compassionate. People think it will hurt you to talk, but talking keeps the person alive for you. Or they fear they will be reminding you – as if you had forgotten.

It is an absolute safety valve to be allowed to talk, which is why I joined CRUSE, the support group for widows and widowers. There people can cry because everyone understands, but you'll hear gales of laughter too.

> *Jean Baker, quoted in an article entitled 'Please Don't Say That' in The Sunday Times magazine.*

Those who don't know what to say may feel inspired by a lovely Irish tradition, described by Danny Danziger in The Independent (Jan. 27th 1992):

At the very end of the service, before the funeral, the people come up and they hold your hand, and they say a phrase that will ring many bells in Irish ears: that is, 'I am very sorry for your trouble.'

Or, as Elsie Sieben wrote in The Compassionate Friends Newsletter (Spring 1985):

Hug me, tell me you care and that you're sorry this has happened.

Be available to me – often if you can – and let me talk and cry without judging me.

Just love me and I will always remember you as a true friend.

And Virginia Ironside in The Times (July 29th 1992) related how surprised she was to be consoled by letters after her father's death:

I will never let another death go by without dropping the relatives a line. Letters that say things like: 'He will live on for ever in your heart' – trite lines I'd usually wrinkle a lip at – seem to have huge significance, laden with meaning. 'I am down the road if you want an ear,' came from an old schoolfriend I barely know. And a lovely line from my son's godfather: 'These sad deaths are like signposts which direct you into a new and unknown route. I can only wish you well.'

Simply helping the bereaved person with household tasks can be important. Dr Colebrook, who lost his son in a motorbike accident, wrote in the BMJ (Dec 31st 1983) that he felt that he had experienced outstanding support from a local girl, an old college friend of his wife, who simply took over the housekeeping and looked after arrangements at home.

Consolations

Jenny Kander offers consolation of a sort in The Compassionate Friends paper (No. 16) on 'The Death of an Only Child':

Grief, for a time, can seem larger than life. Your anguish is your response to that, but do not relate solely to your pain; remember your child, however painful the memories at first; recall your lives together, however short or long they were, so that restoration may take place and, in time, you will realise that he or she is still with you in the deepest sense, bonded to you and living within your heart. You are parents of your child for eternity. Nothing can alter that. Nothing can take that away.

At some stages of bereavement the sense that the dead person is present is powerful and disturbing. Of course it is psychologically quite accurate to say that someone we love is within us, an indwelling presence. This is in itself a comfort. But when the longed for appearance of the person in the flesh does not occur, then there is anguish. Where is that physical, substantive presence that we miss? To contain the spirit of the dead person within the self is at once a comfort and an agony, but the bereaved person often wants a larger context for this containment, a context that will take some of the burden away and at the same time be soothing and healing. In this sense the child may feel nearer to a dead person whilst up in an aeroplane because he or she has been told that the spirit is 'up there'. The more sophisticated adult may feel the same soothing presence, inside himself or herself, yet enclosed in something larger, in a religious building for example, within the uplifting and inspiring confines of a cathedral. Or in music which has the same grandeur and peace of containing the spirit. Or in the chanted words of prayer. The bereaved person, then, craves some form of communion within which he or she can share the agony and beauty of containing the spirit of the dead. We may call this religious, or we may call it therapeutic. The distinction only matters to the observer. If the bereaved person is religious, the practice of religion will have a therapeutic effect. If he or she seeks comfort in a conventional therapeutic setting, it is likely to have the intensity of a religious experience. Religion, after all, is largely about reconciling life and death.

Professional mourners, women who attend a funeral service and wail or keen, are traditional in many cultures, and this is one way of sharing the burden of the dead spirit. In Crete this method of joining the living to the dead has been brought to a fine art.

Keening

An essential element in the lament singing is that women identify with each other. Each woman's recollection of her own grief serves to remind and intensify the grief of others. A skilled lamenter has to move her audience to 'ponos' (pain) and thus, symbolically, to lead the living to the dead The depth of these laments has thus a metaphysical dimension.

From a paper by Sonias Greger, sent to The Natural Death Centre, entitled
'Woman – Man – Peasant – Central Administration'.

There are many who claim to join the living to the dead in a more direct sense, through psychic guidance and evocations, or through the gift of vision.

Help from the spirit world?

Suddenly I gasped, as a flash of headlights shot over the hill – the old man was going to walk right out in front of a car. But just then, something strange happened – I stood transfixed, as a ghostly gleaming-white mist appeared behind him. It quickly condensed into the radiant form of a middle-aged spirit woman. Strangely unruffled by the gale, her hair was completely unmoved, not a drop of rain had wet it, and her flowing white spirit robes were bone-dry.

All at once she stooped down, drew back her arm and delivered a swift blow to the back of the man's knees. My heart jumped into my throat as he fell backwards like a collapsing house of cards, landing on the pavement with his legs in the gutter. Just a second later, a reckless car hurled around the blind bend at over 50 miles per hour, missing his feet by half an inch – then zoomed past the bus queue, splashing us with muddy water.

Brushing the rain from my eyelashes, I watched the ghostly woman kneel down, kiss the old man's troubled brow, smile, and then vanish into the dark night – fading back into the spirit world, from whence she came.

I've had these psychic abilities from my earliest years, visions of other worlds beyond death.

From 'Voices from Heaven' by Stephen O'Brien.

There is no reliable guide to life after death. Guidebooks abound, but the paths they indicate are varied to the point of confusion. A theologian asks the question, Where do the dead go when they pass over? He reviews the possibilities, beginning with nowhere:

Living in God

Perhaps there is nowhere to go. Perhaps people, burdened with fear, want and sorrow, just dance into the arms of death, as Schopenhauer said, wondering what the tragic comedy of life is supposed to mean – and finding out it ends in nothing. Those who have died are then shadows of the past. Nothing remains of them except for the loving scratches or hideous scar they etched on our world, and our memories.

Then, he considers the opposite option, that of reincarnation:

Perhaps our inner Atma is made of incorruptible stuff, as Hindus maintain. At death the spark of our soul then divests itself of one mortal body to start life again in another disposable shell. Our deceased relatives and friends could then be at any station on the spiralling track of reincarnation. They might even have reached their destination, nirvana, where they merge back into the infinite ocean of Atmas.

Or maybe the dead await judgement:

Perhaps the dead roam as shades in the netherworld, populating the Old Testament *she'ol*. The psalms describe this abyss under the earth as a house of darkness, a bottomless pit, a land of forgetfulness. All the dead can do is bide their time till their fate will be sealed at the universal judgement.

He ends by advocating a truly spiritual understanding:

We can meaningfully speak of heaven and hell, as long as we remember that they are dimensions of life, not locations in outer space. We can say the dead merge back into God if we realise She/He is an ocean of love who does not swamp our littleness. Properly understood, the time-honoured phrase coined by Kohelet puts it rather well: those who have died live in God.

> *From 'Learning to live with life after death' by John Wijngaards*
> *in The Times (Nov. 4th 1991).*

Stephen Levine talks of the comfort to be had in facing up to the worst that human life can bring.

Fierce journey towards freedom

I've been with many people whose grief has been beyond bearing. And in some ways it has been the best thing that ever happened to them. For they come to plumb the depths of their being.

When we experience grief, we are not just experiencing the loss of our son or daughter, our husband or wife, our parent or loved one. We are dropped into the very pit of despair and longing. We are touching the reservoir of loss itself. We experience the long-held fear and doubt and grief that has always been there. It is not an experience that most would choose, though the confrontation with this area of deep holding seems to be an initiation often encountered along the fierce journey toward freedom.

> *Stephen Levine, quoted in Raft, The Journal of the Buddhist Hospice Trust.*

Sogyal Rinpoche in his excellent book 'The Tibetan Book of Living and Dying' advises helping your dead friend and the healing of your own grief by invoking, perhaps with a mantra, any enlightened being who inspires you, and imagining tremendous rays of light streaming out towards you from that being, filling up your heart. And then: 'Imagine you are sending this blessing, the light of healing compassion of the enlightened beings, to your loved one who has died.'

If the hardest death to bear is an untimely one, and the hardest untimely death is a child's death, and the hardest child's death is one that is accompanied by feelings of great guilt amongst the survivors, then we can surely trust the parents who report their thoughts and feelings in The Compassionate Friends publications. Yes, Margaret Hayworth warns, if death causes *persistent* self-accusatory thoughts, then probably professional therapeutic help should be sought (Newsletter, Summer 1992). But a way that helps is to give yourself permission to forgive yourself, by writing a letter to your child listing regrets and stating your need for forgiveness. For the rest, she shares Kübler-Ross and Levine's spiritual perspective on suffering as an opportunity for the soul to develop. The American spiritual teacher Ram Dass developed these arguments in a public talk where he was responding to a father whose son had drowned. The father was in despair: 'They say that God is perfect but all I can think is that God made a mistake. I cannot believe there would be any good reason for Him to allow this to happen.' Ram Dass replied, in part:

I feel such pain for the loss you and your wife have suffered. The grief that parents experience over the loss of a child is perhaps the deepest grief of all because it seems to upset the natural order of things.

What I can share with you from a spiritual vantage point cannot really allay your grief. Perhaps however it may allow you and your son to know each other in a new way, and that other way of knowing may give balance to the grief.

Because your son was attractive and was your son, and so warm and vibrant, you got to know him through his uniqueness and his separateness. There is another way of knowing a person, which we know through our intuitive heart. This way of knowing one another is subtle, so it is often hidden behind the more obvious ways of knowing people through senses and thought. But if we know what to look for and cultivate that intuitive way of knowing, we find out for ourselves that we are each indeed more than just bodies and personalities.

The soul has an agenda in taking birth itself as a human being. It has certain work to do and complete while on the earth plane and it uses the body and personality to carry out that work. And when the work is finished it leaves this plane. The wisest beings with whom I have made contact in this lifetime all assure me that a soul leaves the physical plane neither a moment too early nor a moment too late. Human birth is a bit like entering in the fourth grade, and we stay just as long as it is necessary to achieve what we need from that specific grade or form, and then we are naturally ready to go on for further evolution by leaving this plane.

I can sense from the description and pictures of your son, the purity of his heart and the beauty of his soul. And I suspect that though you considered his work on earth just at the beginning, for his soul the work was completed. Even the manner of his leaving was part of his work. For your personality, the pain is shattering and seemingly unbearable. You wake crying and find life now meaningless. Such suffering is what the personality would avoid at all costs if it were able. For your soul, however, it is an entirely different matter. For your soul, suffering is that which forces you to grow spiritually, and brings you closer to awakening to whom you in truth are. I realise even as I say all these things to you, that it is really too much for me to ask of you that you understand the way in which the manner of your son's death was his soul's gift to your soul. I suspect all that seems topsy-turvy to you. But you did ask me how I understand such tragic events, and this is my truth that I am honoured to share with you.

Probably your suffering and attachment to him and sense of loss is felt by his soul. Although he now understands what has happened, why it had to happen the way it did and why you are suffering as you are, I am sure he is surrounding you with healing energy; and as you are able to quiet your mind, I suspect that you will feel it. It of course acts to your benefit even if you don't feel it . To the extent that you are able, sit quietly and just hang out with your son, talking to him as you normally would about the many experiences you shared together. In doing so, look to see the thread of spirit that pervaded each experience. Imagine that you and he are souls who met on earth this time as father and son. How many times in your years together did the love between you nearly rend the veil of mystery that would have allowed you to recognise the truth of soul that lay at the root of your relationship? It takes only a moment for two people to recognise their bond as souls. Souls know no time. And now, even though your son is no longer embodied, you and he can recognise each other.

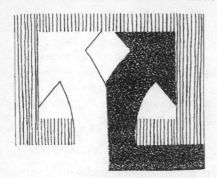

Chapter 9
A MANIFESTO FOR THE DYING

The Natural Death Centre has drawn up the following provisional Declaration of Rights of the Person Dying at Home. The attainment of many of these rights lies in the Utopian future, and would require a fairly drastic redirection of NHS resources and a reanimation of Neighbourhood Care type schemes in both urban and rural areas. The statements that follow are thus more in the realm of wishes than enforceable rights; and are limited by how much a family can cope with, since so much of the caring depends on the family at present. Your suggested improvements to this Declaration would be welcomed. It could be made into a more personal declaration by crossing out bits that do not apply to you or by adding others.

A Declaration of the Rights of the Person Dying at Home

• I have the right to sufficient support from the National Health Service and the community to enable me to die at home, if I so wish, whether or not I have relatives to care for me.

• I have the right not to die alone; although with the right to be left alone, if desired.

• I have the right to expect the local priest or other community leader to ask the neighbourhood to support me and those caring for me.

• I have the right to have 'midwives for the dying' or their equivalent to attend to my physical, emotional and spiritual needs.

• I have the right to the same expertise of pain relief as I would obtain if occupying a hospital or hospice bed.

• I have the right not to be taken without my consent to hospital as my condition deteriorates, or, if a hospital operation is required to relieve pain, I have the right to be brought home again afterwards.

• I have the right to have any Living Will I have signed respected and, if not fully conscious myself, to have the wishes of my appointed proxy respected.

• I have the right to reject heart stimulants, blood transfusions or other medical interventions to prolong my life.

• I have the right, to the extent that I so wish, to be told the truth about my condition and about the purposes of, alternatives to, and consequences of, any proposed treatments.

• I have the right to fast as death approaches, if I so desire, without being subjected to forced feeding in any form.

• I have the right to discuss my death and dying, my funeral or any other related matters openly with those caring for me.

• I have the right to as conscious and dignified a death as possible in the circumstances.

• I have the right, if I so express the wish and if the circumstances allow, for my body to remain undisturbed at home after death for a period, and for my funeral to be handled by my relatives and friends, if they so desire, without intervention by undertakers.

All comments please to The Natural Death Centre, 20 Heber Road, London NW2 6AA (tel 081 208 2853; fax 081 452 6434).

Policy changes needed

This book and indeed the above Declaration have implied the need for a number of changes in policies and practices relating to dying and death. These are summarised here:

Education

• Children need less exposure to violent death on television and in the media and yet they need to be more involved in the natural dying of their relatives and friends; to have the opportunity to view the body if they wish and to participate in the funeral. Teachers in schools can help where appropriate by introducing relevant literature to do with bereavement or, for instance, by helping the children to make Memory Books or Memory Boxes that compile their thoughts and memories and photos of the dead or dying person.

• A number of people learn first aid, which they may or may not ever need to use. But everybody would benefit from learning the basics about preparing for dying and about looking after the dying person, if only to be better prepared for their own death. A one day (or weekend) first-aid-style course in practical care for the dying should be popularised, and open to the general public, not just to the nursing profession.

• Death needs to become less 'socially invisible'. Towards this end, it will help to have an annual English Day of the Dead, along the lines of the Mexican Day of the Dead, both as an opportunity for rituals in remembrance of friends and relatives who have died, with a flavour of festival to it, and also as a chance for debate, discussions and exhibitions related to death and dying. The Natural Death Centre intends to help popularise English Days of the Dead on the third Sunday in April each year.

The National Health Service and the community

• The natural death movement must be as insistent as the natural birth movement in pressing for changes in the NHS. First, there needs to be a feasibility study leading to a pilot project that would look at the relative costs for a particular region if the policy were to become one of enabling the terminally ill to die at home rather than in hospital or elsewhere; and the study would encourage and collect suggestions from carers about how services for the dying could be improved. Second, the Marie Curie, Macmillan and other nursing and hospice home-care services need to be adapted, or new organisations founded, for extending services to people dying of other causes besides cancer, motor neurone disease and AIDS. Third, there needs in the long term to be a new 'holistic' profession of 'Midwives for the Dying', trained to look after the physical, emotional and spiritual needs of the dying and their carers; backed up by a network of volunteer 'Personal Assistants' for the dying, who will sit with the dying, carry out errands for the carers, provide transport, etc. Fourth, we need the Canadian experimental 'brokerage' scheme whereby invalids or terminal patients and their carers identify their own financial and other needs, interviewing and selecting would-be helpers, with generous funding coming from the state. Fifth, respite breaks for carers should be frequently and flexibly available, preferably by a vast extension of the Crossroads-type arrangements whereby a replacement carer comes into the home and takes over all the tasks involved.

• There are many Neighbourhood Watch anti-crime schemes that have provided the foundations for neighbours to get to know each other. There need to be grants for pilot projects to extend these into Neighbourhood *Care* schemes where neighbours would gradually begin to care for each other in crisis, including helping the dying, their carers, and the bereaved. It would be natural in many areas for the local doctor, priest or other respected figurehead to provide the impetus to get such schemes going. For example, Harriet Copperman writes in 'Dying at Home' of an instance where the vicar 'organised a rota of people to sit with a patient who lived alone, in order that he could die at home'.

Spirituality

• There needs to be an English Book of the Dead (there are already several American ones) that would translate Tibetan insights into the experience of dying and the reports from those who have had Near-Death Experiences into anglicised and even Christian rituals that could become part of a pre-arranged Dying Service for those wanting it – for instance an elaboration of the 'go towards the light' message whispered into the ear of the dying person, along with breathing and other meditations; and perhaps accompanied by music such as that offered by the Chalice of Repose at a hospice in the United States. People could be encouraged to design their own Dying Plans specifying the kind of material of this nature that they might like.

• People seem to appreciate dying close to nature, as near outdoors as the elements will allow. Nature needs to be brought into the house or even the hospital – not only flowers, but branches, trees and animals.

Hospital

• A hospital palliative care ward should have as much a 'home from home' atmosphere and design as possible – imagine, for instance, a country house hospital with open fires and meals around long tables, with patients' interests accommodated, whether for pets, music or complementary treatments.

• Dr Marie Louise Grennert's excellent palliative care work at the Malmo Geriatric and Rehabilitation Clinic in Sweden (tel 010 46 40 33 10 00) deserves copying. To encourage patients to talk freely, she has an informal discussion with each one at the outset and asks: 'What are your most pressing problems right now? What do you want from the care provided here? What is your outlook on the future? Where do you get your strength or inner resources from? How do you feel about entering this palliative care ward?' Next-of-kin also talk with the doctor about anything that is on their mind, not just medical matters – and are invited back to the hospital two weeks after the death for a further talk. Two hours or so after the death, all the ward staff gather briefly to discuss the patient who has died, any problems that arose and any lessons that can be learnt.

• In the hospital setting, the partner needs acceptance as part of the caring team (that is, if both partner and patient would like this). Ideally, just as a parent can sometimes stay with a child in hospital, the partner should be able to share a bed with the dying person, as is possible at home, or to have another bed alongside.

• The medical carers need to maintain reassuring physical contact with the dying. One American hospital renowned for its excellent palliative care was filmed looking after a dying woman who was rigged up to the most high tech equipment. She died with the medical team in full attendance and with an accurate record kept of the exact time of her death. But nobody held her hand or had anything to do with her as a person or even said a word of blessing over her dead body.

• Where it suits their particular style, doctors and nurses in hospital could evolve a brief religious or humanist ritual (depending on their own belief systems and that of the patient) to say together over the body of someone who has just died.

• The nursing staff could show carers and visitors simple techniques such as scalp massage and Boerstler's breath relaxation method (see p. 111) which can be helpful to the dying person and which give family and friends a feeling of involvement.

• How to support the dying person and a knowledge of NDEs and of the various kinds of basic information in this Handbook should become an integral and important part of the training of doctors and nurses. (Project 2000 nurses should not be able to use their 'supernumary status' to 'opt out' of this subject in their training.) Medical staff need encouragement to recognise the difference between healing and curing, and to acknowledge that sometimes death is not a failure on their part. All Accident and Emergency department staff should be trained in dealing with the bereaved, and each such unit should have a counsellor on call (as suggested in the Nursing Times, Jan. 8th 1992). Counselling help, discussions groups, talks by experts and other support must be available to all personnel caring for the dying (as suggested by Pam Williams, see the booklist).

• Doctors should use tests such as the Ether test and the Icard test that are completely reliable indicators of death, for the reassurance of those worried about people being embalmed, buried or cremated alive.

• Some hospitals incinerate miscarried foetuses with the hospital waste. A better approach is that of the Aberdeen Maternity Hospital where since 1985 a service is held at the local crematorium every three months attended by the hospital and those families and friends who wish to come. The main point it that parents should have some choice about what happens to the body – and about viewing the body.

• Permission needs to be granted for the resumption of research into the use of the psychoactive and empathogen drugs with the terminally ill – drugs that in the right setting apparently not only relieve pain, depression, tension and anxiety, but help the patient gain a perspective on their situation. Mescaline, LSD, ketamine and MDMA have all produced promising results in these areas. Readers are referred particularly to the Bethesda Hospital work with terminally ill cancer patients written up by Dr Stanislav Grof in 'The Human Encounter with Death', where 71% of their patients rated an improvement in their emotional condition after participation in the experiment.

• Whilst mindful of the exceptions – for instance, Mother Teresa with her great zest for life, who had a heart pacemaker fitted at the age of 82 – and whilst accepting that the patient's own wishes come first, we believe it would be helpful in some cases if doctors were to take very evidently frail and elderly patients and their carers through a detailed series of questions aimed at ascertaining that person's perceived quality of life, before pressurising a patient to accept a major operation and the subsequent stresses and strains of 'maximum recovery' treatment.

• When dealing with the very elderly and the dying, cardiopulmonary resuscitation given by emergency teams should be reserved for those patients who want it, or whose relatives request it on their behalf, or who stand a good chance of surviving and being discharged (currently about 6% of those patients to whom it is given). This routine assault on the very elderly and dying should be something a patient has to be 'opted in' for, rather than 'opted out' from as at present. (See 'Whose Life Is It Anyway?' by nurse Pam

Williams, an unpublished paper in The Natural Death Centre library.)

• The legal standing of Living Wills should be confirmed by an act of parliament, if only to give more secure legal protection to any medical carer who follows a patient's requests.

• All patients should be offered the opportunity of drawing up a Living Will before entering hospital for serious treatment. Indeed, GPs should discuss a Living Will with all their patients who reach pension age, and should encourage them to lodge a copy of their Living Will at the surgery, and to carry on their persons a summary credit-card-size Living Will card, giving the doctor's phone number. The US government in 1987 concluded that Living Wills could save its health service $5 billion a year ('one out of every seven health care dollars are spent on the last six months of life'). Here then is a reform that would not only save the NHS money but that would improve the quality of living and dying.

Euthanasia and suicide

The word 'euthanasia' comes from the Greek for 'good death' and in the Shorter Oxford English Dictionary has the definition of 'a quiet and easy death or the means of procuring this or the action of inducing this'. With such a definition it seems hard to imagine who could be against it – even to enter a hospice could count as slow euthanasia. It may reassure relatives of those who have committed suicide to know that our culture's present stand against suicide and euthanasia has not been shared at other times and in other cultures. For Christians (as The Compassionate Friends outline in a paper on suicide) it stems from a decision of the church Council of Braga in AD 562 to refuse funeral rites to all suicides. This in turn came about because early Christians were killing themselves in worrying numbers – martyrs had all their transgressions wiped out and were glorified by the church, and Christian suicide was very prevalent and acceptable in the fifth century. The Christians had inherited the Roman attitude to suicide. They saw it as a virtuous act if undertaken with dignity, just as the Greek stoics before them viewed death and suicide with equanimity. Plato too felt that if life became 'immoderate' through disease, then suicide was a justified and reasonable act.

The arguments in favour of doctor-assisted active euthanasia include the following: that a small percentage of terminal pain cannot be controlled by drugs; that some patients are either insufficiently mobile or conscious to take their own lives unassisted; and that the drugs required for a swift and painless exit are unobtainable without a prescription.

The arguments against include: that pain relief as practised in hospices is a very advanced art; that it is against the Hippocratic Oath for a doctor to kill a patient; that it is not for the doctor to play God and to decide that a patient's time is up; that the soul may have lessons to learn from the body's helplessness, dependency and suffering – the 'labour pains' of dying; and, most powerfully, that it is a slippery slope – once mercy killing is legalised, where will it end?

The Inuits and the Japanese used to practise euthanasia by hypothermia – the elderly person passed out in the freezing cold and died within hours. In nature, some animals who realise their time has come refuse all food, just as, traditionally, American Indians who had decided that 'now is a good time to die' thereafter refused all food. The *slowness* of this kind of dying seems to be the crux of the matter. Rather than a possibly impulsive decision regretted in the event – as suggested, for instance, by the positive and almost mystical transformations experienced by those few who survived suicide jumps from Golden Gate Bridge – fasting to death requires commitment and perseverance.

In its early stages, fasting can sometimes have an almost mystical effect, helping people to feel centered and spiritual. If they then change their mind when viewing their condition from this new perspective, they can simply start accepting food again. Death by fasting has been described in this book as a 'gentle way to die' (in the case of Caroline Walker) and as being 'like a leaf falling from a tree' (in the case of Scott Nearing). Da Free John (in 'Easy Death') has talked of it as 'a kind of traditional yoga for conscious death; people who traditionally died in this way were philosophically disposed toward intuitive transcendence and gradual transition'. It can be a slow, orderly and graceful process that allows the person time to come to terms with his or her dying. (Derek Humphry, however, warns in his book 'Final Exit – The Practicalities of Self-Deliverance and Assisted Suicide for the Dying' – on public sale in the UK or $16-95 from the Hemlock Society, PO Box 11830, Eugene, Oregon 97440, USA, tel 0101 503 342 5748 – that self-starvation can sometimes lead to severe indigestion, muscle weakness, mental incapacity and painful dehydration. Among the self-administered methods he recommends instead are 4.5 grams of secobarbital in combination with brallobarbital, mixed with alcohol and pudding, taken on an empty stomach, followed by a plastic bag secured by rubber band over the head. Hardly a slow, conscious or dignified death.) As a way of dying, fasting is tough on the relatives, watching the patient become more and more skeletal. But perhaps the fact that it is hard on the relatives is an additional safeguard against pressure on the elderly person from potential beneficiaries from the estate. Fasting is also a way that absolves doctors or nurses from ethically problematic involvement, as long as the terminally ill person makes clear his or her rejection of enforced feeding, preferably through filling in a Living Will.

Our tentative conclusions, therefore, are:

• Euthanasia actively assisted by doctor or relative should remain illegal, but judges should be given more scope for leniency in their sentencing, should such cases come to court (as recommended by the Lord Nathan's select committee on murder and life imprisonment in 1989).

• The Natural Death Centre would like to see research into alternatives to active euthanasia, such as better relief of pain, anxiety and depression in terminal care. Our guess is that the breakthrough will come through the use of drugs that enhance the circulation of the neurotransmitter 5-HT.

Funerals

• Given that our investigations show that none of the mainstream coffin manufacturers will sell a coffin directly to a member of the public and that funeral directors do not see themselves as 'coffin shops' – if they grudgingly sell just a coffin they tend to add an extravagant mark-up – The Natural Death Centre recommends that the Office of Fair Trading issue a requirement that funeral suppliers and directors sell coffins to the general public without undue profit.

• Just as members of the National Association of Funeral Directors (NAFD) have to offer a basic funeral as one of their options – although only 10 out of 18 in one small study informed the member of the public of this option – so they should also be obliged to offer a basic container for those not wanting a coffin. This could be, as in the United States, either an unfinished wood box or a cardboard, pressboard or other rigid container (supported by a plank of wood if necessary).

• Given that 97% of people are 'hooked' the moment they contact an undertaker, and do not shop around, The Natural Death Centre recommends the adoption of regulations similar to the 1984 funeral rules of American Federal Trade Commission, whereby funeral directors are obliged:

(a) to give a price breakdown over the phone (several of the funeral directors in our survey refused to do so).

(b) to give a written and itemised breakdown of prices, to be displayed on the premises and to be readily available for visitors to take away. In the 'Which?' survey of February 1992, a third of funeral directors did not have proper price lists and in a Tyne Tees TV investigation only two out of 18 displayed prices. The Consumer Affairs Ministry at the Department of Trade and Industry has been in endless debate with the NAFD in an attempt to persuade the latter 'to require members to itemise the costs of the components of the various funeral packages offered in estimates and price information'. We are not confident that by the time this book is published these efforts will have been crowned with success. Of the replies to our questionnaire to 2,800 funeral directors, only one – congratulations to George Brooke of Dewsbury in West Yorkshire – sent us a fully itemised price list (the normal undertaker's price list hides many of the funeral costs behind an inflated price for the coffin). The NAFD should find out from George Brooke what a proper list entails, and then publicise this to their members.

(c) to give an *itemised estimate* before the funeral, so that you can add or subtract items to get what you want.

(d) to charge a fee for embalming only if authorised by the family or required by law – eg for transport out of the country.

(e) to disclose in writing what service fee, if any, is being added by the funeral director to the cost of disbursements, or if he or she is getting a refund, discount or rebate from the disbursement supplier.

• There should also be an enforcement of the requirement that funeral directors reveal clearly on their paperwork and premises if they are part of a larger firm. (The latter, unlike most chains in other businesses, have pushed up prices, and they will tend to bring about a bland uniformity of style.) One small firm complained in the Funeral Service Journal that 'certain multinationals openly admit they do not display ownership on the premises or paperwork, which is against trading law. Even those that do, go under a pseudonym to fool the public.'

• The Ministry of Agriculture, Fisheries and Food (MAFF) should alter its proposed requirement that those buried at sea must have an undertaker's name, phone number and case number on a narrow plastic band around the waist. This requirement would militate against those not using undertakers. It should be enough for the band to carry the name, telephone number and case number of any registrar of deaths or any solicitor.

• The government should take up Jonathan Porritt's suggestion (reported in the D-i-y chapter) that Memorial Groves (where a tree is planted by the body) should be included in its planned Community Forests.

• The Social Security, the Births and Deaths Registrar, the Citizens Advice Bureau and many crematoria make useful printed information available to the public about what happens after a death. This information should include the fact that it is possible to organise a funeral without using undertakers and how to go about it – or at least should include a reference to The Natural Death Centre.

• The Funeral Service Journal carries fairly regular reprints of news items about funeral directors found guilty of crime or fraud. Whilst we are against the registration of funeral directors – it would tend to leave trade associations such as the National Association of Funeral Directors (NAFD) with a near-monopoly of power – the rules on pre-paid funeral plans need tightening. For instance, a funeral director with an unspent record for any crime involving fraud should not be able to take cash from the public for pre-paid funeral plans.

• The National Association of Funeral Directors needs to Improve its self-policing and in particular its complaints procedure. All complaints should be acknowledged within ten days and dealt with within three months. The Natural Death Centre complained to the NAFD about a funeral director who claimed on TV that, Oh yes, she would sell coffins to members of the public, when in reality she wanted to charge £300 for the cheapest coffin that she was prepared to sell on its own. We had just been told by another funeral director that he obtained his cheapest coffin for £20, with the handles, lining and name plate adding perhaps another £10. Our complaint was that this mark-up of up to 1000% was an offence against Section 2 of their Association's own code, the principle that undertakers will at all times 'make fair charges in respect of merchandise supplied'. Despite faxing this complaint and a reminder, it took about five months to receive a very lame reply to the effect that the funeral directors have overheads and that they have to polish the coffin, put on the fittings and store it.

• The NAFD should insist that its members familiarise themselves with its code and obey it – not only as regards price lists (Rule 8: 'Every member will have readily available to the general public a price list') but also as regards the basic funeral they are obliged to offer. Rule 15 states that 'Appropriate reductions should be allowed for services in the basic funeral not required, and these reductions reflected in the bill.' Six funeral directors in our survey who claim NAFD membership, and who are no doubt admirable in other ways, refuse such reductions, even, for instance, if a family were to provide its own bearers.

• Members of the public do not shop around in the trauma of bereavement. We recommend in this book that they get a friend who is less involved do so on their behalf, to find a funeral director that suits their particular requirements. But it would also be of assistance to the public if there were regularly published comparative surveys of price and services, drawn up on a regional basis, naming particular establishments. This book is a first step towards such a goal.

• Many people have written to The Natural Death Centre wanting what amounts to a 'disposal service' for their body after death. All local authorities should make agreements with undertakers to supply a cut-rate basic funeral to residents. As an experiment, some might want to go further and offer a 'disposal service', with a simple body container and no hearse, for those members of the public who want this. One correspondent has taken the idea to an extreme and writes that he feels strongly that any such disposal service should not charge 'more than £25 for 60 kilos of rubbish'. This does not fit with the Natural Death Centre's view of the mystery and dignity of death – and of the importance of the rite of physical farewell to a person's body – but we accept that for some people a disposal service is all that they want.

• Local authorities, church authorities or the government should offer financial incentives to churchyards to re-open their graveyards. At the moment it can be to a church's financial advantage to declare a graveyard closed, and to pass its maintenance over to the local authority. Churches should adopt the Belgian practice, outlined by Tony Walter in 'Funerals and How to Improve Them', whereby a ten-year grave is bought. If a further ten years is not then paid for, a notice is pinned to the grave, giving one year's grace before the grave is made available for re-use. In this way, local burials remain possible and graves are well tended.

• New crematoria should adopt Tony Walter's design proposals for 'theatre in the round' with the coffin stage centre (see The Good Funeral Guide chapter for more on this).

• UK crematoria, as in the United States, should offer a cheap 'alternative container' for those not requiring a standard coffin. In most instances this is a cardboard coffin costing from $15 to $50. Funeral directors feel that they are losing business by selling just coffins. The crematoria should not feel this constraint to the same extent, although they may fear that undertakers will take their clients elsewhere.

• Only one doctor should have to sign for cremation, as recommended by the Brodrick Committee in 1971. In many cases at present the second doctor neither examines the body nor positively identifies it, yet a second £30 fee is charged.

• There are many commercial opportunities that entrepreneurs could seize on within the UK funeral trade, particularly as the Green movement's sixties generation ages and becomes responsible for organising the funerals of parents and friends. The first undertakers to offer an entirely Green funeral would do rather well – one option could consist, for example, of a horse drawn cart (or wheel bier for short distances), the body in a coffin of recycled newspaper or similar, followed by burial in a wildlife reserve cemetery. Another option would be to offer a posh rentable coffin for display plus a cheap combustible inner coffin.

• Likewise, the d-i-y superstores could offer flatpack coffins. Sainsbury's Homebase wrote to Jane Spottiswoode to say that they would not sell coffins as their stores are intended for family shopping 'based on the future and therefore not associated with death', whereas of course death in the future is one certainty that every family faces! Argus wrote to say that the sale of coffins would require a 'truly personal service' – in fact all that is required is the assurance that the coffin is big enough: two or three standard sizes should suffice.

• There is scope too for a Death Supermarket like Roc'Eclerc (and Fun'Eclerc) in Paris which now has over forty branches in France as a whole. They sell urns, wreaths, headstones and other funeral objects. Their prices would need cutting, however, for the UK – their coffins start at the high price of 1,995 francs (£238). Roc'Eclerc was started by Michel Leclerc, who specialises in undercutting monopolies. (Their Paris address is 85 Avenue General de Gaulle, Creteil-L'échat, L'échat, Val de Mar 94, France, tel 010 331 4980 4865 or 4207 7513; fax 010 331 4980 4866 or 4742 7321). Having already moved into Belgium and Switzerland, they have tentative plans to expand to the UK.

• The rules about the styles of memorial permitted in churchyards, cemeteries and crematoria should be relaxed, with any design or type of stone allowed. The disliked Albert Memorial monstrosities of one era become the much-loved tourist attractions of the future. And as one vicar complained in the journal Funerals: 'I can't tell you how often I deal with clients who are deeply upset because they have set their heart on some appropriate memorial which has then been forbidden.'

• Birthdays are recognised social occasions. Deathdays could be recognised too. On the first anniversary of the death, it could become the accepted practice for there to be a meal for close friends and relatives, and at subsequent deathdays just the simple gesture at mealtime of a toast to the person's memory or those present telling a story or memory about the one whose anniversary it is – thus passing on family lore to the next generations.

This may be the appropriate moment to wish you, dear reader, a peaceful deathday. May death for you be as graceful as Walt Whitman imagined it could be:

Come, lovely and soothing Death,
Undulate round the world, serenely arriving, arriving,
In the day, in the night, to all, to each,
Sooner or later, delicate death.
From 'Leaves of Grass' by Walt Whitman.

Chapter 10

USEFUL
RESOURCES

Booklist

✪✪✪ = *HIGHLY RECOMMENDED from a Natural Death perspective.*
NDC = *Can be ordered through the Natural Death Centre book service.*

• Ainsworth-Smith, Ian and Speck, Peter **Letting Go – Caring for the dying and bereaved**, SPCK, 1982, 154 pp, £6-99, ISBN 0 281 03861 0.

• Alexander, Helen (ed), **Living with Dying**, £2-75 incl. p&p (cheques to 'BSS') from Living with Dying, PO Box 7, London W3 6XJ.

• Aleksander, Tobe, **A Practical Guide to Coping with Death**, Channel 4 TV, 1992, 47pp for 34p stamp and SAE from Coping With Death, PO Box 4000, London W3 6XJ.

• Arya, Pandit Usharbudh, **Meditation and the Art of Dying**, Himalayan, 1985, 180 pp, $9-95, ISBN 0 89389 056 1.

• Bailey, Alice, **Death – The great adventure**, Lucis Press, 1985, 144 pp, £4-50, ISBN 085330 138 7.

• Bender, Mike and Lloyd, Christa and Cooper, Alison, **The Quality of Dying – in residential homes, nursing homes and hospital wards**, Winslow Press,1990, 108 pp, ISBN 0 86388 077.

• Benn, June (ed), **Memorials – An anthology of poetry and prose**, Ravette, 1986.

• Boerstler, Richard, **Letting Go – A holistic and meditative approach to living and dying**, Associates in Thanatology, 1985, 60 pp, $3-95 plus $2 p&p, ISBN 0 9607928 0 5 T (see Videos and Tapes below, for address).

• Boston, Sarah and Trezise, Rachael, **Merely Mortal – Coping with dying, death and bereavement**, Methuen, 1987, 214 pp, £3-95, ISBN 0 413 15590 0.

• Bowlby, John, **Loss, Sadness and Depression**, Penguin, 1980, £8-99, ISBN 0 14 013839 0. Psychoanalytic exploration of children's reactions to loss of mother.

• Brotchie, Jane, **Help at Hand – The home carer's survival guide**, Bedford Square Press, 1990, 148 pp, £6-95, ISBN 0 7199 1282 2.

• Buckman, Dr Robert, **I Don't Know What To Say – How to help and support someone who is dying**, Macmillan Papermac, 1990, 247 pp, £8-99, ISBN 0 333 54035 2.

• Cancerlink, **Caring for the Very Sick Person At Home**, available free (see Cancerlink, under Organisations below). A helpful 25 page pamphlet.

• Cannon, Geoffrey, **The Good Fight – The life and work of Caroline Walker**, Ebury Press, 1989, 179 pp, £4-99, ISBN 0 7126 3769 9.

• Carlson, Lisa, **Caring For Your Own Dead**, Upper Access, 1987, 344 pp, $12-50, ISBN 0 942679 01 6.

• Collick, Elizabeth, **Through Grief**, available from CRUSE (see under Organisations below), £4.60 inc. p&p.

• Copperman, Harriet, **Dying at Home**, Wiley, 1988, 158 pp, £5-50, ISBN 0 471 26278 1.

• Davies, Douglas, **Cremation Today and Tomorrow**, Grove Books, 46 pp, £3-50, ISBN 1 85174 165 8.

• Davies, Russell, **Law of Burial, Cremation and Exhumation**, Shaw and Sons, 1982.

• Davies, Simon, **Death Meditation**, a non-sectarian booklet available from the author at 44 St Gerrard's Road, Lostock Hall, Preston, Lancs PR5 5TS.

• Dickenson, Donna and Johnson, Malcolm (eds), **Death, Dying and Bereavement**, Sage, 1993, 355 pp, £12-95. This is the reader for the Open University course on death and dying.

• Doyle, Derek, **Coping with a Dying Relative**, Macdonald, 1983, 96 pp, £2-95, ISBN 0 86334 026 1.

• Doyle, Derek, **Domiciliary Terminal Care**, Churchill Livingstone, 1987, £6-95. Aimed at GPs and community nurses but covering pain, diet, equipment and counselling.

• NDC✪✪✪ Duda, Deborah, **Coming Home – A guide to dying at home with dignity**, Aurora Press (PO Box 573, Santa Fe, New Mexico 87504, USA, tel 0101 505 989 9804, USA), 1987, 404 pp, £11-95 from Airlift (tel 071 607 5792), ISBN 0 943358 31 0.

• England, Audrey (ed), **Helping Ourselves**, £2 from The Compassionate Friends (see under Organisations below). For those who have lost a child.

• Enright, D. J. (ed), **The Oxford Book of Death**, OUP, 1987, 351 pp, £5-95, ISBN 0 19 282013 3.

• ✪✪✪ Foos-Graber, Anya, **Deathing – An intelligent alternative for the final moments of life**, Nicolas-Hays, 1989, 397 pp, £11-95 from Airlift (tel 071 607 5792), ISBN 0 89254 016 8.

• Foster, Margaret, **Have the Men had Enough?**, Penguin, 1990. About looking after someone with Alzheimer's Disease.

• Fremantle, Francesca and Trungpa, Chögyam (eds), **The Tibetan Book of the Dead**, Shambhala, 1975, 120 pp, $3-95, ISBN 0 394 73064 X.

• Garcia, Marlene, **How to Write a Will and Gain Probate**, Kogan Paul, 1989.

• Glaser, Barney and Strauss, A. L., **Awareness of Dying**, Aldine Publishing, 1965, ISBN 0 202 30001 3. Hospital-based research.

• Gold, E. J., **The Lazy Man's Guide to Death and Dying**, IDHHB Publishing, (PO Box 370, Nevada City, CA 95959, USA, tel 0101 916 477 1116), 1983, $17-49, ISBN 0 89556 041 0. Tibetan-style approach, but jokey and graphically punchy. Only a few damaged copies left at present. For UK, see also 'Gold' under Videos and Tapes, below.

• Gold, E. J., **The Labyrinth Reader's Course**, IDHHB Publishing, (PO Box 370, Nevada City, CA 95959, USA, tel 0101 916 477 1116), $50. A course for learning how to guide the soul on its way. For UK, see also 'Gold' under Videos and Tapes, below.

• Gold, E. J., **The New American Book of the Dead**, IDHHB Publishing (PO Box 370, Nevada City, CA 95959, USA, tel 0101 916 477 1116), 1983, $12-50, ISBN 0 89556 051 8. Describes in plain English how to help the person through and beyond death, with readings, from a Tibetan-style perspective. For UK, see also 'Gold' under Videos and Tapes, below.

• Green, J. and Green, M. **Dealing with Death**, Chapman & Hall, 1992, ISBN 0 412 36410 7. Wide coverage of legal, technical and religious aspects.

• Green, Jennifer, **Death With Dignity – Meeting the spiritual needs of patients in a multi-cultural society**, Nursing Times (Macmillan Magazines), 15 pp, ISBN 0 333 54971 6.

• Grey, Margot, **Return from Death – An exploration of the Near-Death Experience**,

Arkana (Penguin), 1987, 206 pp, £5-99, ISBN 0 14 019051 1.

• ✪✪✪ Grof, Stanislav and Halifax, Joan, **The Human Encounter with Death**, Souvenir Press, 1978, 240 pp, £2-95, ISBN 0 285 64874 8. Out of print, alas.

• Grollman, E., **Talking About Death**, Beacon Press (Boston), 1970. For parent and child to read together.

• Grosz, Anton, **Letters to a Dying Friend – What comes next, based on the Tibetan Book of the Dead**, Quest, 1989, 169 pp, $9-95, ISBN 0 8356 0640 6.

• Harding, Douglas, **The Little Book of Life and Death**, Arkana (Penguin), 1988, 150 pp, £4-99, ISBN 0 14 019174 7.

• Hastings, Diana, **Crisis Point, A survivor's guide to living**, Papermac (Macmillan), 1989, ISBN 0 333 48267 0. Has a good chapter on dying.

• Hicks, Cherryl, **Who Cares? Looking after people at home**, Virago, 1988, 271 pp, £5-95, ISBN 0 86068 834 8. Well-argued case for better provision for carers.

• Hinton, John, **Dying**, Penguin, 1972, 221 pp, £4-99, ISBN 0 14 020866 6.

• Hockey, Jennifer, **Experiences of Death – An anthropological account**, Edinburgh University Press, 1990, 218 pp, £30, ISBN 0 7486 0221 6.

• Hockey, Jennifer, **Making the Most of a Funeral**, CRUSE (see under Organisation below), 1992, 54 pp, £2-50, ISBN 0 900321 04 0. Useful suggestions aimed at priests, such as: involve the family, no rushing, use symbols and include the children.

• Huxley, Laura, **This Timeless Moment – A personal view of Aldous Huxley**, Chatto and Windus, 1969, 330 pp, ISBN 7011 1439 8. Tells the story of his dying.

• Illingworth, Mary, **How to Direct Your Own Funeral**, Bookstall Publications (79A Gloucester Road, Bristol BS7 8AS, tel 0272 246248), 1992, booklet, 49 pp, £10)

• John, Da Free, **Easy Death – Talks and essays on the inherent and ultimate transcendence of death and everything else**, Dawn Horse Press, 1983, 410 pp, $10-95, ISBN 0 913922 57 9.

• Jones, Mary, **Secret Flowers – Mourning and the adaptation to loss**, Women's Press, 1988, 81 pp, £2-95, ISBN 0 7043 4122 0. About coming to terms with the death of her husband from cancer.

• Kamath, M. V., **Philosophy of Death and Dying**, Himalayan International Institute of Yoga, Honesdale, PA, USA, 1978.

• Kapleau, Philip, **The Wheel of Life and Death – A practical and spiritual guide**, Rider (Century Hutchinson), 1989, 371 pp, £8-95, ISBN 0 7126 3621 8.

• Keleman, Stanley, **Living Your Dying**, Center Press, 1974, 156 pp, $7-95 (£6-50), ISBN 0 934320 09 8.

• Kellehear, Allan, **Dying of Cancer – The final year of life**, Harwood Academic, 1990, 246 pp, $40, ISBN 3 7186 5070 3.

• Kohner, Nancy, **Caring at Home: A handbook for people looking after someone at home**, National Extension College, 1988, £2-50 from the Kings Fund Centre, 126 Albert St, London NW1 (tel 071 267 6111).

• Kohner, Nancy, and Mares, Penny, **Who Cares Now? Caring for an older person**, BBC Education, 1991, £1 incl. p&p from Who Cares Now?, PO Box 7, London W3 6XJ.

• Knapp, Ronald J., **Beyond Endurance, When a Child Dies**, Schocken Books (USA), 1986, £7-95, ISBN 0 8052 0823 2. Records all aspects of the experience of the bereaved parent (including where the child was murdered). Knapp really listened to the 135 families he interviewed.

• Krementz, J., **How it Feels when a Parent Dies**, Gollancz, 1986. Stories from 18 children.

• Kübler-Ross, Elisabeth, **AIDS – The Ultimate Challenge**, Collier Books (Macmillan, New York),1987, 330 pp, $4-95, ISBN 0 02 059001 6. In UK £6-20 (incl. p&p) from Elisabeth Kübler-Ross Foundation (see Organisations below).

• Kübler-Ross, Elisabeth, (ed), **Death – The Final Stage of Growth**, Spectrum (Prentice-Hall), 1975, 179 pp, $2-95, ISBN 0 13 196998 6. In UK £6-20 (incl. p&p) from Elisabeth Kübler-Ross Foundation (see Organisations below).

• Kübler-Ross, Elisabeth, **Living with Death and Dying**, Souvenir Press, 1982, 181 pp, £7-95, ISBN 0 285 64957 4. In UK £8-20 (incl. p&p) from Elisabeth Kübler-Ross Foundation (see Organisations below).

• Kübler-Ross, Elisabeth, **On Children and Death**, Collier Books (Macmillan, New York), 1985, 279 pp, $5-95, ISBN 0 02 076670 X. In UK £6 (incl. p&p) from Elisabeth Kübler-Ross Foundation (see Organisations below).

• Kübler-Ross, Elisabeth, **On Death and Dying**, Tavistock Publications (Routledge), 1973, 272 pp, £9-99, ISBN 0 415 04015 9. In UK £11-24 (incl. p&p) from Elisabeth Kübler-Ross Foundation (see Organisations below).

• Kübler-Ross, Elisabeth, **On Life After Death**, Celestial Arts (Berkeley, California), 1991, 82 pp, $7-95, ISBN 0 89087 653 3. In UK £6-95 (incl. p&p) from Elisabeth Kübler-Ross Foundation (see Organisations below).

• Kübler-Ross, Elisabeth, photos by Warshaw, Mal, **To Live Until We Say Goodbye**, Prentice-Hall, 1978, 160 pp, $10-99 (£8-95). In UK £10-45 (incl. p&p) from Elisabeth Kübler-Ross Foundation (see Organisations below).

• Kupferman, Jeanette, **When the Crying's Done**, Robson Books. Her experience of widowhood, moving and courageous.

• Lake, Dr Tony, **Living With Grief**, Sheldon Press, 1984. Sensitively written.

• Lamerton, Richard, **Care of the Dying**, Pelican, 1980, 240 pp, £4-99, ISBN 0 14 022275 8.

• Lamm, Maurice, **The Jewish Way in Death and Mourning**, Jonathan David Publishers (NY), 1989.

• Leary, Timothy and Metzner, Ralph and Alpert, Richard, **The Psychedelic Experience – A manual based on the Tibetan Book of the Dead**, Citadel, 1990, 157 pp, $7-95, ISBN 0 8065 0552 4.

• Levine, Stephen, **A Gradual Awakening**, Gateway Books (The Hollies, Wellow, Bath BA2 8QJ), 1979, £5-95.

• Levine, Stephen, **Guided Meditations, Exploration, Healings**, Gateway Books, 1992, £8-95.

• Levine, Stephen, **Meetings at the Edge**, Gateway Books, 1982, £6-95.

• ✪✪✪ Levine, Stephen, **Healing into Life & Death**, Gateway Books, 1990, 290 pp, £7-95, ISBN 0 946551 48 0. Contains a number of useful meditations.

• NDC✪✪✪ Levine, Stephen, **Who Dies? – An investigation of conscious living and conscious dying**, Gateway Books, 1986, 317 pp, £7-95, ISBN 0 946551 45 6.

• Lewis, C. S., **A Grief Observed**, Faber & Faber, 1966 (reprinted1985), £1-95.

• Lewis, Martyn, **Tears and Smiles: The hospice handbook**, Michael O'Mara Books, 1989.

• Litten, Julian, **The English Way of Death – The common funeral since 1450**, Robert Hale, 1991, 254 pp, £25, ISBN 0 7090 4350 3.

• Lodö, Lama, **Bardo Teachings**, Snow Lion (Ithaca, NY) 1987. For the Buddhist stages of death

• Lorimer, David, **Whole in One – The Near-Death Experience and the ethic of interconnectedness**, Arkana (Penguin),1990, 340 pp, £6-99, ISBN 0 14 019258 1.

• MacIlanan, Maggie, and Kelley, Patricia, **Final Gifts**, Hodder and Stoughton, £9-99, ISBN 0 340 57471 X. 'The subtleties of communicating with the dying.'

• Manning, Doug, **Don't Take My Grief Away – What to do when you lose a loved one**, Harper & Row, 1984.

• Mathias, Beverley and Spiers, Desmond, **A Handbook on Death and Bereavement –** Helping Children Understand, National Libary for the Handicapped Child, 1992, ISBN 0 948664 10 X.

• Melonie, Bryan and Ingpen, Robert, **Beginnings and Endings, With Lifetimes in Between**, Bantam Books (USA), 1983, £4-95, ISBN 1 850288 038 X. For children 8 to 11.

• Messenger, Dally, **Ceremonies for Today**, Armadale (Brian Zouch Publications, Victoria), 1979. Examples of Australian life-centred funerals.

• Mooney, Bel, **Perspectives for Living**, John Murray. A collection of interviews with bereaved people.

• Morgan, Ernest, **Dealing Creatively with Death**, Barclay House, 1990, 167 pp, $11-95, ISBN 0 935016 79 1.

• Morse, Melvyn, **Closer to the Light**, Ivy Books (Ballantine, New York), 1990, 237 pp, ISBN 0 8041 0832 3.

• Mullin, Glenn H., **Death and Dying – The Tibetan tradition**, Arkana (Penguin), 1986, 251 pp, £5-95, ISBN 1 85063 024 0.

• Nearing, Helen, **Loving and Leaving the Good Life**, Chelsea Green Publishing Company (Post Mills, Vermont, USA), 1992, 197 pp, $19-95, ISBN 0 930031 54 7; £10 hardback in UK (p & p extra) from Kathleen Jannaway, 47 Highlands, Leatherhead, Surrey KT22 8NQ. The life and dying of Scott Nearing.

• Neuberger, Julia, **Caring for Dying People of Different Faiths**, Austen Cornish, 59 pp, £5-50, ISBN 1 870065 00 X.

• Neuberger, Julia and White, John (eds), **A Necessary End – Attitudes to death**, Papermac (Macmillan), 1991, 178 pp, £10-99, ISBN 0 333 48276 X.

• Nuttall, Derek, **The Early Days of Grieving**, Beaconsfield.

• Owens, Dr R. G. and Naylor, F., GP, **Living While Dying – What to do and what to say when you are, or someone close to you is dying**, Thorsons, 1989, 112 pp, £4-99, ISBN 0 7225 1620 7.

• Parrish-Harra, Carol, **A New Age Handbook of Death and Dying**, De Vorss (Marina del Rey, California) 1982, 138 pp, $5-95, ISBN 0 87516 470 6. Poignant about the loss of her own children, and with a psychic dimension.

• Riemer, Jack (ed), **Jewish Reflections on Death and Mourning**, Shocken Books (NY), 1976.

• Ring, Kenneth, **Heading Toward Omega – In search of the meaning of the Near-Death Experience**, Quill, 1985, 348 pp, $8-95, ISBN 0 688 06268 7.

• Rinpochay, Lati and Hopkins, Jeffrey, **Death, Intermediate State and Rebirth**, Rider, 1979.

• ✪✪✪ Rinpoche, Sogyal, **The Tibetan Book of Living and Dying**, Rider/Random House, 1992, 427 pp, hardback, £16-99, ISBN 0 7126 5437 2. Superb and compassionate book on spiritual help for the dying, and well adapted for the Westerner. It gives the background of the teachings, rather than being a prayer book to use. (See also Rigpa in Organisations, below.)

• Rose, Xenia, **Widow's Journey – A return to living**, Souvenir Press, 1992, 204 pp, £13-95, ISBN 0 285 65098 X.

• St Christopher's Hospice, **Someone Special Has Died**, St Christopher's Hospice (see Organisations below), 8 pp. An illustrated booklet for children.

• St Christopher's Hospice, **Your Parent Has Died**, St Christopher's Hospice (see Organisations below), 1991.

• Sanders, Dr Catherine, **Surviving Grief and Learning to Live Again**, John Wiley and Sons Inc (New York), 1992, 223 pp, $10-95, ISBN 0 471 53471 4.

• Saunders, Cicely, **Hospice and Palliative Care – An interdisciplinary approach**, Edward Arnold, 1990, 120 pp, ISBN 0 340 54462 7.

• Schiff, Harriet Sarnoff, **The Bereaved Parent**, Souvenir Press, 1979 (& 1992), 146 pp, £6-99, ISBN 0 285 64891 8.

• Smith, E. Lester, **Our Last Adventure – A commonsense guide to death and after**, Theosophical Publishing, 1985, 100 pp, £4-95, ISBN 0 7229 5122 1.

• ✪✪✪ Social Security, Department of, **What To Do After A Death**, Leaflet D49 available free from DSS Leaflets Unit, PO Box 21, Stanmore, Middx HA7 1AY (or phone 0800 666555, best between 4-30pm and 7pm), 1990, 60 pp.

• ✪✪✪ Spottiswoode, Jane, **Undertaken with Love**, Robert Hale, 1991, 175 pp, £12-95 hardback, £5-95 paperback, ISBN 0 7090 4394 5. About a funeral without an undertaker.

• ✪✪✪ Staudacher, Carol, **Beyond Grief – A guide to recovering from the death of a loved one**, Condor (Souvenir Press), 1988, 244 pp, £8-95, ISBN 0 285 65069 6.

• Stedeford, Averil, **Facing Death – Patients, families and professionals**, Heinemann, 1988, £10-95, ISBN 0 433 31550 4. Dealing with physical pain, fear of death, etc.

• Stickney, Doris, **Waterbugs and Butterflies**, Mowbrays, 1987, booklet, 95p, ISBN 0 26466 904 5. Explaining death to children under 5.

• Stillbirth and Neo-Natal Death Society (SANDS), **The Loss of Your Baby**, booklet for bereaved parents (see Organisations below).

• Stuart, Alexander and Totterdel, Ann, **5¹/₂ x 3 – The short life and death of Joe Buffalo Stuart**, Vintage, 1991, 306 pp, £5-99, ISBN 0 09 988330 9.

• NDC✪✪✪ Taylor, Allegra, **Acquainted with the Night – A year on the frontier of death**, Fontana (Harper Collins), 1989, 187 pp, £3-99, ISBN 0 00 637249 X.

• Wallbank, Susan, **Facing Grief - bereavement and the young adult**, available from CRUSE (see under Organisations below), £7.95 inc. p&p.

• ✪✪✪ Walter, Dr Tony, **Funerals – And how to improve them**, Hodder & Stoughton, 1990, 307 pp, £9-99, ISBN 0 340 53125 8.

• Waugh, Evelyn, **The Loved One**, Penguin, 1951, 127 pp, £3-99, ISBN 0 14 018249 7. A satire on the funeral industry in the United States.

• Wells, Rosemary, **Helping Children Cope with Grief: Facing a death in the family**, Sheldon Press, 1988, £2-95.

• Wertheimer, Alison, **A Special Scar**, Routledge, 1991, ISBN 0 41501 763 7. Experiences of people bereaved through suicide, excellent for both the bereaved and professionals.

• ✪✪✪ Which? Books, **What To Do When Someone Dies**, Consumers' Association (credit card orders, tel 0992 587773),1991, 142 pp, £9-95 incl. p&p, ISBN 0 340 56631 0.

• Which? Books, **Wills and Probate**, Consumers' Association (credit card orders, tel 0992

587773),1991, 224 pp, £9-95 incl. p&p, ISBN 0 340 56632 9.
• White, John, **A Practical Guide to Death and Dying**, Quest, 1988, 196 pp, $7-50, ISBN 0 8356 0633 3.
• Wilber, Ken, **Grace and Grit**, Shambhala, 1992. About the death of his wife from cancer.
• Wilkins, Robert, **The Fireside Book of Death**, Robert Hale,1990, 256 pp, £14-95, ISBN 0 7090 4144 6.
• Williams, Pam, **Knowing About Caring for the Dying** from author, c/o College of Nursing Midwifery, Barnsley Hospital, Gawber Rd, Barnsley S75 2EP. How nurses' training is now and how it could be improved.
❂❂❂Willson, Jane Wynne, **Funerals Without God – A practical guide to non-religious funerals**, British Humanist Association (see under Organisations below), 1989, 58 pp, £3 incl. p&p, ISBN 0 901825 14 X.
• Worden, William, **Grief Counselling and Grief Therapy**, Tavistock (Routledge), 1989, £7-99, ISBN 0 415 02923 6.
• Zaleski, Carol, **Otherworld Journeys – Accounts of Near-Death Experience in medieval and modern times**, OUP (New York), 1987, 274 pp, $8-95, ISBN 0 19 505665 5.

BOOKSHOPS: The Natural Death Centre book service, c/o Institute for Social Inventions, 20 Heber Road, London NW2 6AA (tel 081 208 2853; fax 081 452 6434) sells (or will pass on your order for) the three highly recommended books above which are marked 'NDC❂❂❂'. Please add 20% for postage and packing (50% foreign airmail) and make any cheque payable to 'ISI'. Further copies of this present Handbook are also also obtainable from the Centre for £11 incl. p&p. If urgent, phone your order through for these books, giving your Access, Visa or Mastercard number. Please add the extra 4% which the bank charges for this credit card service. Otherwise, probably one of the best bookshops in London for books on dying is **Watkins**, 21 Cecil Court, London WC2N 4EZ (tel 071 836 2182); sometimes good for American imports is **Compendium Bookshop**, 234 Camden High St, London NW1 8QS (tel 071 484 8944), or **Airlift** distributors (tel 071 607 5792 for mail order). **St Christopher's Hospice** have a book service too: 51-59 Lawrie Park Road, London SE26 6DZ (tel 081 778 9252). Outside London, **Meditec**, Jackson's Yard, Brewery Hill, Grantham, Lincs NG31 6DW (tel 0476 590505) has a large catalogue of mail order books on death and dying. The Natural Death Centre can help with fuller details on publishers' addresses, etc, for some of the books on this booklist, if required.

Tapes and videos

• Ananda Network Cassette Library, c/o Ray Wills, 5 Grayswood Point, Norley Vale, Roehampton, London SW15 4BT (tel 081 789 6170). The Ananda Network has a library of cassettes and videotapes which they will loan for free, with talks on living, dying, death and rebirth, mainly from a **Buddhist perspective**.
• Boerstler, Richard, **Letting Go: A Holistic and Meditative Approach to Death and Dying**, Associates in Thanatology, 115 Blue Rock Road, South Yarmouth, MA 02664, USA. Half hour video ($29 incl. p&p) about this simple method, make sure it is playable on your UK machine – The Natural Death Centre, address below, may be able to lend you their poor-quality copy. See also book version, above. Joanna Gilpin, Laurel Cottage, West Horrington, Wells BA5 3ED (tel 0749 675832) runs seminars on this method.
• British Holistic Medical Association (see Organisations below) – tapes at $9-95 incl. p&p

include Imagery for **Relaxation**, **Coping with Persistent Pain**, **Coping with Stress**, **Introducing Meditation** and **The Breath of Life** (relaxation).

• Collick, Elizabeth, **Through Grief**, tape available from CRUSE (see under Organisations below), £3-90 inc. p&p. Also available as a book (see above). Offers sensible maxims.

• Gold, E. J., tapes ($15)– **Bardo Dreams**, **The Lazy Man's Guide to Death and Dying** and **How I Raised Myself from the Dead in 49 Days or Less** – also Gold's books in the UK from Donald Suckling, 2 Boyswell House, Scholes, Wigan WN1 3QG (tel 0942 43551).

• Jones, Ken, **Caring as a Spiritual Practice**, £27 video from Meridian Trust (tel 071 289 5443). Promoting the sharing of common generosity of spirit.

• Kübler-Ross, Elisabeth, **Life, Death & Life After Death** (audiotape £6), **Aids, Life and Love** (a video conversation), and other such tapes and videos, all from The Elisabeth Kübler-Ross Foundation (see Organisations below).

• **Levine, Stephen** tapes are available from Gateway Books (see Levine's books, above, for address) at £6-96 each, incl. p&p. His tapes (and his schedule of workshops) are also available from Warm Rock Tapes, PO Box 108, Chamisal, NM 87521, USA. Send two international reply coupons for details.

• Long, Barry, **May I Speak to you of Death**, audiotape from the Barry Long Foundation, Whistlands, Langley Marsh, Wiveliscombe, Somerset TA4 2UJ (tel 0984 23426).

• Marie Curie Memorial Foundation, **Caring for your Relative at Home**, useful VHS video £25 (incl. booklet) from Marie Curie (see Organisations below). New EC DIrectives put a caution on its recommendations for lifting patients (see our chapter four).

• Mental Health Media Council, 380 Harrow Road, London W9 2HU (tel 071 286 2346) puts out a catalogue (price £3-50) of films and videos available for sale or hire in the UK on the subjects of **Death and Bereavement**, many of them aimed at professionals, some about euthanasia, others on Near-Death Experiences, etc.

• **Relaxation for Living**, 168/170 Oatlands Drive, Weybridge, Surrey KT13 9ET (tel 0932 858355). Tapes, classes on relaxation, 85p article on easing grief, large SAE for info.

• Roach, Steve: his **Structures from Silence** music (and a 60 minute piece on the album World's Edge) re-creates the sounds he heard during his Near-Death Experience (tel USA 0101 602 760 0004; fax 0101 602 760 0551; UK distributor Laurence Aston at TM records, tel 0734 312 580; fax 0734 312 582). Also Gilles Bédard in Quebec (tel 0101 514 279 2413; fax 0101 514 279 3033) is working with Roach to produce a Soundquest to Omega album of NDE music.

• **Tibetan Book of the Dead** reading at a cremation in Ladakh – Fields of the Senses video, part 3 of Tibet: A Buddhist Trilogy by Thread Cross Films, Bath.

• Yeshe, Lama, **Death and the Transference of Consciousness**, a video about the Tibetan view of death and life. £32 from Meridian Trust (tel 071 289 5443).

Useful organisations and individuals

• **Age Concern**, Astral House, 1268 London Road, London SW16 4ER (tel 081 679 8000). Age Concern has a will-writing service which can help you draw up a simple will for £40, based on a questionnaire you fill in. Also leaflets (send SAE) on arranging a funeral, etc.

• **Alder Centre**, Royal Liverpool Children's NHS Trust, Eaton Road, Liverpool L12 2AP (tel 051 228 4811; helpline 051 228 9759 from 7pm to 10pm every evening). For all those affected by a child's death. Counselling, groups, befriending (see also The Compassionate Friends).

• **Alzheimer's Disease Society**, 158-160 Balham High Road, London SW12 9BN (tel 081 675 6557). Information on aids, services and resources.

• **Ananda Network**. This is a fine initiative: the Network's volunteers offer companisionship to the dying or bereaved of any religion or none. See Buddhist Hospice Trust (below) for address. One of its volunteers, Caroline Sherwood (Parsonage Farm Cottage, Stoney Stratton, Shepton Mallet BA4 6EA, tel 0749 830827), offers counselling and teaching by phone or mail for people wanting help with fear of death or associated issues.

• **Asian Family Counselling Service**, 8-12 Lancaster Road, Southall UB1 1NW (tel 081 813 8321).

• **Association for Children with Life-threatening Conditions and their families** (ACT), Institute of Child Health, Royal Hospital for Sick Children, St Michael's Hill, Bristol BS2 8BJ (tel 0272 221556). Advice and information.

• **Association for Death Education and Counselling**, 638 Prospect Avenue, Hartford, CT 06105-4298, USA (tel 0101203 232 4825). Conferences and courses.

• **Association of Crossroads Care Attendant Schemes**, 10 Regents Place, Rugby, Warwickshire CV21 2PN (tel 0788 573653). Trained carers who take over from the regular carer completely in looking after a disabled person at home, so as to give the carer a break.

• **Association to Aid Sexual and Personal Relationship of the Disabled** (SPOD), 286 Camden Road, London N7 OBJ (tel 071 607 8851). Information and advice for clients.

• **BACUP** (British Association of Cancer United Patients), 3 Bath Place, Rivington St, London EC2A 3JR. Free advice about cancer from nurse specialists (tel 0800 181199) and free counselling sessions in the London area (tel 071 696 9000).

• **Bristol Cancer Help Centre**, Grove House, Cornwallis Grove, Clifton, Bristol BS8 4PG (tel 0272 743216). Holistic treatment and publications.

• **British Association for Counselling**, 1 Regent Place, Rugby, Warwickshire CV21 2PJ (tel 0788 578328; office 550899). Has information on organisations, counsellors and therapists nationwide that you can pay to see – although some are free.

• **British Holistic Medical Association**, 179 Gloucester Place, London NW1 6DX (tel 071 262 5299). Self-help breathing, relaxation, meditation and diet books and tapes (see Tapes and Videos, above) and an informative newsletter.

• **British Humanist Association**, 14 Lambs Conduit Passage, London WC1R 4AH (tel 071 430 0908). Can provide officiant (normally charging £50-£60) for non-religious funeral. See also Jane Wynne Willson under books, above.

• **British Organ Donor Society** (BODY), Balsham, Cambridge CB1 6DL (tel 0223 893636). Self-help groups for recipients and families of organ donors, and general enquiries.

• **The Buddhist Hospice Trust**, PO Box 123, Ashford, Kent TN24 9TF (tel c/o Ray Wills 081 789 6170). A particularly friendly organisation. 'It was established in 1986 to explore Buddhist approaches to dying, death and bereavement. It is a non-sectarian and welcomes both Buddhists and non-Buddhists alike. Its purpose is to bring together, in a creative way, the teachings of the Buddha and the philosophy of modern hospice care.' In fact it confesses that it is at this stage just a network of people, 'a hospice of the heart', rather than a building. Has a quarterly magazine Raft (£4 subs.). Volunteers in its Ananda Network are prepared to sit with and befriend the terminally ill. See also Tapes and Videos, above.

• **CALL Centre** (Cancer Aid and Listening Line), Swan Buildings, 20 Swan St, Manchester M4 5JW (tel 061 835 2586 noon-3pm, 061 434 8668 24 hrs). Emotional support and practical advice for cancer patients and families.

• **CancerLink**, 17 Britannia Street, London WC1X 9JN (tel 071 833 2451). A central information and publishing resource for cancer patients and their families. One of its aims is to organise local self-help groups. Useful pamphlets on everything from sexuality to complementary alternative treatments and caring for the dying at home.

• **Care for the Carers Council**, 143 High St, Lewes, East Sussex BN7 1XT (tel 0273 476819). Advice, information and support, primarily for the East Sussex area.

• **Carer's National Association**, 29 Chilworth Mews, London W2 3RG (tel helpline 071 723 8117). Advice for carers and newly bereaved. Phone to find out your local branch.

• **The Center for Attitudinal Healing**, 19 Main St, Tiburon, California 94920, USA (tel 0101 415 435 5022). Works with children facing serious illnesses, and with children whose parents have cancer, etc. Their video 'Under the Sun' (which emphasises that health is inner peace and that the present instant is the only time there is) may be available on loan from the Buddhist Hospice Trust (see above).

• **The Cemetery Journal**, 46 Broadmead, Hitchin, Herts SG4 9LX (£6 sub). A delight-fully irreverent newsletter on many aspects of death.

• **Child Death Helpline** – tel 071 829 8685. For anyone affected by the death of a child. Parent volunteers take calls on Mondays and Thursdays 7pm to 10pm.

• **Citizens Advice Bureau**, free, impartial, confidential advice about death, bereavement, financial and all other matters, etc. See your local phone book or contact the HQ, Myddelton House, 115-123 Pentonville Rd, London N1 9LZ (tel 071 833 2181; fax 071 833 4371) for details of your nearest branch.

• **The Compassionate Friends**, 53 North Street, Bristol BS3 1EN (tel 0272 539 639). Befriending bereaved adults. Also a very fine newsletter and a postal lending library for books.

• **The Cot Death Society**, 116 Alt Road, Formby, Merseyside L37 8BW (tel 07048 70005).

• **Counsel and Care, advice and help for older people**, Twyman House, 16 Bonny St, London NW1 9PG (tel 071 485 1550). May be able to give a grant for nursing care, also provides counselling for those elderly people needing it, and helps find London homes.

• **Court of Protection** – if you need to apply to manage the affairs of someone who has become mentally incapacitated – The Public Trust Office, Protection Division, Stewart House, 24 Kingsway, London WC2B 6JX (tel 071 269 7300).

• **Cremation Society of Great Britain**, 2nd Floor, Brecon House, 16/16a Albion Place, Maidstone, Kent ME14 5DZ (tel 0622 688292). Can tell you the crematorium nearest you. Publish a free booklet on 'What You Should Know About Cremation', and a directory of crematoria (£16-50).

• **CRUSE** (for all those who have suffered a bereavement: socials and advice, counselling and excellent publications), Cruse House, 126 Sheen Road, Richmond, Surrey TW9 1UR (tel 081 940 4818). Counsellor available on 081 332 7227 weekdays 9.30am to 5pm.

• **Death and Immortality Course**, c/o David Badham, St David's University College, Lampeter, Dyfed, Wales SA48 7ED (tel 0570 422351). (Described in Chapter 4.)

• **Death Studies** journal, Taylor and Francis Ltd, 4 John St, London WC1N 2ET, subs. £39.

• **Disablement Income Group**, Mill Mead Business Centre, Mill Mead Road, London N17 9QU (tel 081 801 8013). Advice on negotiating the nightmare bureaucracy of benefits and services.

• **Disabled Living Foundation**, 380-384 Harrow Road, London W9 2HU (tel 071 289 6111). Advice on incontinence, equipment and aids.

• **Disaster Action**, 11 Lamb St, London E1 6EA (tel 071 377 6691). For those bereaved following a major disaster such as plane crash.

• **Elisabeth Kübler-Ross Foundation**, PO Box 212, London NW8 7NW. In the USA the Foundation's phone number is 0101 703 396 3441). It organises workshops and sells books, tapes and videos (see above).

• **Equipment for the Disabled**, Mary Marlborough Lodge, Nuffield Orthopaedic Centre, Headington, Oxford OX3 7LD (tel 0865 750103). Booklets on a range of aids.

• **The Family Welfare Association**, 501-505 Kingsland Road, Dalston, London E8 4AU (tel 071 254 6251). Gives grants to individuals and families.

• **Federation of British Cremation Authorities**, 41 Salisbury Road, Carshalton, Surrey SM5 3HA (tel 081 669 4521).

• **Federation of Independent Advice Centres**, 13 Stockwell Road, London SW9 9AU (tel 071 274 1839). Phone for the nearest grassroots or specialist agency to you.

• **The Foundation for the Study of Infant Deaths** (information, fundraising for cot deaths research, befriending service, local groups), 35 Belgrave Square, London SW1X 8QB (tel 071 235 0965; helpline: 071 235 1721).

• **Funerals**, The Old Dairy, 1 Church Farm Cottages, Church Rd, Yapton, West Sussex BN18 OEP (tel 0243 553684). A magazine sent free to the funeral trade.

• **Funeral Service Journal**, 121 London Rd, Knebworth, Herts SG3 6EX (tel 0438 814441). The best of the funeral trade journals. Founded 1885.

• **Helen House – A Hospice for Children**, 37 Leopold Street, Oxford OX4 1QT (tel 0865 728251). There are other children's hospices in Yorkshire, Birmingham, Manchester and Cambridge, with more planned.

• **Help the Hospices**, 34-44 Britannia St, London WC1X 9JG (tel 071 278 5668). Helps fund hospices' projects, equipment, education and research.

• **Hospice Arts**, Dr David Frampton, Chelmsford Hospice, 212 New London Road, Chelmsford CM2 9AE (tel 0245 358130 or c/o 071 377 8484). Helps hospices to run art projects.

• **The Hospice Information Service**, at St. Christopher's Hospice, 51-59 Lawrie Park Road, Sydenham, London SE26 6DZ (tel 081 778 9252; fax 081-659 8680). A very helpful organisation that puts out a regular newsletter giving the latest developments on the domestic and international scene and provides information about local hospices. Also issues a series of fact sheets including 'Setting Up and Running a Home Care Service.'

• **Ian Rennie Hospice at Home**, Little Rothschild House, 71 Marsworth Road, Pitstone, Bedford LU7 9AX (tel 0296 661667). Trained nurses provide free full nursing breaks for those caring for the terminally ill in the Buckinghamshire area.

• **International Association for Near-Death Experiences**, David Lorimer, Garden Cottage, Newhouse Farm, Northington Down, Alresford, Hants SO24 9UB (tel & fax 0962 734031).

• **Intractable Pain Society** (IPS), Bradford Royal Infirmary, Duckworth Lane, Bradford, West Yorks, BD9 6RJ. Able to supply information concerning the locality of pain clinics. Membership of the society is limited to the medical profession only.

• **Jewish Bereavement Counselling Service**, 1 Cyprus Gardens, London N3 1SP (tel 081 349 0839 answerphone; 071 387 4399 ext 227 office hours).

• **John Bell and Croyden**, 50 Wigmore St, London W1, tel 071 935 5555 ext 212. Chemist for specialist medical requirements, everything from a sheepskin rug (£35) to a walking frame(£42-50). Publishes a 150 page catalogue aimed at professionals.

• **Kübler-Ross Foundation**, see Elizabeth Kübler-Ross, above.

• **Law Centres** can provide free advice about wills etc for those who are hard-up. See the Helplines page in the front of your local Thomson Phone Directory or phone 071 387 8570 to find your nearest one.

• **Lesbian and Gay Bereavement Project**, Vaughan M. Williams Centre, Colindale Hospital, London NW9 5GJ (tel 081 455 8894 helpline, 081 200 0511 admin. 3-6pm). Can also advise about funerals which acknowledge the partner.

• **London Association of Bereavement Services**, 68 Chalton Street, London NW1 1JR (tel 071 388 2153). Supporting and linking London bereavement services.

• **London Lighthouse**, 111-117 Lancaster Road, London W11 1QT (tel 071 792 1200). 'A centre for people facing the challenge of AIDS.' London Lighthouse has facilities for its own funeral and memorial services.

• **Macmillan nurses**, c/o Cancer Relief Macmillan Fund, 15-19 Britten St, London SW3 3TZ (tel 071 351 7811). The Fund's nurses can help with emotional support, pain and symptom control. It provides financial assistance for some cancer patients and financially supports or helps funding of organisations caring for patients with cancer.

• **Malik, Yvonne**, Sweet Briar, Wray, Near Lancaster LA2 8QN (tel 05242 21767). Consultant to the Natural Death Centre and artist, who designed Memory Boxes (see the end of our chapter five), accepts commissions for painting coffins and for meditative glass engravings (see our chapter six).

• **Marie Curie Cancer Care**, 28 Belgrave Square, London SW1X 8QG (tel 071 235 3325) Phone for information about this organisation's hospice centres, and advice about the availability of night nurses, who are free, but normally obtained through your health authority's community nursing manager.

• **Memorial Advisory Bureau**, 139 Kensington High St, London W8 6SX (tel 071 937 0052). Advice on technical and legal aspects of memorials.

• **Memorials by Artists**, Snape Priory, Saxmundham, Suffolk, IP17 1SA (tel 0728 88 8934). £5 booklet, incl. postage and packing, second edition, contains articles, advice and 37 photographs.

• **Miscarriage Association**, Clayton Hospital, Northgate, Wakefield WF1 3JF (tel 0924 200799). Support groups and information.

• **Motor Neurone Disease Association**, PO Box 246, Northampton NN1 2PR (tel 0604 250505/22269). Advice, information, equipment loan. Regional advisers. Financial help.

• **National Black Bereavement Foundation**, 25 Baysham St, Camden, London NW1 (tel 071 388 5551).

• **National Information for Parents of Prematures – Education, Resources and Support** (NIPPERS), PO Box 1553, Wedmore, Somerset BS28 4LZ (tel 0934 733123). Support group and newsletter for parents whose babies die in special care baby units.

• **National Association of Bereavement Services**, 20 Norton Folgate, London E1 6DB (tel 071 247 1080 referrals; 071 247 0617 admin).

• **National Association of Funeral Directors**, 618 Warwick Road, Solihull, West Midlands B91 1AA (tel 021 711 1343). Its members' Code of Practice is available free. If complaining about a funeral director, you are supposed to write first to the funeral director for satisfaction, though there is nothing to prevent you going direct to the

Association or to the trading standards department (see local council's phone number) or to a small claims court. The Association's magazine is called 'The Funeral Director'.

• **National Association of Memorial Masons**, Crown Buildings, High Street, Aylesbury, Bucks HP20 1SL (tel 0296 434 750). Code of ethics for members. It offers arbitration.

• **National Association of Widows**, 54-57 Allison Street, Digbeth, Birmingham B5 5TH (tel 021 643 8348). Pamphlets and a survival guide, plus local branch socials.

• **National Federation of Spiritual Healers**, Old Manor Farm Studio, Church Street, Sunbury-on-Thames TW16 6RG (tel 0932 783164).

• **Natural Death Centre**, 20 Heber Road, London NW2 6AA (tel 081 208 2853). The Centre researched this present book. Please send any updates to this address. Further copies of this book are available from the Centre for £10-95 incl. p&p.

• **Office of Fair Trading**, Field House, 15-25 Breams Buildings, London EC4A 1PR (tel 071 242 8526; fax 071 269 8543). Christopher Wright in its Competition Policy Division 2 has been dealing with the Natural Death Centre's complaints about competition issues relating to the funeral trade. Its report 'Funerals' (1989) is interesting.

• **Open University 'Death and Dying' course**, c/o Prof Malcolm Johnson, Dept of Health and Social Welfare, Walton Hall, Milton Keynes MK7 6AA (tel 0908 653695; fax 0908 653744). (Described in the chapter on Training.)

• **Pagan Hospice and Funeral Trust** in the UK, BM Box 3337, London WC1 3XX.

• **Parents of Murdered Children Support Group**, 92 Corbett Tay Road, Upminster, Essex RM14 2BA (tel 0708 640400).

• **P. A. T. Dog**, c/o Lesley Scott-Ordish, Rocky Bank, 4 New Road, Ditton, Maidstone, Kent ME20 7AD (tel 0732 848499). Arranges dogs to visit the sick and the elderly.

• **Probate Registry**, Personal Applications Dept, 2nd Floor, Principal Registry, Family Division, Somerset House, Strand, London WC2R 1LP (tel 071 936 6983 or 6974).

• **Rainbow Trust**, Rainbow House, 47 Eastwick Drive, Great Bookham, Surrey KT23 3PU (tel 0372 453309). Help and respite haven for terminally ill children and their families.

• **React**, 73 Whitehall Park Road, London W4 3NB (tel 081 995 8188). Money and equipment for children with reduced life expectancy. Applications via doctor or a professional worker.

• **Red Cross Medical Loans Service**: see local phone book, branches can supply medical equipment for short term loan – wheelchairs, commodes, etc. Or contact British Red Cross, 3 Grosvenor Crescent, London SW1X 7EE (tel 071 235 5454).

• **Rigpa**, 330 Caledonian Road, London N1 1BB (tel 071 700 0185). Tibetan Buddhist centre founded Sogyal Rinpoche. Runs courses on death and dying (see also Sogyal Rinpoche's book, above; and Tibetan approach, below).

• **Samaritans**, 10 The Grove, Slough, Berks SL1 1QP (tel 0753 532713). Or see local phone book. For those in despair or suicidal.

• **Shadow of Suicide** (SOS), 6 Denmark St, Bristol BS1 5DQ (tel 0272 292778). Support for parents (and possibly grandparents and siblings) where a child (of any age, including adult) has committed suicide.

• **Shanti Nilaya** now known as Elisabeth Kübler Ross Foundation (see above).

• **Social Security**, for how to claim benefits, etc, phone free to 0800 666555 (often no reply; easier to get through from 4-30pm to 7pm) or go via your local office, under H for Health and Social Security in your local phone book. Potentially relevant leaflets to ask for include 'Help when someone Dies' (FB29), 'National insurance for widows' (NI51), 'Rates of war pensions and allowances' (MPL 154), 'War widows and other dependants' (MPL 152),

'What to do after a death' (D49) and 'Widow's benefits' (NP 45).

• **Spiritual healing** (see also National Federation of): John Avery, 31 Wakefield Gardens, London SE19 2NR (tel 081 653 3982), who 'works more and more with the terminally ill'. Rosy Creasy, 165 Lower Richmond Road, Putney, London SW15 1LY (tel 081 788 6214). 'I use colour, sound and visualisation to help people to love themselves.'
Philippa Pullar, 7 St Mary's Grove, London SW13 OJA (tel 081 789 0243). Author of 'Spiritual and Lay Healing', she draws comfort from her own Near-Death Experience.
Inga Marie Solders, Roslagsgatan 19B, S-11355 Stockholm, Sweden (tel 010 468 612 5809), believes she can help the soul to pass over the river of death.
• **The Starlight Foundation**, 8A Bloomsbury Square, London WC1A 2LP (tel 071 430 1642), attempts to grant the wishes of critically ill children.
• **The Stillbirth and Neonatal Death Society (SANDS)**, 28 Portland Place, London W1N 4DE (tel 071 436 5881). Befriending, local groups, information and publications.
• **Terence Higgins Trust**, 52-54 Grays Inn Road, London WC1X 8JU (admin tel 071 831 0330; helpline 12 noon to 10pm daily tel 071 242 1010). A registered charity to inform, advise and help on AIDS and HIV infection.
• **Tibetan approach:** Ngakpa Chogyam Rinpoche can give talks and empowerments on the theme of death and dying. His secretary's address is 5 Court Close, Whitchurch, Cardiff CF4 1JR (tel 0222 620332). (See also Rigpa, above.)
• **Transition (Caochladh)**, c/o Steve Gwyn Davies, Council for Voluntary Organisations, Bridge Road, Portree, Isle of Skye IV51 9ER (tel 0478 2921 or 047852 271). Offers friendship, information and positive support for people who are dying or concerned about dying. 'Shares aims of Natural Death Centre, would like a Scottish or UK network.'
• **Twins and Multiple Births Association – Bereavement Support Group**, PO Box 30, Little Sutton, South Wirral L66 1TH (tel 051 348 0020).
• **Unitarian Churches**, c/o Matthew Smith, Unitarian Information Officer, Essex Hall, 1-6 Essex St, Strand, London WC2R 3HY, tel 071 240 2384. Unitarian ministers conduct flexible funerals without dogma.
• **Victim Support**, National Office, Cranmer House, 39 Brixton Road, London SW9 6DZ (tel 071 735 9166). Trained volunteers offer one-to-one help to victims of crime.
• **Voluntary Euthanasia Society**, 13 Prince of Wales Terrace, London W8 5PG (tel 071 937 7770). The Society pioneered the Living Will (advance directive) in the UK and is pressing for a parliamentary bill to give it definite legal backing.
• **Voluntary Euthanasia Society of Scotland**, 17 Hart Street, Edinburgh EH1 3RN (tel 031 556 4404). Christopher Grant Docker there is very knowledgeable about the varieties of Living Will texts worldwide.
• **War Widows Association of Great Britain**, 17 The Earl's Croft, Coventry CV3 5ES (tel 0203 503298). Advice for all war widows. Can supply a local contact.
• **Welfare State International**, 'the celebratory arts company,' The Ellers, Ulverston, Cumbria LA12 1AA (tel 0229 581127; fax 0229 581232). Artistic director John Fox offers consultancies for imaginative memorial services, lanterns, urns, etc.
• **Yad b'Yad** (Hebrew for 'Hand in Hand'), a Jewish child bereavement project. The contact person is Louise Heilbron (tel 081 444 7134).

INDEX